# RECORDING &
# PRODUCTION TECHNIQUES

## For The Recording Musician

Paul White

publications
LIMITED

Published by:
SOS Publications Limited,
Media House, Burrel Road, St. Ives,
Cambridgeshire, PE17 4LE, England.


© Paul White 1993.


ISBN  0-9522195-0-6

Editors:
Debbie Poyser.
Ian Gilby.


Cover Design:
Paul White.


Layout and Setting:
Sound Design, St. Ives, Cambridgeshire.


Printing:
Black Bear Press, Cambridge.

# YOU'VE DONE SEQUENCING, SAMPLING AND QUANTISING. NOW COMES THE HARD BIT.

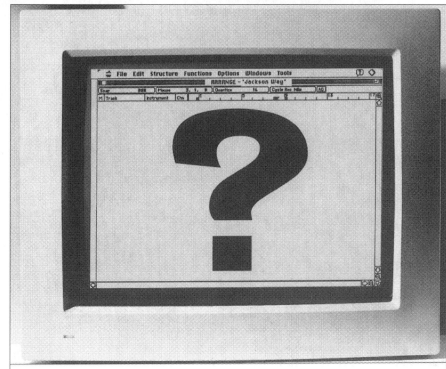

IN the last five years computers have revolutionised music. Virtually any sound you want is available on disk and can be incorporated into your track. Everything can be arranged so that it's machine perfect and then, with some of the more sophisticated packages, you can add a few "human" touches.

All of which is fine and dandy if you've made a policy decision to stay away from anything other than

electronic sound sources. The problem comes when you want to add a vocal part or maybe a slug of grunge guitar.

Enter the Fostex X-28H. It's a four-track high speed recorder which can be used to record up to eight individual sound sources at once.

Yes, you can sync midi devices into it. And, yes, you can plug all manner of outboard gear into the back of it.

In fact functionally the Fostex X-28H is pretty well identical to a Neve console. Okay, so maybe it's a bit smaller and the EQ isn't quite as flexible and you have to move the faders yourself but in essence you're working with the same piece of kit.

And of course once you own one, you'll have made the move from making tracks to recording songs.

A quick flourish of a pen on the coupon will get you more technical info and the address of your nearest Fostex dealer.

# CONTENTS

# INTRODUCTION

A great deal of mystery surrounds the art of the professional record producer and studio engineer, for it is now recognised that their contribution to a record can be equal to that of the artist. Indeed, some producers have assumed a Svengali-like role, taking command of all stages of a project, from songwriting to final mix. In such cases, it has been known for the artist to make only a minor musical contribution; examples of this are rare and come to our attention only because of the publicity they attract, but they serve to demonstrate the enormous influence that can be exercised by the producer. However, the vast majority of producers work closely with the recording engineer and artist, the sole aim being the production of a commercially viable record.

The backgrounds and experiences of producers vary widely: some producers are competent engineers, while others come from a musical background and rely solely on the studio engineer to interpret their needs. As you will discover, it is the diversity of backgrounds and approaches that makes record production such a lively and involving subject.

The aim of this book is to explain the role of the producer and his relationship with the artist, recording engineer and record company. But I won't be neglecting the engineering side of things, and will also be covering the techniques that can be used to create specific sounds and musical effects. Equally valuable, you'll find information on liaising with clients and planning sessions; all aspects of a session are covered — from setting up to the final mix.

After the chapters devoted to the mix, you'll find a section addressing the little-understood area of post-production, which includes album compilation, audio sweetening, remixing and editing, as well as the final steps in producing a professional recorded product.

The recording and engineering techniques discussed in this book will be of benefit to the commercial studio engineer and potential record producer as well as the home recordist. In addition to the author's own experience, much of the information has been distilled from long conversations with top producers and engineers worldwide and is applicable to a wide range of musical styles and disciplines.

# A LITTLE HISTORY

When you consider the flamboyant personalities and rock 'n' roll lifestyles associated with the music business over the past two or three decades, it might come as quite a surprise to learn that in the early days of recording, the whole process was very formal — and, by modern standards, very basic. The first records ever made were recorded in mono, with very simple mixing techniques used to record what was, in effect, a live performance.

The only tools at the engineer's disposal in these early days were level faders; the first mixers had no EQ, so if the engineer wanted a different sound, he had to achieve it either by selecting a different mic or by changing the mic position. If a more ambient sound was needed, the only way of achieving this was to use a 'live' room; consequently, many improvised techniques, such as using reverberant concrete stairwells to add reverb to a mix, were pioneered during this period .

It was also commonplace for studios to build dedicated echo rooms in their basements. These were essentially large reflective rooms with angled surfaces, often tiled. A loudspeaker and microphone would be set up in the room, then any sound needing treatment would be fed into the room. The signal picked up by the mic would be added back into the mix, in much the same way as we add digital effects using the effects return channels on a multitrack console.

# COMPANY MEN

In these early days, engineers and producers were full-time employees of the record company which also owned the studio. Because of this arrangement, the same people would work on a wide range of musical styles, covering classical, jazz, pop, ballads and so forth — which is why many of the 'old-school' engineers and producers are so versatile. In those days, efficiency was the prime objective, and because of the live way of working, whole albums were regularly completed in a single four-hour session; the Beatles album Please Please Me, for example, was recorded in one 13-hour day! Engineers — wearing white lab coats — remained on one side of the control room glass, with the artists on the other. Rarely, if ever, was an artist allowed into the control room during a session!

What we now call record production was then split between two people; the musical director and the producer. This is a close parallel to the way in which things are still done in the film industry — the producer looking after the business side, and the director concentrating on artistic considerations. The musical director would be responsible for the musical arrangements, the quality of the musical performance and the sound and mix of the final recording. In turn, he would be under pressure from the producer to work quickly while spending as little money as possible! In the days when all non-pop backing music was provided by orchestras, a little wasted time could add up to a lot of money, and even today this is an area of concern. One major consideration is that orchestras tend not to be booked by the minute but in blocks of half an hour or so, depending on which country you are working in and the rules of the particular union to which the musicians belong. This means that 'just one more' take can take you into the next block of time, which can add hundreds or even thousands of pounds to the cost of a session.

# LOW-TECH

Technology improved to allow stereo recording, and this was soon followed by four-track recording, which allowed singers to overdub their parts rather than tying up a live band or orchestra for every take. Basic EQ and pan pots were added to the mixing consoles, and the plate reverb was developed to eliminate the need for a live room. It was with this fairly basic technology that many of the classic pop records of the sixties were made, though many of the early Phil Spector-produced hits were recorded in mono. During this decade, the only real effects unit was the tape echo, though guitar amps were being built with integral electronic tremolo and spring reverb.

Around this time, improvisation was a vital ingredient to achieving a distinctive commercial sound and with no hi-tech processing to help, this involved a lot of experimentation. Rooms with interesting acoustics were pressed into service, while double-tracking was taken to extremes by some producers, who would hire in several guitar players, for example, to play identical parts.

When flanging was first discovered, it had to be created manually by recording the same piece of music onto two tape recorders, which would then be started at the same time. By using slight hand pressure on the tape reels of first one and then the other machine, the sync between the two machines could be made to drift in and out, giving rise to the characteristic whooshing sound used on so many psychedelic records. At the time, this effect could only be added after the recording; there was no way to achieve it live.

# CHANGING ROLES

The role of producer and musical director gradually merged, and if a producer lacked the specialised musical knowledge to arrange songs, he would hire in an arranger when required. Even so, the producer was still very much tied to his record company, and the relationship between George Martin and the Beatles was probably the greatest incentive to challenge the status quo. All the world knew just what an influence George Martin had on the Beatles and few doubt that he was a key figure in ensuring their continued success.

This relationship inspired many producers to go freelance, which gave them the opportunity to negotiate royalties, or 'points', with the artist's management, at the same time allowing producers to specialise. Prior to this, the 'tied' producer had to make the best of any job that came his way, regardless of its musical style. And regardless of the commercial success of a record, the producer still only received his basic salary.

Things were changing, though, and it was also around this time that recording engineers were allowed to turn up for work without a tie! Rigidly-defined morning and afternoon recording sessions also became more flexible, with some musicians being allowed to record during the night. Musicians were even managing to get into the control room!

From this time the whole system became more flexible, with freelance studios springing up to accommodate the growing number of freelance projects. No longer was it set in stone that an artiste had to record at his or her record company's studio with the company engineer and in-house producer. The more forward-thinking record companies recognised that certain projects could benefit from being handled by producers who favoured a certain musical style or who had a good track record in producing hit records. Inevitably these producers built up relationships with engineers they found it easy to work with, and so the freelance engineer was created. Now a musical act could benefit from working in the most appropriate studio with a sympathetic producer and an engineer who knew the producer's requirements.

This slackening of the old regime was a double-edged sword. On the positive side, it did allow the right people to work together and some great records were made, but in the late sixties and early seventies when the music business still made a lot of money, this freedom was frequently abused. Aside from the stories of all-night recording sessions consisting of sex, drugs and very little rock and roll, work was seldom approached with any sense of economy. Bands would book studios for months on end and actually write the songs in there! Artist mismanagement was rife, and many young bands didn't realise that at the end of the day, it was their own money which was being wasted.

# ADVANCES

Much of this waste of resources and time was down to a basic misunderstanding of what a record company advance really is. It isn't just free spending money! When a company signs a band, they generally make available a sum of money for the band to live on and to enable them to go into the studio and make a record. All the studio expenses and any other cash advanced is ultimately deducted from the artists' royalties once the record starts to sell. If the record doesn't sell, then it's the record company, not the artist, who loses out — but in the past it was quite common for bands to have a hit single and then find that they received none of the proceeds from it because their share had all been frittered away in recording time, chauffeured cars and expensive catering. In other words, a record company advance should be considered as an unsecured, interest-free loan which is repaid when the artist's records begin to sell.

Over the past decade, the music business has suffered a considerable decline, partly because consumers now have interests other than collecting records and partly, so the record companies argue, because of unauthorised cassette copying. The truth probably goes deeper than that; the original sixties music generation are now middle-aged, with enough money to buy records but with little chance to hear any music that might appeal to them. It could be that the national obsession with the Top 40 has served only to alienate a great many potential record buyers; it is up to record companies and record producers to redress this situation.

# WITH A KORG 'O' SERIES
# YOUR SET WON'T BE DISC AFTER DISC,

# IT'LL BE SONG AFTER SONG.

There's nothing worse. You've got the audience hanging on your every note, baying for more.

Instead, all they hear is the silence while you load up the disk for your next song.

It can kill a live set stone dead. But now, Korg have come up with the perfect solution: a 48,000 note internal sequencer that lets you play your songs one after another without having to play computer operator.

Clever? You've heard nothing yet.

'O' Series keyboards have 32 voices, giving plenty of capacity for the richest arrangements without any risk of sounds being suddenly 'snatched' away.

On top of that, each of those voices has its own enhancement circuit, letting you achieve almost infitesimal variations in the texture and colour of sound.

There are even two samples per programme, allowing you to create stereo voices without tying up your FX.

If you like the sound of all this write to Korg (UK) Ltd. 8-9 The Crystal Centre, Elmgrove Road, Harrow, Middlesex HA1 2YR and find out more about the 'O' Series. The keyboards that make performances less of a performance.

# KORG
### BREAKING SOUND BARRIERS

# THE MODERN PRODUCER

Today's producer requires a significantly different range of skills to those of his sixties counterpart, though the underlying objectives of bringing in a commercially successful project at the right budget are still at the top of the list. Nowadays, the producer must have a flair for music (though he doesn't have to be a musician), he must have the right contacts, he must be able to plan finances and, not to be underestimated, it is essential that he be able to handle people.

Most producers come from a musical rather than an engineering background and have made their contacts during their years in the business. They will have worked in studios and, during that time, will have made contact with engineers, record company staff and other musicians who may be able to help out on future sessions. Current producers also tend to be familiar with MIDI, as much pre-production work is done using MIDI sequencing systems.

I have interviewed a great many of the top record producers over the past few years and nearly all have a different approach to the subject, so there's no absolute definition or job specification. Some are competent recording engineers, while others need a house engineer to do virtually everything for them. Some may only fine-tune the arrangements presented by the artists, while others may rewrite the whole thing and even replace band members with session musicians. The only bottom line is results and different producers have different ways of getting from A to B; the important thing is to get to B! There is one point, however, on which most seem to agree and that is that the ability to handle people in a stressful environment is very near the top of the list of qualities whihc a producer needs. Working against the clock in an expensive recording studio can be very stressful, especially when things aren't going right, and the producer must shoulder the responsibility for ensuring that a creative atmosphere is maintained.

# MUSICAL STYLE

A great many record producers build a reputation for working in a particular style, but the more astute among them have realised that styles change, and if you allow yourself to get pigeon-holed, you run the risk of becoming out of fashion and hence out of work. Even so, it is only natural for producers to relate better to some styles of music than to others, and even the most broad-based producers tend to have pet areas in which they particularly like to work. The main thing is to appreciate the risks and take care to ensure you don't get left out in the cold when styles change, as they inevitably do. This may be a particularly apt warning in these times when dance music is so successful, but the production techniques are so different to traditional pop work that a dance-only producer might be hard-pushed to find work in any other area.

# PROJECT PLANNING

At one time, records were invariably made in the studio belonging to the record company with in-house engineering staff. In recent years however, alternative working methods have been developed, which have advantages both creatively and for the recording budget. After spending some time talking to the artists and their record company, a producer will, typically, listen to demos of their material and pick out the tracks that he thinks are most suitable for the album/single.

This is done in consultation with the artist, but at the end of the day, the producer has the last word. Having said this, a lot depends on the band and on their track record and standing in the business — a top band with a proven chart track record will certainly have more say over which of their songs are chosen and how those songs are recorded. A new band, on the other hand, is likely to have rather less influence.

Even at this stage, it's important for the producer to develop a comfortable rapport with the artist. They will be working very closely together, and so it is essential to build a mutual trust and respect, otherwise friction can easily occur when the going gets tough. The emphasis is on teamwork, and the producer is there to function as team leader.

# THE ENGINEER

Recording engineers come from a variety of backgrounds, though most appear to have had some connection with music prior to getting into recording. Traditionally, the aspiring recording engineer started out in a commercial studio, making tea and maintaining the tape filing system while picking up what he could about recording from the resident engineer. He'd then work on a few pet projects during studio down time, help out on sessions and eventually, be in the right place at the right time to control a session of his own. Most of the tales I've been told include stories of ludicrously long working hours, poverty pay and an almost total lack of sleep. Even so, most successful producers have a 'right place at the right time' story and recognise this event as the turning point in their careers.

Over the years, I've answered countless enquiries from people who want to get into record production or studio engineering. Unfortunately, a lot more people want to do the job than there are vacancies available, and the old 'tea boy' entry into the business can no longer be relied upon. There are so many engineers around that studios can afford to demand some level of experience from would-be applicants; the trick is to gain experience without actually doing the job.

# RECORDING COURSES

Recording courses are available in several guises, from cheap and cheerful weekend introductory sessions run in budget studios to full-time courses at recognised educational establishments. There's no doubt that these courses can help to get you started, but they offer no guarantee of a job. Likewise, you can run a home studio and learn a great deal about recording that way, but this still doesn't guarantee you the job of your dreams. However, all experience is useful, and if it makes you better equipped than the next candidate, then it's worth it.

But being able to physically do the job is only the first prerequisite — you also need the right attitude. Engineering can be a very stressful job and, like the record producer, you have to be able to work with often highly-strung musicians in a confined, potentially stressful environment for long periods. You have to be able to think on your feet and anticipate problems, and you have to accept that nobody is going to suggest you take a tea break, let alone half an hour off for something so trivial as a meal! If anything goes wrong in a studio, it's always the engineer's fault (justified or not) so you need to be broad shouldered as well as possessed of infinite stamina.

An engineer doesn't have to be a record producer, but even so, a good engineer will anticipate a producer's demands so that when the producer wants to try out a little vocal compression or reverb, the engineer already has them patched in with suitable settings. Some producers are really not deserving of the title and the bulk of the creative work then falls to the engineer. However, in these cases, the engineer seldom receives any credit for his input — it's still the producer's name which ends up on the record sleeve.

## WHY DO IT?

You might well ask why anyone becomes a recording engineer, because the work is arduous, not at all well paid and very often demands that you work anti-social hours — both in the number of hours worked and the time of night you eventually get to finish work. I can't even pretend to answer the question, but there seems to be an endless stream of people just waiting to take their place in that smoke-filled sweat-box that is the working recording studio control room. I've done a lot of engineering over the past decade and a half, but I've never been in the position of having to do it full time, all the time, so I've grown to enjoy it. If you're determined to be a recording engineer, then you'll get there in the end, but you have to be persistent — if you can't take banging your head against closed doors, you probably don't have the resilience for the job anyway.

# Gateway

## The School of Recording, Music Technology and Music Business Studies

**In Partnership with the School of Music
at
*Kingston University***

**Full Time and Part Time Diploma Courses.**

**One 24 track, Two 16 Track Teaching Studios, Four Pre Production rooms for practical work and a new Music Technology Teaching Suite.**

**There are also many short intensive courses throughout the year, including live sound, sequencing and sampling courses**

**For more details please call Gateway.**

Gateway. The School of Music, Kingston Hill Centre, Surrey, KT2 7LB
081-549-0014

# PLANNING A SESSION

The planning for a recording project starts as soon as the artists meet the producer. In some circumstances, the artists themselves will be in a position to choose which producer they work with, but it is more often the case that the record company chooses the producer because of his or her track record with certain musical styles. Establishing a rapport with the artists is the first step towards establishing confidence, as is an exploration of the artists' own ideas as to how their material should be handled.

Some acts readily accept that they need the guidance of an experienced producer, but as musicians tend to be pretty self-opinionated types, it is also possible that they will resent the imposition of a third party who has the final say over their material. A good producer will tackle this problem at once by exploring the artists' own ideas and only then suggesting possible changes, rather than taking a hard line by dictating the way he intends things to be.

## DEMO

As previously mentioned, most producers will first listen to the artists' own demos. Some producers like to copy the demo cassette to open reel tape and then edit the tape to form a more workable arrangement. The edited demos are then played back to the musicians before proceeding. Taking this pre-production procedure even further, some musician/producers might want to program their subsequent ideas for the final song into a sequencer and present various options to the artists.

An experienced producer might draw the attention of the artists to sections that don't work well and then elicit their ideas as to how the problem can be rectified. With any luck, they can be subtly coaxed until they draw the conclusions that the producer has already come to — it's much easier if the artists think the ideas have come from them, as they are less likely to resist them!

## SESSION PLAYERS

A more sensitive issue arises when band members have to be supplemented or even replaced by session musicians. This has to be handled carefully to avoid damaging fragile egos, and it helps if the redundant band members can play at least some part in the recording. For example, the drummer who has been replaced by a drum machine might sit in on the rhythm programming and, in addition, may be asked to play a few live fills — it all depends on the producer and on his personal approach to the job.

Some producers may want to use MIDI sequencing extensively, in which case the preliminary programming will be done next, and the artists may play little part in this. Artists can easily feel insecure in such circumstances, so it helps to get them as involved as is practical and to solicit their approval when things are changed. Even getting the drummer to record some of his own drum sounds into a sampler can be enough — the secret is to make everyone feel involved.

## THE BUDGET

Once the preliminary ground has been covered, the next step depends on the producer's approach and on the available budget. It can be artistically fruitful to allow a band to experiment as they go along, but when it comes to bringing a project in on time and to budget, the producer with a positive plan is likely to be more successful. In any event, a producer with definite ideas can't afford to give too much leeway, as he will have a pretty good idea at this stage of how the finished product should sound.

There are producers who like to be more open-ended, but a sensible approach is to do any experimental work in a low-budget facility or home studio and then move into the more costly facility when all the uncertainties have been taken care of. If the majority of a project can be undertaken in a musician's home or programming suite, it can be completed at a much lower cost than a traditional studio recording.

# SMPTE AND SEQUENCING

Whether MIDI is being used or not, it helps to stripe the multitrack tape with SMPTE (Society of Motion Picture and Television Engineers) time code, in case sequenced parts have to be added later and to facilitate automated mixing. SMPTE code should be striped to the tape at the prevailing TV frame rate, which is 30fps (frames per second) in the USA and 25fps in Europe. The other frame rate of 24fps is used exclusively for film work, and so-called 'drop-frame' should be avoided unless the project specifies it.

Even if the majority of the musical parts are to be sequenced at the mixing stage, it helps to put a rough stereo mix of the sequenced backing onto tape; this will allow the artists to work on their overdubs without having to worry about loading sequences. Strangely enough, though the prevailing wisdom is that sequencing MIDI parts directly into the mix is the right way to go, a surprising number of professional producers still like to record their sequenced instruments to tape. When asked why, they tend to reply that they feel more comfortable having something concrete on tape rather than relying on the vagaries of software. Additionally, they may profess to like what analogue tape does to the sound. They might also comment that making a commitment at this stage saves procrastination later on, but providing the time code track stays intact, it is still possible to lock up the sequencer and change a sound or melody line right up to the final mix. Perhaps this approach gives the best of both worlds, in that the producer feels a commitment has been made, yet he or she still has the complete flexibility afforded by the sequencer should it be necessary to revert to the original sequence.

There's another very valid reason for recording sequenced parts onto tape, and that is that the available synths, drum machines and samplers might not have sufficient polyphony to cope with the entire performance in one take. In this instance, the sequence must be played through with some parts muted and the different sections recorded to tape in several passes. This might involve adding effects as the sounds go to tape, simply because several different instrumental or percussion sounds may have to share the same tape tracks.

Before leaving the subject of sequencing, it is the producer's responsibility to ensure that backup disks are made of any working material and that proper notes are kept to describe sounds, effects and so forth. The producer also has to decide whether to work with the available instruments or whether to hire in extra equipment.

# VOCALS

The best time to record vocals depends on which producer you ask! Some like to get the main vocal down as soon as the bare bones of the musical backing have been recorded; their justification for this is that it allows any further instrumentation to be fitted in around the vocal line. In any event, it helps to get a guide vocal down first for the same reason — and it also helps the other players navigate their way through the song. Often the singer gives his or her best performance when recording the guide track because there is less pressure to get it dead right. A good producer will keep the guide vocal until the end of the session just in case.

In home recording, we tend to record a vocal part all the way through and then run through it again, dropping in any phrases that weren't up to scratch. Some professionals work in this way too, but they are more likely to record several complete takes on separate tracks, from which the producer will compile one good, composite vocal track. The best phrases will be bounced down onto a new track, and if the desk is fitted with mute automation, this process is very simple. If no mute automation is available, the different phrases must be 'brought up' manually, using either the channel mute buttons or the channel faders. Good notes are essential in order to keep track of the wanted phrases during this process.

# HARDWARE

Though frivolous experimentation is a waste of time and money, it is well worth setting aside a little time to try out different mics and compressors as the vocalist warms up, to see which give the best result. There are certain esoteric models known for their good vocal sound but, as is often found to be the case, what works magic for one singer may be quite unsuitable for another.

It is common practice to apply a degree of compression to vocals as they are recorded; this helps to get a good working level onto tape and evens out the worst variations in level. Further compression can be used during the mix, as required. Proper attention should also be paid to giving the singer a workable foldback or monitor mix. Most singers work best with a reasonable amount of monitor reverb to help them pitch their notes. If a singer has problems working with enclosed headphones, try a semi-enclosed type or suggest that they work with one can on and one can off. Spill from the phones into the vocal mic is unlikely to be a problem except at very high monitoring levels or where a click track is involved.

# DRUMS

If the session requires a lot of real drums, it may be most cost-effective to book some time in a studio which has a good live room, but may have fairly basic 16 or 24-track equipment. It is important to ensure that the tape machine is compatible with those available in the studios that may be used for other parts of the project.

Most pop music tends to make use of sequenced drum parts, often augmented by manual percussion, manual hi-hat and cymbal parts and the odd tom fill. This is an easy way to work because the basic drum rhythm is locked into the sequencer. On the other hand, if the session demands real drums all the way through, and some instruments are to be MIDI sequenced, then the drummer usually has to play to a click track generated by the sequencer. Top session drummers can do this effortlessly, but drummers used to setting the tempo rather than following it may take some time to adapt.

# TAP TEMPO

If a less rigid approach to timing is beneficial, it is possible to record the rhythm section 'live' and then use a tap-tempo facility to create a sequencer tempo map of the actual performance. This usually involves tapping a button in time with the original performance, and it helps to have at least two bars of extra count-in to get the tempo in sync. However, such an approach is rare in pop music and even very proficient drummers tend to make use of some sequenced rhythm parts, both for convenience and to produce a very exact tempo.

Sequencing the snare and bass drum parts avoids all the problems of snare rattle or toms booming whenever the bass drum is hit, yet if the player's own drums are sampled and then triggered by a sequencer, the end result can still be very authentic. As a rule, hi-hat and cymbal parts should be played live where a human feel is sought, though for dance music, which is more mechanical, totally sequenced drum parts invariably work better.

# DRUM MIKING

Recording drums probably involves more decision making than any other aspect of the session, but other than a suitable room, all you need is a good basic desk and a selection of suitable drum mics. Rock drum sounds tend to be recorded with the emphasis on the close mics, with the overhead or ambient mics used to fill in the cymbals. The exception is where a very big, ambient drum sound is required, in which case a studio with a large live room is needed, with additional ambience mics placed at a distance from the kit.

Jazz drums tend to be recorded the other way around — the stereo mic pair providing the main contribution, and close mics used to fill out the sound and fine-tune the balance.

# GUITAR

Guitar parts may be DI'd using one of the available studio preamps or speaker simulators, though for heavy rock, the miked sound is still the preferred option. Ultimately there is no best way; it's all down to personal choice. In many instances, chordal and rhythm parts can be DI'd very satisfactorily, while lead solos might benefit from the interaction between the amplifier and the guitar, especially if feedback is used to prolong sustained notes. Once again, one can mic up either a large stack or a small combo. Both produce their own distinctive sound, though a large setup needs a large studio to produce the best results. A small valve combo such as a Fender Champ or low wattage Mesa Boogie can produce excellent results in a small project studio.

Different results can be achieved by varying mic position and by choosing either dynamic or capacitor microphones. If two guitar parts need to be separated in some way, recording one with a dynamic mic and the other with a capacitor mic can help. Further differences can be created by using humbucking or single-coil pickups or by the subtle application of effects such as chorus. Additionally, EQ can be used both on the amplifier and the mixing console to emphasise different parts of the sound spectrum, and of course, the two parts can be panned to different sides of the stereo image. If the resulting sound is still confused, the guitar parts themselves should be examined to see if they are too similar or too busy. Sometimes playing a chordal part in a more restrained and simple way or applying a little string damping solves the problem.

# ACOUSTIC GUITARS

Acoustic guitars invariably sound better when miked up, regardless of how good the internal bug or pickup system may be. Important acoustic parts can be recorded in stereo, but where the guitar forms part of a complex arrangement, a mono recording may well give more stability. Because of the problems of sound leakage when working with acoustic instruments, acoustic guitars are invariably overdubbed individually, using closed headphones to prevent spill from the backing track.

If a song needs to start with several bars of solo acoustic guitar, but that guitar part must be recorded as an overdub, it is important that the correct number of count-in bars is provided, with a suitable click track or guide hi-hat part. If you ever have to pick up a project where this has not been done, it is possible to turn the tape over so that it plays backwards and then record extra beats at the introduction of the song to extend the count-in to a suitable length. A short, dry sound is best for this, otherwise the timing may appear to shift slightly when the sound is heard in reverse, as it will be once the tape is played back normally.

# PSYCHOLOGY

Recording can be a stressful experience, and it is part of the producer's job to be aware of mood problems and to tackle them as they arise. Open discussion should be encouraged if it is not allowed to run on too long, and any individual who is clearly in a less than ideal mood can often be diverted by giving them something useful to do, such as looking after a fader level or supervising drop-in points.

The good producer will also recognise the point at which an artist has worked too long to be giving of their best and he'll change the order of work to give that person a break if at all possible. Perhaps the worst time is when someone is repeatedly incapable of getting their part right; insisting on a break at this point can often be far more productive than allowing the person to struggle on stubbornly. Positive encouragement is the key, because as soon as you start to criticise a musician, his or her confidence is likely to suffer and the final performance will be so much worse for it.

If you can afford the tape tracks to keep a previous take while allowing the performer to do another, the feeling of security this gives may enable the player to give a more relaxed performance. The use of drugs and the excessive use of alcohol should be discouraged because of their detrimental effect on musical ability.

# CORRECTIVE EDITING

In extreme cases of inability to perform, it may be possible to edit together several attempts to provide one good version. For example, a one-off good vocal chorus can be 'spun in' for each chorus, using a sampler or open reel stereo recorder, while several dreadful guitar solos can often be edited to produce one good one. Session players can sometimes be used to perform critical sections with greater precision than the original musicians, but if these sections are to be edited, great care has to be taken to match the sounds. Even if the same guitar and amplifier is used to play part of a solo, the sound can be quite different simply because of the players' individual techniques.

Once all the necessary parts are safely on tape, then it's time for the mix. However, unless time really is tight, this should be done on a different day so that it can be heard with fresh ears.

# ARRANGING

When presented with a song to arrange, the producer has to consider not only the musical construction of the piece, but also the way in which the various sounds fit together. Thus arrangement can be divided into three distinct areas:

• The order in which the various musical sections are presented (intro, verse, chorus, bridge, middle eight and so on).

• The musical lines and rhythms which make up each part.

• The sounds chosen to play these lines and rhythms.

The order in which a song is arranged is very important — commercial material tends to work to a fairly rigid formula in that a distinct intro is followed by between three and five minutes of music. The traditional, melodic pop song tends to have:

• An easily recognisable verse/chorus structure, usually with a middle eight (which, despite its name, doesn't need to be exactly eight bars long).

- One or two 'bridge' sections.

- An instrumental solo, though this is not invariably included.

The chorus will be repeated frequently, the song often fading out over a repeated chorus line. Though musical fashions change very quickly, this traditional song structure has proved to be one of life's survivors.

Because of the fickle nature of the commercial music market, a song has to attract the interest of the listener very quickly, and once the intro is over, it usually pays to get to the chorus pretty quickly. This may be achieved by such devices as:

- Shortening the first verse.

- Using a modified version of the chorus as an intro.

- Coming straight in with the chorus after the intro.

Another useful device is to use only part of the chorus when it first occurs; this creates a sense of anticipation, helping to keep the listener interested. Indeed, the ability to create an atmosphere of anticipation is the hallmark of a good songwriter, and often the ends of verses or link sections will contain musical hooks which make the listener want to reach the chorus. What makes a good hook is less easy to quantify.

# THE NAME THAT REVERBERATES THROUGH THE WORLD'S GREAT STUDIOS

## FOR THE PRICE OF THOSE THAT DON'T!

# EFFECTS IN THE MIX

Artificial effects have become an integral part of modern music recording, but it is wrong to think of an effect as something that is added at the last minute to provide a kind of superficial gloss. It is also wrong to assume that using an effect will cover up a mistake or a piece of poor playing, because in most instances, it will simply draw attention to it.

Reverberation needs to be added to most recordings to simulate a natural acoustic environment and as an effect, it occupies a unique position. All other effects are employed for artistic reasons; it helps to plan the type of effect that will be used very early on in a session rather than groping around for something which might or might not work at the last minute. Indeed, some effects form an integral part of the sounds used in a composition, while certain delay-based effects may help determine the rhythm of a piece of music. In the studio, the producer has to decide which effects, if any, need to be added during the recording stage and which can be left until the mix. The home recordist faces the same decisions, though some decisions may be determined by the number of tape tracks and effects units available.

## RECORDING WITH EFFECTS

Though leaving all effects until the mix gives more room for manoeuvre, it is not always the best way to work, even if the facilities exist to make this practical. Sometimes it helps to record an effect to tape with the original instrument. A good engineer or producer will know instinctively when an effect should be added during recording and when it should be left until the end. Indeed, the very open-endedness of leaving everything to the mix can have a detrimental effect on the production of a piece of music; several producers I've spoken to recently believe it's a good idea to commit yourself to something fairly rigid at an early stage. Failure to do so can lead to a huge amount of time being wasted in exploring different possibilities when all that was needed was a clear sense of direction at the outset. To make matters worse, we now have MIDI sequencers synchronised to tape, mix automation and hard disk digital editing. All these technologies, while wonderful and extremely useful in themselves, can divert much time and effort from the task in hand. Ask anyone who has used an automated mixing system and they'll invariably tell you the mix takes at least twice as long as it did on a manual desk!

# ARTISTIC CONSIDERATIONS

When it comes to adding effects, we have to consider both the artistic and logistic effects of either recording them to tape or saving them until the mix. The factors in favour of recording the effect to tape with the original instrument are that:

• The player may feel more comfortable and put in a better performance.

• Committing effects to tape saves time at the mixing stage...

• ... and frees up the effects unit in question for a different task later in the session; for example, a multi-effects unit could provide an echo or delay during recording and then be used to furnish reverb during mixdown.

Conversely, if effects are changed or left out at the recording stage, the original musical performance may no longer work. This is very often the case when delay effects are used, as the musician 'plays' to the effect, but it can apply equally to chorus-type treatments which are often used on guitar parts.

There are negative aspects to recording the effects to tape too, especially if the number of tracks is limited — for example:

• Recording an instrument in mono only takes one tape track, but if you want to add an effect, then you need two tape tracks to keep the effect in stereo.

• Committing effects to tape deprives you of the opportunity to later fine tune the effect, to change its pan position relative to the dry track and to change its level in the mix.

In truth, there are occasions when one or the other approach is most appropriate and it is unwise to develop too rigid a method of working which might deprive you of flexibility when you most need it. If time is limited, recording as many effects as possible while tracking certainly saves time when you come to mix.

# GUITAR EFFECTS

Guitar parts tend to be recorded with their basic effects, such as overdrive, spring reverb, and expressive pedal effects such as wah wah. Some analogue effects pedals produce a more musical sound than their better specified rackmount counterparts, especially chorus and flange units, while stereo reverb treatments can safely be left to the final mix. Don't be tempted to dismiss an effects pedal purely because of its technical spec — if it sounds good, use it. If it's too noisy, distorts, or causes some other problem, discuss it with the player using the pedal and see if you can simulate the sound with your own equipment.

Even if you decide to add the effect at the final mix, you should be able to arrange things so that the player can hear his part with the required effect while playing via the headphone monitoring system. This can usually be achieved by feeding the effect to the monitor mix but without recording it to tape.

● TIP ●

If it really is necessary to leave a guitar treatment open-ended, it may help to record the sound the player wants on one tape track and a straight, clean, DI'd output from the guitar (via a DI box) on a spare track. This way, it is possible to feed the dry guitar track through an amplifier with the desired effects and overdrive settings, then mic it up, recording the result onto a further spare tape track or over the original guitar part. Figure 5.1 illustrates how this is done.

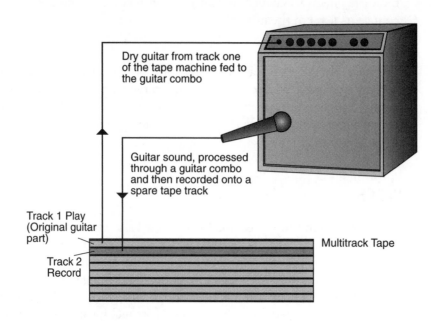

Dry guitar from track one
of the tape machine fed to
the guitar combo

Guitar sound, processed
through a guitar combo
and then recorded onto a
spare tape track

Track 1 Play
(Original guitar
part)

Track 2
Record

Multitrack Tape

**Figure 5.1: Re-recording a Guitar Track via a Combo Amplifier**

# LOGISTICS

In some circumstances, it is necessary to record effects with the performance purely because there aren't enough effects units or console sends to go around at the mix. Similarly, if tracks have to be bounced together to conserve space on tape, then the necessary effects must be added during the bounce. If track restrictions mean that the bounced signal ends up on a single track, then any added effects will also be mono. This is particularly common in home studios, and the usual outcome is that many of the effects which should have been in stereo end up being in mono. There is no easy way around this, but it is possible to give some semblance of stereo spread to a mono track by processing it at the final mixing stage with an additional stereo reverb treatment. If the track needs little in the way of added reverb, a short, bright plate or an early reflections program will create a sense of depth and width without making the sound seem as though extra reverb has been added at all.

If the main restriction is in the number of console sends, then consider using the channel insert points or direct outputs as sends when adding individual effects to individual tracks. If you have sufficient spare input channels on the mixer, use these as effects returns to enable you to make use of the EQ and pan controls. Ensure that the effects sends are turned down on any channels used as returns or unwanted feedback may result.

# INNOVATIVE EFFECTS

While most effects can be generated using either dedicated effects units or digital multi-effects processors, it is possible to create something a little out of the ordinary by using just a little ingenuity. Indeed, most of the recordings still regarded as pop classics were made in the days when very few effects units were available and engineers had to improvise. Fine examples can be heard on records by the Beatles and early Pink Floyd to name just two.

# BACKWARDS REVERB

Some of the most powerful effects are the most simple to create, and one of my favourites is true 'backwards reverb'. This is quite unlike the canned reverse effects that come as standard on most reverb units, because it actually comes before the sound that caused it. Obviously this can't be done in real life, and it can't be done in real time either, because the reverb unit would have to know what sound was coming next. Nevertheless, it can be done on tape and it is relatively easy.

## ● TECHNIQUE ●

• Record the original take dry onto the multitrack tape, then turn the tape over so the track plays backwards — from the end of the song to the start. (Turning the tape over also reverses the track order, so that on an 8-track machine, track 1 becomes track 8 and vice versa, so make sure you don't record over any wanted stuff while the tape is reversed.)

• With the recording now running backwards, the track to be treated is used to feed a conventional stereo reverb set to a medium to long decay setting (2 to 10 seconds) and the reverb recorded onto an empty track (or pair of tracks if you can afford the luxury of keeping it in stereo).

• Once the reverb has been recorded, the tape can be replaced the right way round and played normally. Now the reverb will start to build up a couple of seconds before the track starts and produce an unnatural pre-echo effect. This works very nicely on vocals, but can also be used on instrumental sounds or drums.

• Panning the dry sound to one side of the mix and the reverse reverb to the other creates a strong sense of movement, and it is worthwhile experimenting with combined effects such as adding artificial reverse reverb to the track at the same time and panning this to the other extreme.

# DUCKER

### ● TECHNIQUE ●

Another interesting trick is to set up a compressor as a ducker and trigger it from the vocal track. The backwards reverb vocal track is then processed via the ducker so that the reverse effect only surfaces between vocal phrases. This is shown in Figure 5.2.

A normal, short reverb can also be added to the vocal track to make it sound natural. The secret is not to overdo it. The reverse sound doesn't have to be used all the way through a song — it can be brought in and out of the mix as required at the touch of a fader.

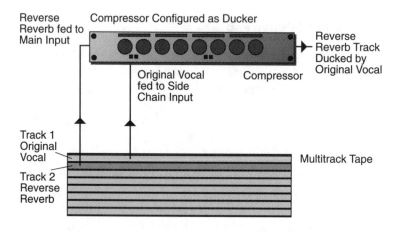

Figure 5.2: Ducked Reverse Reverb

# PITCHED REVERB

### ● TECHNIQUE ●

Normally, a reverb unit will be fed directly from the track being treated, but there are a couple of tricks that can make the effects more interesting. One technique is to feed the effects send through a pitch shifter before it goes to the reverb unit and drop the pitch by an octave. This means that the original sound will be unchanged but its reverb will be an octave lower than normal. Used on musical sounds, the pitch shift must either be an octave up or an octave down to maintain a true musical relationship, but in the case of drums and percussion, smaller shifts can be used.

# REVERB AND FLANGE

### ● TIP ●

Flanging is a very dramatic effect but, by the same token, it can be too obvious. However, if we patch in a flanger between the desk's aux send output and the input to the reverb unit, the result is far more subtle than would be achieved by putting the flanger after the reverb output, and helps add sparkle and interest to vocal sounds.

This works nicely with synthesized string sounds, as the flanger creates a sense of detail and movement in the reverberant sound without changing the dry part of the sound. And the fact that the flanger comes before the reverb rather than after it means that the cyclic nature of the effect is broken up by the multiple delays of the reverb unit, resulting in a less obvious treatment.

# REAL SHIFT

It is well known that pitch shifters can be used to thicken a vocal or instrumental track by providing a slightly detuned version of the original. But, with a little thought, the pitch shifter may be used in a much more convincing way. This technique requires a spare tape track.

### ● TECHNIQUE ●

• The idea is to double the original vocal part by singing along to the original on tape. Now there's nothing new in this — in fact it's the classic method of double-tracking a line to make it sound fatter or fuller. The difference is that, this time, we take the signal feeding the singer's headphone monitor system and process that through the pitch shifter so that it is between 5 and 10 cents sharp or flat. The sound quality of the pitch shifter is of little importance as it is used only for monitoring during performance.

• The singer now pitches his or her performance to the shifted sound, with the result that the new take is exactly the right amount out of pitch with the first to create a natural chorus effect.

• If the pitch shifter has a delay function, a few tens of milliseconds of delay can be added to shift the second take slightly in time as well as pitch. The advantage, apart from having a real as opposed to a synthesised second take, is that the quality of recording is uncompromised by unnecessary signal processing.

• With instruments, there is no need even to use a pitch shifter — all that is necessary is to change the tape speed slightly, using the varispeed control, and then record a second take without retuning the instrument. Once the tape is replayed at the normal speed, the two slightly out-of-tune takes will produce a chorus effects far more natural than that from any chorus pedal.

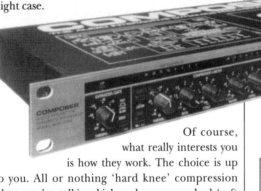
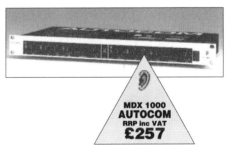

# VOCALS

Even those used to working in an all-MIDI environment will need to work with microphones when it comes to getting vocals onto tape. Recording vocals is essentially very simple, but it still surprises me how many people really struggle to get an acceptable vocal sound. In reality, the first necessity is a vocalist who can actually perform well, but taking that for granted, the rest is down to choosing the right type of microphone, putting it in the right position and using the correct degree of compression to control it without choking the life out of it.

Pop shields should be used as a matter of course, and the engineer should have an effective de-essing system available when the singer's vocal characteristics demand one. A suitable reverb or ambience treatment is invariably needed to add realism to vocals recorded in a dead studio, and both the engineer and producer should work to put the singer at his or her ease in order to stimulate the best performance possible.

It is the producer's responsibility to check that the vocal is of sufficient quality throughout and any lines containing errors in either lyrical delivery, timing or pitch should be replaced, ideally during the same session to maintain a continuity of sound. The producer will also need to supervise any harmony parts or double tracking.

## COMPOSITE TAKES

It helps to have photocopies of the lyric sheet on hand before the session gets under way so that the producer can add comments and underline any phrases or words that need patching up as they arise. Some producers are happy to get one reasonable take down on tape and then patch this up by replacing sections, while others prefer to capture several complete takes and then use the best sections from each. In 8 or 16-track studios, the first method is less wasteful of tape tracks and the final mix is easier to handle.

If the singer isn't comfortable singing isolated sections of the song, try running the tape all the way through and simply punching in and out of record on the lines you want to replace. This way, the singer can concentrate on creating a whole performance, even though what you finally use will be the result of several different takes. Even with this method, though, you'll often find that one specific line is giving trouble so you may have to tackle this in isolation until it's right. So long as the singer gets a couple of lines 'run' into it, everyone should be happy.

The second method of producing a composite take — recording several complete takes and then using the best sections from each — is best suited to larger systems; a mixer with mute automation makes it much easier to switch between vocal takes than attempting to do it manually. Often the composite vocal track will be bounced to a spare tape track and the original tracks freed up for re-use. This may mean holding up the session for a while to allow the vocal track to be sorted out but it's one thing less to worry about when you come to mix.

Ultimately, it doesn't matter what method you use, as long as you end up with vocal take you're happy with. And if that means putting the best vocal chorus into a large-memory sampler and then firing it back into the mix at the appropriate points using MIDI triggering, then that's fine too. After all, this is only the modern equivalent of 'spinning in', where vocal sections such as choruses were transferred to a two-track open reel machine which was then cued up and started manually to do the same job. This may sound tricky, but if marker pencil cue marks are put on the back of the tape and lined up with some feature on the machine, the results can be quite repeatable.

# VOCAL MONITORING

Most vocal monitoring is done with headphones, and two types are commonly used. Fully-enclosed headphones are less prone to spillage problems, but some vocalists find that they have trouble singing in tune because the boxed-in feeling distracts them. This is why you often see videos of recording sessions where the singer has one phone on and the other off.

Semi-enclosed phones are more comfortable to work with but they leak more sound, so you could end up with a little of the backing track on the vocal track. This is not normally serious — as long as you don't suddenly decide to use part of the take unaccompanied! The leakage problem may also occur if any sort of click track is being used — basic pulsed tone metronomes tend to spill quite badly.

The quality of monitoring can have a profound effect on the quality of a vocal performance, so take the time needed to set up a good foldback mix for the singer and add sufficient reverb to the headphone mix to make him or her feel comfortable. The room temperature can also affect a singer's ability to pitch — don't automatically blame the singer if something isn't going quite right. A song is only as good as its vocal part, so make every possible effort to keep the singer relaxed and in a creative frame of mind.

# THE RIGHT MIC

Generally, live vocal mics are dynamic models and incorporate a deliberate treble boost of a few dBs at around 5kHz in order to render the vocal more intelligible. While undoubtedly useful in preserving clarity of diction, such a 'presence peak' is not necessarily a good thing in the studio, where the general aim is to capture as natural a performance as possible.

Most professional studios will use a capacitor mic for vocal use, because these have a high sensitivity and a wide frequency response extending up to 20kHz or so. Dynamic microphones, on the other hand, tend to perform poorly above 16kHz or thereabouts and they are less sensitive than capacitors — which could lead to problems with electronic noise if the vocalist has a quiet voice. However, some rock vocalists prefer to use dynamic mics in the studio because it gives them a fatter sound and they use the mic so close to the mouth that low sensitivity is no longer a problem.

The wide frequency response of capacitor microphones can emphasise sibilance (a whistling sound accompanying S and T sounds) in a performer's voice; the problem is further aggravated by large amounts of compression or bright reverb treatments. The usual cure for sibilance is to use a de-esser to attenuate the sibilant sounds, but in some cases, a more pragmatic approach might be to use a suitable dynamic microphone, as the limited frequency response will tend to hide the problem. It may also be possible to choose a capacitor microphone with a warmer characteristic. This need to match microphone characteristics to vocalists is the main reason a well-equipped studio will have so many different vocal mics.

● TIP ●

No single microphone is ideal for all vocalists. If a singer has a bright voice, then a mic with a presence peak may tend to make the overall sound appear excessively harsh, whereas the same mic used on a singer with an indistinct or soft voice could yield a significant improvement. Attempting to achieve the same effect by means of EQ seldom succeeds, and for this reason, I would recommend recording vocals with little or no EQ; if the sound isn't right, then try a different mic or change its position slightly before resorting to EQ.

# MIC PATTERN

Unidirectional or Cardioid pattern mics are the preferred choice for live performance because of their ability to reject off-axis sounds, thus minimising both the spill from other performers and acoustic feedback. In the studio, vocals tend to be recorded as separate overdubs where the singer monitors the backing mix via headphones, and in this case the need to use a Cardioid pattern mic is not so great. However, unless the studio is acoustically quite dead it may be a good idea to use a directional mic anyway, to minimise the effect of the room acoustic on the recorded sound — unless the room acoustic just happens to provide the sound you want. Figure 6.1 shows the directional characteristics available from different types of microphone.

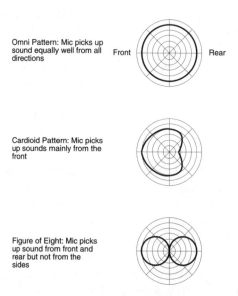

Omni Pattern: Mic picks up sound equally well from all directions    Front    Rear

Cardioid Pattern: Mic picks up sounds mainly from the front

Figure of Eight: Mic picks up sound from front and rear but not from the sides

Figure 6.1: The Common Polar Patterns

In circumstances where the room does make a positive contribution to the sound (as it may when recording choral music in a church, for example), the result will invariably sound more natural recorded via an Omni (Omnidirectional) pattern microphone. As a general rule, Omni pattern mics produce a more accurate overall picture than an equivalent Cardioid because they have the same nominal response in all directions, with the result that both direct and indirect sound is accurately captured.

Microphones should be mounted on a solid boom stand and a shock-mount cradle employed if available. However, some singers can't perform properly without a hand-held mic, in which case you should give them one to hold, set up another mic on a stand a couple of feet in front of them, and tell them that you need a mix of the sound from both mics. The recording is invariably made using just the output from the stand-mounted mic!

# POP SHIELDS

Most engineers experience problems with microphone popping, and experience has shown that simple foam wind shields are virtually useless. The popping is caused by blasts of air from the performer's mouth slamming into the microphone diaphragm and giving rise to a high level, low frequency output signal, which comes over as a loud, bassy thump.

Commercial pop filters use a fine plastic or metal gauze stretched over a circular frame somewhere between four and six inches in a diameter and positioned between the performer and the microphone. Normal sound, which consists of vibrations within the air, is not affected, but blasts of moving air are intercepted and their energy dissipated harmlessly as turbulence.

### ● TIP ●

Commercial pop shields are very expensive, so here's how to make your own. For the grille, a piece of fine nylon stocking works perfectly. This may be stretched over a wire frame (many engineers use wire coat-hangers) and is then positioned between the microphone and the singer's mouth as shown in Figure 6.2.

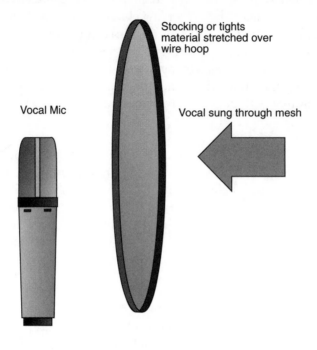

Stocking or tights
material stretched over
wire hoop

Vocal Mic

Vocal sung through mesh

**Figure 6.2: Improvised Pop Shield**

A tidier alternative is to use a wooden embroidery hoop to hold the stocking material. Another ready-made option is a frying pan splash guard. These comprise a fine metal mesh fixed to a wire hoop with a handle; the provision of this handle makes it easy to tape the filter to a mic stand.

# MIC POSITIONING

Working too close to a microphone will cause significant changes in both level and tone as the singer moves his or her head. A working distance of between six inches and two feet from the mic is most appropriate to studio work. Most studio vocal recordings are done in a relatively dead environment so that reverb can be added artificially during the mix. In a professional studio, there is likely to be a dedicated vocal booth, but excellent home recordings can be made simply by keeping the microphone well away from the walls of the room and improvising sound absorbers using bedding draped over clothes driers and suchlike. In general, the deader the environment the better, and if the acoustic is still less than ideal, work closer to the mic to improve the ratio of direct to reflected sound.

# VOCAL GROUPS

If several vocalists are to be recorded at one time, the distance between mics should be at least three times the distance between the microphone and the vocalist, to avoid phase cancellation effects due to spill. If you can improvise some form of acoustic screening, so much the better.

For larger groups of singers, such as choirs or ensembles, it may be desirable to record them in stereo using a pair of coincident cardioids or an M&S pair. For larger choral recordings, more control is available if you use one stereo pair for each section of the chorus, with the microphone pairs mounted above and in front of the performers.

## ● TIP ●

To create the illusion of space when multitracking backing vocals or groups of backing vocalists, try setting up a stereo pair of mics in the room and then moving the performers for each new recording. For example, you could record three tracks with the singers positioned left, then centre, then right of the mics. On playback, this will create the illusion of the three groups of people existing at the same time in a real stereo soundspace. The singers can be made to sound slightly different using established tricks, such as varispeeding the tape slightly for each overdub. These techniques are described later in this chapter when double tracking is explained.

# COMPRESSION

Compression is invariably needed in pop music production to keep the vocal level nice and even. A degree of compression applied during the recording will help keep the level going onto tape sensibly high and at the same time guard against loud peaks that might otherwise cause tape overload and subsequent distortion. Soft-knee compressors are least obtrusive in this application and should be set to give a gain reduction of 10dB or so during the louder sections.

A singer with a very wide dynamic range, on the other hand, may need a ratio type controller set to a ratio of 4:1, or even higher, to really keep the peaks under control. This is where an experienced engineer is a great asset, as he'll know from the first run-through just how much compression will be required. As a rule, choose a fast or programme-dependent attack time and a release time of around half a second.

It is safer to apply less compression than you need, because you can always add more compression when you come to mix. The effect of too much compression added at the recording stage may ruin an otherwise perfect take and will be impossible to correct later. The majority of engineers will use additional compression when mixing, but again you have to take care not to overdo it, because compression also brings out any noise and sibilance present in the recording. The use of an Exciter to brighten a vocal track may also bring up the sibilance to an unacceptable level, in which case you may have to resort to using a de-esser.

A gate or expander is useful to clean up the spaces between words and phrases, but as the setting up is quite critical, these should only be used on the mix and never while recording. That way you can take as many passes as you need to get it right.

# EQUALISATION

Vocals will often need some equalisation to make them 'sit' well with the backing track, while over-sibilant vocals may require dynamic EQ processing using a de-esser. No two singers have exactly the same voice characteristics, so any EQ treatment is likely to be different depending on the singer. However, modifications in certain general areas of the audio spectrum can be considered appropriate to the vast majority of voices, though final EQ settings will have to be tuned by ear with regard to the specific singer being recorded.

• Any top boost should be applied quite high up at 6-12kHz, but watch out for sibilance creeping in. However, don't settle for a dull vocal sound simply because using the right EQ brings up the sibilance; if you have to use a de-esser to save the day, then do it.

• Boosting in the 1-2kHz range gives a rather honky, cheap sound to the vocals and so is not recommended except as a special effect. I try to keep vocals as flat as possible and tend to use the shelving high control to add just a hint of top rather than anything more drastic.

• Presence can be added with just a little boost at 3-4kHz, but be moderate or the sound quality will suffer. After all, vocals are the most natural sound in the world and our ears soon register the fact that they've been tampered with.

• If you're mixing several backing vocals, rolling off a touch of bass might help the vocal to sit better in the mix without sounding muddy. On its own, the equalised backing vocal might sound terribly thin, but once in the track, the chances are that it will sound perfectly normal, yet won't fill up the vulnerable lower-mid area of the spectrum with unwanted energy.

# DOUBLE TRACKING

Double tracking is a popular trick used to add depth to a voice. It may be used to compensate for a weak voice, or creatively to add impact to choruses and so on. Traditionally, the singer performs the same part twice (or more) onto two tape tracks and then the two tracks are played back together to give the effect of two singers in unison. Alternative technological tricks may be used to fake the effect, but if a singer is capable of duplicating a performance pretty accurately in pitch and timing, the real way always sounds better.

● TIP ●

A common problem with double-tracked parts is that words may start together but often sound ragged because the word endings aren't in sync. Nowhere is this more evident than in the case of words ending with 't' or 's' sounds, and a simple dodge is to perform the second take in a deliberately sloppy manner by missing off or fading the ends of tricky words. When the two tracks are played together, the result will sound much tighter. The same applies to backing harmony vocal parts.

● TIP ●

To create a little difference between the two vocal lines, you could varispeed the multitrack up or down by a semitone or so before recording the second part. This will give the voice a different character when the tape is returned to normal speed; it's a trick is often used by radio jingle writers to create the effect of a large vocal group when overdubbing just one or two singers.

● TIP ●

Another useful trick is to use a delay line to delay the headphone mix by 50mS or so when recording the second track. This has the effect of making the singer perform the second part 50mS later than the first part, giving a short delay effect when the tape is replayed normally. This creates a nice rich effect without compromising the sound quality, because what goes to tape hasn't actually been passed through the delay unit. This means that any old delay will do the trick, even an old tape echo or guitar foot-pedal.

# FAKING IT

Inevitably, some singers can never perform a song the same way twice, in which case any attempt at real double tracking will sound messy and unacceptable. This is where ADT, or Automatic Double Tracking, comes to the rescue. Originally, this effect was created using an open reel machine running at high speed to function as a very short delay unit, or by using the short delay setting on a tape echo unit. By fine-tuning the delay so that the original sound and its repeat just start to separate, you get the effect of two voices singing slightly out of time with each other.

The effect isn't entirely convincing because the pitching of the delayed part is just too perfect, but later electronic attempts to simulate the effect using chorus or pitch shift circuitry can sound rather more realistic:

## ● TECHNIQUE ●

• A short delay of between 30 and 100mS is added to the sound but the delay is either subtly chorused or processed via a pitch shifter to give a detuning effect of between 5 and 10 cents (one cent is one hundredth of a semitone).

• Further depth can be added by panning the original and delayed signals to opposite sides of the stereo mix.

• If you only have a basic DDL, then you can use this to simultaneously delay the sound and to vary the pitch — a kind of delayed chorus setting. After getting the delay time right by ear, adjust the modulation depth and speed so that the pitch wavering effect is just audible — a modulation rate of 2-3Hz combined with a very shallow modulation depth should do the trick nicely. The longer the delay time, the less modulation depth you'll need to create the required degree of pitch shifting.

# REVERB AND AMBIENCE

Even before digital reverb units came along, some way of adding life to vocals had to be found, because the dead studio recording environment made them sound quite lifeless without further treatment. Reverb is part of our everyday lives — we exist in reflective environments, so any sound we hear that is totally devoid of any reverb or ambience sounds unnaturally limp. In the early days, live echo rooms, spring reverb units and echo plates were all used to add reverberation to recordings, the most successful probably being the plate. This comprised a large steel plate suspended in a rigid frame and driven into vibration by a voice coil similar to that on a loudspeaker. The resulting vibrations were picked up by two or more

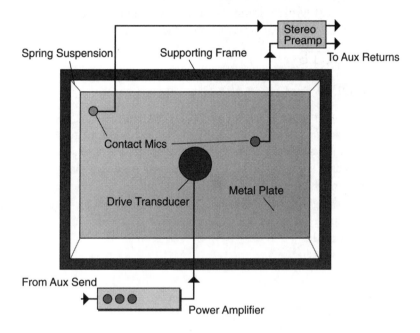

**Figure 6.3: Reverb Plate**

surface-mounted contact mics and amplified before being fed back into the mix. The final effect was brighter than natural reverb, but it was a musically pleasant sound, which is why most modern digital units have plate simulation modes as well as rooms, halls and chambers. Figure 6.3 shows how a plate works.

Picking the right reverb setting is where the producer's artistic input is vital, because there are many ways of approaching any musical project, with no particular way being more right than others. Even so, there are a few guidelines based largely on common sense:

● TECHNIQUE ●

• Bright reverb settings give the vocal an attractive 'sizzle', as long as they are not so bright as to bring the level of sibilance up to an unacceptable degree.

• If the song is a ballad, a longer, softer reverb might create a more appropriate atmosphere.

• Short ambience settings, rich in early reflections, can be used to add life to a vocal while adding no perceptible reverb at all, and trick settings such as reverse reverb also have their place if used in moderation.

# ADVANCED EFFECTS

### ● TIP ●

You can create a useful effect by setting a DDL to give a single repeat between 50 and 100mS long, and feed this into a reverb unit to give a pre-delay. This creates a deeper sense of space and also separates the reverb from the basic sound a little, which can enhance the clarity. Many multi-effects units have a pre-delay setting included in the reverb parameters, but this little dodge is still useful for those occasions where your main reverb unit is tied up on another job and you have to create an effect using something pretty basic.

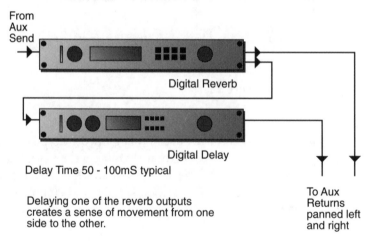

From Aux Send

Digital Reverb

Digital Delay
Delay Time 50 - 100mS typical

Delaying one of the reverb outputs creates a sense of movement from one side to the other.

To Aux Returns panned left and right

**Figure 6.4: Delaying One Reverb Output**

### ● TIP ●

Another production trick can be achieved by putting a delay after the reverb but on only one of the stereo outputs. This splits the reverb so that it starts in one speaker and then moves over to the other. Once again, this treatment adds a sense of movement but without becoming too obvious or gimmicky. Figure 6.4 shows how this might be arranged.

# REVERB PANNING

Reverb panning can also be used to create movement and interest without actually giving the game away, and if your multi-effects unit includes a panner, panning the output of the reverb unit from left to right, ideally at a rate that fits in with the tempo of the song, can be very effective. If you don't have a panner, you can create the same effect by using a gate such as the Drawmer DS201 that has side-chain or key inputs.

## ● TECHNIQUE ●

• Using two sounds programmed into a drum machine (this must have at least two assignable outputs), the two sides of the gate can be triggered alternately via the key inputs. Ideally, the drum machine would be synchronised to the master tape using a MIDI sequencer.

• The stereo reverb is then fed into the main gate inputs and the attack and release times set to give a smooth pan effect. This only takes a little trial and error and is remarkably effective.

• If you have two reverb units, try a reverse setting on one of the reverb units and a conventional reverb setting on the other. Pan one reverb unit left and the other right and you'll find that as the normal reverb decays on one side, the reverse effect will build up on the other, giving a different kind of moving pan effect.

# A MATTER OF TASTE

Almost any effect, no matter how bizarre, can be justified in context — it's all a matter of artistic judgment, which is where a good producer comes into his or her own. I've even heard vocals chopped into short, gated sections and then panned between the speakers, giving an effect like a synchronised, intermittent mic cable fault, but because it was used sparingly and in the right place, it worked. Similarly, a good vocal line can be completely ruined by the gratuitous application of effects. In most cases, clarity of diction is important, in which case the longer the reverb decay time, the lower its level should be in the mix or the sound will become muddled.

# ART BEFORE TECHNOLOGY

By all means combine two or more different reverb units to create a composite effect that enhances the vocal sound, but always keep your artistic aims at the front of your mind and don't let the technology dictate your actions. The technology is there to serve you, not the other way around. Most pop songs rely on a strong, distinctive vocal part and it is up to the producer to achieve that by whatever means possible.

Finally, artists tend to ask for effects they have heard before and many are over-used cliches such as adding repeat echo to the last word in a vocal line or the last word in a song. Occasionally, one of these cliches may still be OK to use, but it is far better to do the unexpected than kill your record with predictability. If you must use a cliche, try to use it in an unexpected way or in an unusual place. For example, adding a gross repeat echo to the very first word in a song might have more impact than using it right at the end.

# Simply the Best!

Packed with authoritative reviews of the latest hi-tech music and recording equipment, hot news from the cutting edge of technology, enlightening hints and tips, regular interviews with top musicians and recording engineers, plus in-depth practical guides to making the most of the gear you have, *Sound On Sound* is the undisputed leader in its field. Check it out at your local newsagent and find out why.

For subscription details call or write to:
SOS Publications Ltd
Media House, Burrel Road,
St. Ives, Cambridgeshire, PE17 4LE, England.
Tel: 0480 461244      Fax: 0480 492422

# DRUMS

I t's probably true to say that now, more than ever, pop records are being made using electronically sequenced drum sounds rather than the real thing. Fashions have a habit of changing, however, and a good engineer should be prepared for all eventualities. The ability to record a real drum kit is a vital skill that no engineer should be without, for even if the majority of work is done with electronic percussion, it is still common practice to overdub real cymbals and percussion to add a spark of humanity to the end result.

## THE KIT

Provided the kit to be recorded is well looked after and fitted with decent heads, it should be possible to get a good sound out of it within half an hour or so. Old heads stretch unevenly and the surface becomes wrinkled, causing a loss of tone which no amount of tuning and damping will fix. Contrary to popular belief, drum tuning doesn't have to be radically changed for recording; a little careful damping is often all that is needed. Furthermore, most drum recording is done using relatively inexpensive dynamic mics, making it possible to mic the entire kit for around the same price as a couple of good vocal mics.

The easiest kit to record is the one that uses single-headed toms. If the toms are double headed, the bottom heads may normally be removed without problems, though you may find that the nut boxes rattle; a little inventive work with a pack of Blu Tak will usually cure this. If you prefer the sound of the toms double-headed, they do require more critical tuning, and the bottom head often needs a little careful damping to prevent it ringing.

# TUNING AND DAMPING

Snare drums usually have metal or wooden shells, though some make use of synthetic materials, and they vary in depth enormously. Metal shells give a brighter tone with quite a lot of ring, while wooden snares tend to be warmer. Whatever the type, it is important to ensure that the snares are in good order and properly adjusted to minimise rattling.

Usually the snare head is tensioned slightly looser than the batter head, though individual drummers will have their own ideas on tuning. As a starting point, all drum heads should be tensioned as evenly as possible; tapping the head around the edges should give the same pitch all the way around the head. Every drum has a natural range of tuning and it will be evident if the tuning is too far out, as the tone will be either too hard or very lifeless.

Inevitably, the snares will vibrate in sympathy whenever another drum is hit, and though this may be minimised by careful tuning of the snare drum relative to the rest of the kit, it can seldom be eliminated completely. One approach is to gate the snare mic, but this does nothing to remove the buzz picked up by the overhead mics. Some engineers resort to taping coins onto the snare head to pull the head down onto the snares, but in my experience, this compromises the tone of the drum.

An undamped drum has a surprisingly long decay time and, what's worse, it will ring in sympathy whenever other drums are hit. Overdamping, on the other hand, can leave a kit sounding lifeless, yet many inexperienced engineers choke the life out of a kit because they are worried by minor rings and rattles that would probably be inaudible in the context of a complete mix anyway. A little experience will soon show the right amount of damping to use. Internal dampers are rarely used in the studio as they put pressure on the head. Far better to use a pad of tissue or cloth held in place with a strip of studio tape.

One trick often used to give a more dynamic tom sound is to first tune the head evenly, but then slacken off just one tuning lug a touch. This produces a slight pitch drop after the drum is struck, rather like an electronic drum, with the effect related to how hard the drum is hit.

● TIP ●

Most contemporary drummers will have a hole cut in the front head of the kick drum which makes miking very easy, though the hole should be as large as is practical to prevent the remaining material from ringing excessively. Don't be tempted to remove the front head completely, as this can put uneven stress on the drum shell and may cause it to distort. A wooden bass drum beater gives a better-defined sound than cork or felt beaters, and a patch of mole skin or hard plastic taped to the head where the beater hits will add more of a click to the sound. There are specialist drum products for this application, but an old credit card works perfectly well.

● TIP ●

Damping the bass drum is best achieved by placing a folded woollen blanket inside the drum so that it rests on the bottom of the shell and touches the lower part of the rear head. Further damping is unlikely to be necessary, though noise gates are often used to sharpen up the decay of the sound.

# MIKING OPTIONS

Perhaps the most accurate way to mic a drum kit is with a stereo microphone pair (either coincident or spaced) placed between five and ten feet in front of the kit. This arrangement can capture the live sound of the kit very faithfully, but the degree of artistic success is dependent on the actual sound and balance of the drum kit and on the suitability of the room acoustics. If the snare and kick drum need to be made more assertive, additional close mics can be used on these and added to the mix, usually panned to the centre. The mic positions will be similar to those used when a separate mic is used on each drum. This setup is illustrated in Figure 7.1.

This method of miking is not suitable for situations in which spill from other instruments might cause a problem. Furthermore, for pop music work, the natural sound of the kit is often the last thing the producer wants to hear, though it has applications in jazz and suchlike! More often, the kit is recorded with closely positioned mics on the individual drums, with an additional stereo pair located above the kit to capture the ambience.

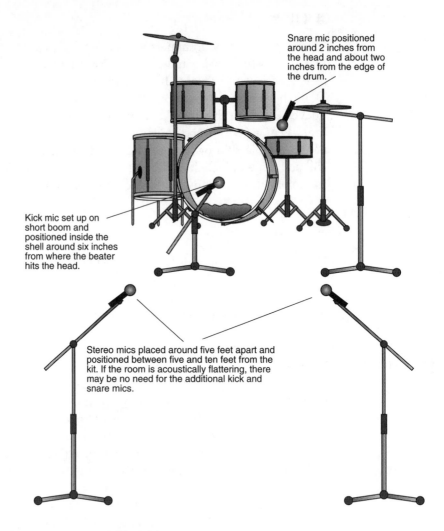

Snare mic positioned around 2 inches from the head and about two inches from the edge of the drum.

Kick mic set up on short boom and positioned inside the shell around six inches from where the beater hits the head.

Stereo mics placed around five feet apart and positioned between five and ten feet from the kit. If the room is acoustically flattering, there may be no need for the additional kick and snare mics.

**Figure 7.1: Basic Kit Miking**

# CLOSE MIKING

• SNARE AND TOMS: Snare drums produce the brightest sound in the kit other than the cymbals, so a dynamic mic with a respectable top end or a capacitor mic is desirable. Most engineers use Cardioid pattern mics for all the drums, to give the greatest immunity from spill, but in reality, Omni mics don't fare much worse than Cardioid in this respect and have the benefit of picking up off-axis sounds more accurately. In other words, they may pick up a touch more spill from the other drums, but at least they'll pick it up accurately. A further benefit is that Omni mics don't suffer from the proximity effect and so are less susceptible to unpredictable tonal changes when used close to an instrument, as is the case when miking drums. The usual mic position for the snare and toms is a couple of inches above the drum head, a couple of inches in from the edge and angled towards the centre of the head. Any damping should be positioned so as not to be between the mic and the drum.

• KICK DRUM: Kick drum mics are invariably mounted on boom stands so that the mic can be positioned inside the drum shell. A good starting position is with the mic pointing directly at the point on the head where the beater hits it and at a distance of six inches or so.

By changing the distance slightly or moving the mic to one side, a significant tonal change can be achieved, giving the engineer a means of controlling the sound at source rather than using EQ. Because of the low frequencies involved, a mic with a good bass response is essential, and it

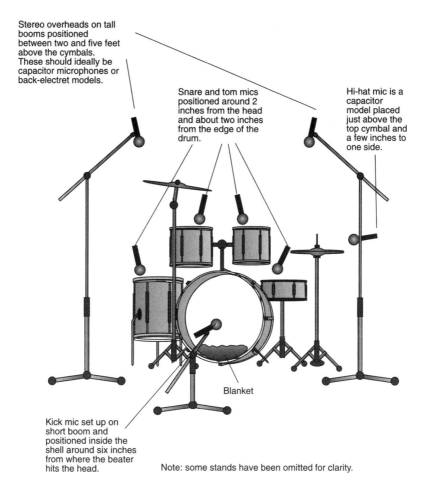

Stereo overheads on tall booms positioned between two and five feet above the cymbals. These should ideally be capacitor microphones or back-electret models.

Snare and tom mics positioned around 2 inches from the head and about two inches from the edge of the drum.

Hi-hat mic is a capacitor model placed just above the top cymbal and a few inches to one side.

Blanket

Kick mic set up on short boom and positioned inside the shell around six inches from where the beater hits the head.

Note: some stands have been omitted for clarity.

**Figure 7.2 Fully Miked Drum Kit**

must be able to stand the high sound levels that occur inside a kick drum. Dynamic Cardioids or Figure-Of-Eights tend to be used in this role.

• CYMBALS: Capacitor mics should be used as overhead/ambience mics to preserve the transient detail of the cymbals; depending on the kit setup, you may find a separate hi-hat mic useful, especially if the close drum mics are to be gated. For the hi-hat mic, a position a few inches from the edge of the cymbals and angled from above or beneath will avoid the mic picking up the sound of air being expelled when the cymbals are closed. Figure 7.2 shows a fully miked kit.

• PERCUSSION: General percussion such as congas may be miked from overhead in either mono or stereo, and unless separation is a problem, the mic distance may be increased to anywhere between one and three feet from the drum. In situations where the mics are placed at a distance, the room will have more of an influence on the sound, whereas close miking will capture little of the room ambience, giving a drier sound which may be processed further during mixing.

# TRACKING

The number of tape tracks allocated to the drum kit depends on the total number of tracks at your disposal and on the requirements of the rest of the instrumentation. Ideally, six tracks should be considered a minimum, divided up as kick, snare, stereo toms and stereo overheads. Check that the overheads are panned the same way as the tom mics! If spare tracks are abundant, then a separate track for each tom might be useful, though in the smaller studio, there may be only four tracks, or even fewer, reserved for drums. In this case, it may be advantageous to mix the bass drum and snare drum together on one track and all the toms on another, keeping just the overheads in stereo. Providing a significant amount of the stereo overhead signal is used in the mix, some degree of stereo imaging will be restored.

# MACHINES AND SAMPLES

Drum machines provide an easy way of obtaining high quality drum sounds, though they need to be programmed by someone with a good feel for percussion if the end result is to be acceptable. Many sequencer users prefer to use their drum machines or samplers merely to provide the sounds, the actual programming being done by playing the drum part in real time either from a MIDI keyboard or some form of MIDI drum pad system. Usually, the part is built up in layers rather than all in one go, and it helps to hold the timing together if a straight guide rhythm is recorded first. This may be quantised, if necessary, before the rest of the drum part is added and then deleted once the recording is complete.

Even the best drum machines sound less than convincing when playing fast tom fills because each beat produces exactly the same sound, unlike a real kit which has subtle variations in tone. For this reason, some producers prefer to program the kick drum and snare parts but play the hi-hats, cymbals and toms on acoustic drums miked conventionally. This eliminates problems such as sympathetic resonances in the bass drum or snare rattles and improves separation, allowing a cleaner result to be obtained. The slight timing errors of a real player make the whole thing sound more human, but the overall sound is cleaner and the essential rhythm elements, the kick and snare, can be made as tight as is desired.

# DRUM SOUND REPLACEMENT

Drum samples can also be used to replace sounds on tape which have been properly played but where the sound is inadequate in some way. This technique relies on the drums being recorded on separate tracks, but on most sessions, at least the kick and snare drums will have their own track.

## ● TECHNIQUE ●

• If tape tracks are limited, gate the sounds while recording to isolate them from any spill; for this application, gates with key filters cope much better than straightforward gates. If there are plenty of available tape tracks, record the drums onto individual tracks and then gate afterwards. This allows more than one take if the gate settings are not properly optimised.

• The output from the gate should then be fed into a pad-to-MIDI converter, though some drum modules have these built in. However, it is essential that the trigger system allows the user to set a retrigger inhibit time, which prevents a sample from being triggered twice in quick succession due to spill breakthrough or a careless stick bounce. Most trigger systems can be made responsive to the loudness of the triggering signal, but in the majority of pop work, the bass and snare levels need to be kept even, so it may be advantageous to turn this facility off or make sure that the input is always high enough to ensure the sample is played at or near its maximum velocity. Figure 6.6 shows a typical setup.

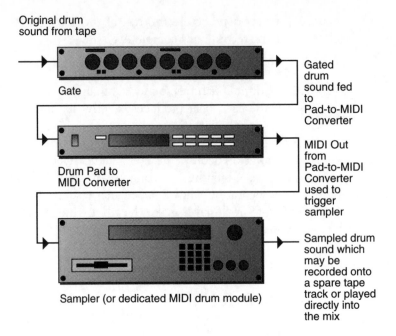

Original drum
sound from tape

Gate

Gated
drum
sound fed
to
Pad-to-MIDI
Converter

Drum Pad to
MIDI Converter

MIDI Out
from
Pad-to-MIDI
Converter
used to
trigger
sampler

Sampler (or dedicated MIDI drum module)

Sampled drum
sound which
may be
recorded onto
a spare tape
track or played
directly into
the mix

**Figure 7.3: Replacing Drum Sounds with Samples**

# PADS

Drum pads provide a convenient means of triggering sampled drum sounds or sounds generated from a drum machine or drum sound module which, especially in the home studio, are less problematic to record than real drums. Pads, played with sticks, invariably allow a more natural feel to be imparted to the playing than is obtained by playing drum parts from a keyboard, and they allow drummers to become involved in sequencer programming rather than leaving it all to the keyboard player. Inexpensive transducers are also available which may be attached to acoustic drums, allowing them to be used in place of pads. Most types are based around simple piezo-electric transducer disks or it is possible to make your own using piezo-electric sounders (normally used as computer bleepers) attached to the drum head by means of a double-sided foam sticky pad. These may be obtained from a variety of electrical component suppliers at very low cost. Figure 7.4 shows how this is done.

While it is commonplace to quantise bass drum and most snare drum parts, it helps to maintain a natural feel if drum fills are left unquantised. When working with a sequencer, it is usually easiest to program drum parts in layers rather than trying to record the whole kit at once, unless you have a set of pads that includes a kick drum and hi-hat pedal. Each pass can be recorded on a different track and then merged when all the parts are complete. As ever, it helps to get the straight rhythmic parts, such as the kick and snare, down first and then overdub the hi-hats, cymbals and fills. If this isn't practical, program a simple guide rhythm and then erase this later.

In order to preserve the feel of the unquantised parts, the quantised parts should be recorded onto one sequencer track and the unquantised parts onto another — if you put them all on the same track, the same quantisation will apply to everything, which is not what you want. My earlier comments regarding mixing programmed and miked drum sounds apply equally when using pads. Natural hi-hats can often help tremendously when trying to make a programmed part sound convincing

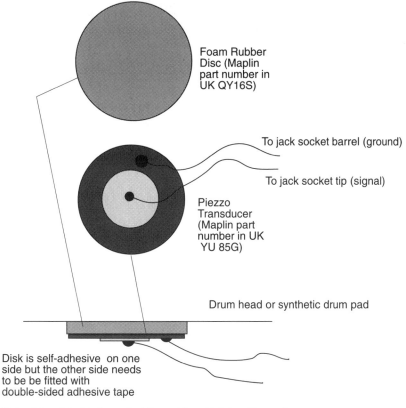

Foam Rubber Disc (Maplin part number in UK QY16S)

To jack socket barrel (ground)

To jack socket tip (signal)

Piezzo Transducer (Maplin part number in UK YU 85G)

Drum head or synthetic drum pad

Disk is self-adhesive on one side but the other side needs to be be fitted with double-sided adhesive tape

Note: It is advisable to protect the soldered joints with small blobs of silicone rubber to prevent vibration damage

**DIY Piezo Drum Transducer**

Drum pads are also ideal for playing tuned percussion such as vibes and marimbas, where only a small selection of notes is required.

### ● TIP ●

When triggering drum samples, it is also possible to create convincing talking drum effects by creating a looped sequencer track containing only pitch bend information on the same MIDI channel as the drum samples. When the drum part is played from either the pads or the sequencer, the bend information is merged with the note data and produces the talking drum effect. Creating the bend information requires a little trial and error but is best done with a typical drum part playing so that the effect can be heard. Subtle pitch bends work best, and if the loop is made an odd length, the pitch bend pattern will appear to be constantly changing. I have used this technique very successfully to make sampled congas sound more like tablas.

# ACOUSTIC GUITARS

Steel-strung acoustic guitars are wonderfully expressive instruments, and their sound encompasses almost all the audio spectrum, with the exception of the lowest couple of octaves. The instrument also has a very wide dynamic range, and while an enthusiastically strummed rhythm part might be relatively loud, a melodic section played with the fingers or with a pick might sound very much quieter. Because of the wide range of acoustic guitars, both in terms of frequency and dynamics, you should use the very best mic you can get your hands on when recording a critical acoustic guitar part. Some of the better dynamic microphones are sensitive enough for all but the quietest playing, but the higher sensitivity of a capacitor model is a distinct advantage. Similarly, the extended frequency range of a capacitor microphone is better able to capture the subtle high frequency detail of the instrument.

Not everyone can afford a top quality capacitor microphone, but a modestly priced back-electret microphone can do almost as good a job for around the same price as a decent dynamic microphone. Further down the scale, even the humble Tandy PZM is capable of creditable results in this application, its main limitation being its lack of sensitivity when compared to a professional studio capacitor microphone.

## MIC POSITIONS

If getting enough level while recording an acoustic guitar is proving a problem, it is tempting to put the microphone very close to the sound-hole. This produces the largest signal, but unfortunately, the tone is likely to be heavily coloured by body resonances, and tends to be both dull and boomy.

These body resonances are part of the natural timbre of the instrument and are what gives the guitar sound its depth, but the essential detail that completes the picture comes from elsewhere. No amount of equalisation can make a good guitar sound out of a bad one, and the key to a good sound is to use the right mic in the right position.

As with all instruments, the various parts of the guitar vibrate in different ways; different parts of the instrument generate different sounds. The strings, the neck vibration, the air within the body and the wood of the body itself all contribute to the overall sound. Add to this the effect of room acoustics and it's easy to see why a single microphone positioned close to one point on the instrument's surface is not going to do it justice; this is why contact mics rarely give a good sound.

It could be argued that the only place you're going to get a good guitar sound is where the audience would normally be — several feet from the guitar. Fortunately, you can get good results far closer than this — after all, the guitarist himself usually hears a passable sound and he's quite close. On top of that, the sound we want to record isn't necessarily the exact sound the audience would hear at a live performance.

# TONE

A steel-strung acoustic rhythm guitar may need to be both brightened and have some bass rolled off to make it sit better in the mix without taking up too much 'space'. Conversely, a solo acoustic guitar is normally miked to sound fairly natural, but even then, the performer may want to vary the sound slightly, either by the choice and positioning of microphones, by the use of equalisation or by some form of electronic enhancement.

# THE RIGHT MICROPHONE

Foremost when recording an acoustic guitar is the choice of microphone, because if the chosen model is insufficiently sensitive or has a restricted frequency response, this reduces our options when we come to position it. Most dynamic microphones are not sufficiently sensitive to do justice to the acoustic guitar, and their lack of top end response leads to a somewhat lifeless sound. However, if a dynamic mic is all you have, you can still get passable results by taking a little extra care. Don't point it directly at the sound hole in an attempt to get enough level, and by the same token, don't place it too close to the guitar. A position between 12 and 18 inches from the guitar is quite near enough and if you're only using a single dynamic

mic, then try aiming it at the point where the neck joins the body. You may end up with a little noise but better that than a dreadful sound. Figure 8.1 shows this approach.

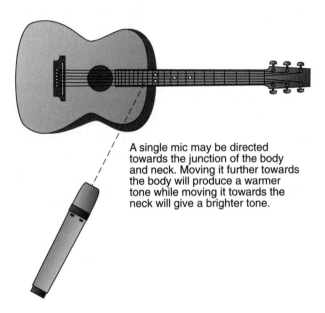

A single mic may be directed towards the junction of the body and neck. Moving it further towards the body will produce a warmer tone while moving it towards the neck will give a brighter tone.

**Figure 8.1: Using a Single Close Microphone**

Ideally, a capacitor or back-electret mic should be used for any serious work and either Omni or Cardioid pattern models may be used. Unless the room acoustics are particularly flattering, I'd be inclined to stick to a Cardioid model — unless two guitars are being recorded together, in which case it may be better to use Omnis rather than Cardioids. This will result in a little more spill between the mics, but because Omnis tend to have a better off-axis response than Cardioids, the spill will at least be sonically accurate.

When using multiple microphones, try to keep in mind the 'three to one' rule for mic positioning. For example, if the mics are placed two feet from the guitars, then make sure they are at least six feet apart. If they are too close to each other relative to their distance from the instruments, the resulting spill will produce significant phase cancelling effects that will colour the sound, usually to its detriment. Getting the desired tone by choosing a suitable mic and mic position always sounds better than using EQ, and if you need a brighter tone, choosing a mic with a presence peak will invariably give a more natural result than applying EQ.

# BEFORE THE SESSION

Unlike electronic keyboards, you can't just assume that a guitar is going to play properly and in tune as soon as it comes out of the box. Intonation problems and buzzes should be fixed before the session starts, and with steel-strung instruments, a relatively new set of strings is a good idea, particularly if you're after a bright sound.

The performer should, ideally, play seated to avoid unnecessary movement of the guitar relative to the microphones. Ensure that the chair doesn't creak and try to exclude other sources of noise such as spill from headphones, especially if you intend to work with a click track. A degree of finger squeak is inevitable, but if it becomes excessive, it can ruin an otherwise excellent performance. There's no complete cure but a dusting of talcum powder on the player's hands might improve matters. There are also commercial string lubricants that may help. Other unwelcome sources of noise include rustling clothing, crackling lyric sheets and excessive breathing noises. Also keep an ear open for ticking watches. It can be argued that breath noises are normal, but if you have several overdubs to do, the result can sound like a chorus of heavy-breathing, dirty phone callers!

# CLICK TRACKS

When working with click tracks, choose a sound for your click that isn't too strident, as some spill is likely, even from enclosed phones. You could route the click signal through a compressor set up in 'duck' mode so that the click track gets louder when the guitar is played louder and quietens down during quiet sections or pauses. This will ensure that the click is audible to the performer at all times, but it will be quietest when there is little else going on to hide it. There are also some processing tricks which help minimise recorded squeaks and breathing, which will be discussed later in this chapter.

# ROOMS AND MIC POSITIONS

Before getting down to the finer points of microphone placement, it is helpful to look at the surroundings in which the recording is to be made. Most instruments are designed to sound best when played in a room with a certain degree of reverberation, and acoustic guitars are no exception. However, most small studios tend to be on the acoustically dead side, so it may pay dividends to look for another room in the building that has hard surfaces to create a more live environment. In the absence of a suitable live room, an artificial live environment can be created by covering the floor with hardboard, shiny side up. Don't worry if the sound still isn't as live as you'd like it to be, as some electronic reverberation can be added at the mixing stage.

As stated earlier, I really can't overemphasise the importance of microphone position when recording acoustic instruments. That's not to say that there's only one right way to do the job, though — there are many different miking methods that produce excellent results. As shown in Figure 8.1, placing a single mic between one and two feet from the instrument, pointing toward the spot where the neck joins the body, is always a good starting point. If the sound is too heavy, the mic can be positioned further away from the sound-hole or moved upwards so that it is 'looking down' on the instrument. To add more weight to the sound, the mic can be brought closer to the sound hole, but make sure that the sound doesn't become boomy as well as full.

This is by no means the only mic position — I've had quite a lot of success pointing the mic over the player's right shoulder, looking down on the guitar body from a distance of between 18 inches and two feet. The theory here is that if the guitar sounds OK to the player, it should sound OK to a mic located close to the player's ear. Figure 8.2 shows this setup. Equally, you might find that pointing the mic at the floor to pick up mainly reflected sound gives a well balanced result.

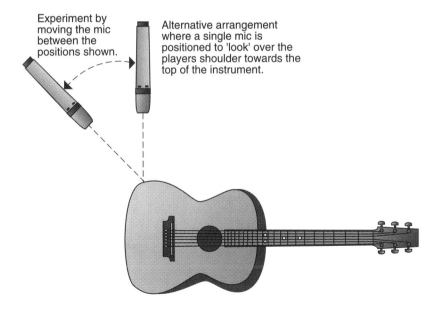

Experiment by moving the mic between the positions shown.

Alternative arrangement where a single mic is positioned to 'look' over the players shoulder towards the top of the instrument.

**Figure 8.2: Miking over the Shoulder**

A good engineer will move around the playing position as the performer warms up, listening for any 'sweet spots'. This careful listening invariably yields some improvement, and when you've identified these 'sweet spots', try moving the mic to hear what difference it makes.

## ● TIP ●

One effective way to find sweet spots is to monitor the output from the mic using good quality closed headphones plugged into the mixer. You then move the mic manually as the guitarist runs through the number. This has the advantage that any colouration of the sound by the microphone or mixing console is taken into account.

# MONO OR STEREO?

If an acoustic guitar line is simply part of a full pop mix, then a mono recording is generally adequate and may even be beneficial as it produces a more stable, solid sound. However, in small acoustic bands or in the case of solo performances, stereo miking greatly enhances the sense of depth and reality. The easiest way to make a stereo recording is to place a stereo pair of

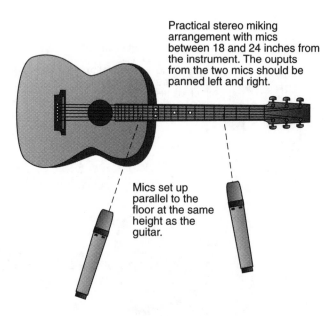

Practical stereo miking arrangement with mics between 18 and 24 inches from the instrument. The ouputs from the two mics should be panned left and right.

Mics set up parallel to the floor at the same height as the guitar.

**Figure 8.3: An Approach to Stereo Miking**

microphones two or three feet in front of the instrument, but in practice, you can use any of the existing stereo miking methods, including M&S pairs, spaced microphones or spaced PZMs.

I'll often pick two mic positions that don't necessarily produce an accurate stereo picture as such, but do provide me with the sound I want, plus a sense of depth. One arrangement that I find works particularly well is to position one mic in the usual end-of-neck or 'looking down' position to capture the main part of the sound and then position another a foot or so away from the neck, pointing towards the headstock or halfway up the neck. This produces a bright, detailed sound that works particularly well with picked or folk-style playing. I'd normally use Cardioid mics, but you could use Omnis if they are available, or even one of each. It really doesn't matter how you get a result so long as you get it! Figure 8.3 shows how the microphones are arranged.

Using two PZM mics, you can obtain a very natural sound by placing these on a table top a couple of feet in front of the performer, with the mics three feet or so apart. Alternatively, these could be set up as a conventional stereo pair, as outlined in the chapter on stereo mic techniques. Even inexpensive Tandy PZMs can sound surprisingly good when placed on a low table in front of the performer. Alternatively, if a guitar is fitted with a bridge transducer, this may be used in conjunction with either one or more microphones to create a stereo effect, though I've never really liked the sound of transducers when compared directly to good microphones.

# EQUALISATION

In an ideal world, equalisation would not be necessary, but in the studio, where reality is not always the main objective, some EQ may be necessary. There is no reason to be afraid of using a lot of equalisation as long as you know what you are trying to achieve, but if in doubt, use as little as you can get away with. If the mic positions were correct and the instrument sounded good in the studio, then you shouldn't need to do much to get a good sound, but often, you may have to contend with a less than perfect recording, in which case a little electronic repair work will be necessary.

One of the most persistent problems with acoustic guitar recordings is boominess. This centres around a certain fixed frequency, and you can find out just what this frequency as follows:

● **TECHNIQUE** ●

• Turn up the boost on your lower mid  equaliser and then sweep through the frequency range until the boominess really jumps out at you.

• Having found this frequency, which will probably lie between 80Hz and 220Hz, you can bring the boost control back into its cut position, applying just enough cut to tame the resonance.

# TOP END

• General brightening can be achieved using the high equaliser on the mixer to add the required degree of top boost. In circumstances where this is insufficient, don't just go on cranking up the top; all you'll do is bring up the noise and make everything sound harsh. Either re-record the track or use an exciter/enhancer to add a little artificial top end.

• Sparkle can be added to the sound by boosting between 5kHz and 10kHz.

• Harshness in the upper mid range can usually be reduced by cutting frequencies between 1kHz and 3kHz.

• The exact frequency you need to work on is best identified by setting the relevant equaliser section to full boost and then sweeping through the frequency range. When you hit the area you need to boost, it should be obvious. All you need to do then is back off the boost until the sound is as you want it. During this process, keep checking the sound against the EQ bypass position because the ear soon gets acclimatised to radical EQ changes and you may not realise you have gone too far.

• In some mixes, you may feel the need to take out all the bottom end to produce a bright, thin rhythm sound. This is common practice and really helps keep the mix sounding clear. The low EQ control may be sufficient to achieve the desired result, but if more cut is needed, try tuning the lower mid control to somewhere between 80Hz and 150Hz and applying more cut with this. It is invariably easier to use EQ cut rather than boost, as there is no danger of overloading the circuitry — with the possible consequence of distortion — and also, the ear is less forgiving of cuts than it is of boost.

# UNWANTED NOISES

Earlier I mentioned the problems caused by string squeaks and over-loud breathing. This can be reduced by the careful use of a parametric equaliser, but accepting that many users don't have these, I have found a way of using the side-chain filters in my gates to achieve the same result. In the Drawmer DS201 gate, as with other models working on a similar principle, the side chain filters are variable frequency, 12dB per octave devices which can be inserted into the audio path simply by selecting the key or side-chain listen mode. This bypasses the gate section and leaves just the filters in series with the input signal as a kind of super equaliser.

The great thing about these filters is that they have a very sharp response, which means that you can take out a high frequency sound without seriously affecting the frequencies directly below. I've had surprising success in filtering both acoustic and electric guitars using these devices, and setting up is quite simple:

## ● TECHNIQUE ●

• Start off with the high filter in its maximum position.

• Now bring it down slowly, while listening to the effect on the recorded sound.

• You should find that you can take the edge off the breath and string squeaks without affecting the tone of the guitar too seriously. Of course, if you turn the filter setting down too far, you'll hear the top go from the guitar as well.

• For a sharper response, you can put both channels of the gate in series, which will produce a filter response of 24dB per octave if you set the filters to the same frequencies.

# FURTHER PROCESSING

Getting the basic guitar sound onto tape and applying a little EQ may be all you need to get exactly the right acoustic guitar sound — on the other hand, it might be just the beginning. There are some engineers who wouldn't dream of recording an acoustic guitar without compressing it at some stage — and it's certainly true that compression does even up the sound a lot. In the case of a strummed rhythm part, compression can smooth out the sound, making it less ragged and more cohesive. By increasing the compressor's attack time to 10mS or so, the attack transients of the guitar remain intact, whereas a short attack time tames the natural attack of the instrument, giving an altogether more consistent sound.

The release time setting of the compressor is also important, because setting it too short can cause the sound to 'pump', especially when a lot of compression has been used. Conversely, setting it too long means that gain reduction may still be applied well after the sound that caused it has fallen back below the threshold resulting in uneven level control. The ideal setting depends on how fast the playing is and on how much pumping can be tolerated, but as a rule, between 250 and 500mS usually does the trick.

Very generally, compressors that sound good on vocals also sound good on acoustic guitars. Soft-knee compressors are normally easier to set up and give consistently decent results, though if you want to juggle the compressor attack time to actually enhance the attack of the instrument, a hard-knee or strict ratio compressor might give you more positive control. By compressing the sound to give a gain reduction of between 6 and 12dB on the loudest sections, it should be possible to even up the sound without inviting too much noise during pauses or quiet sections. If more compression is considered necessary, then consider a compressor with an inbuilt expander gate, or gate the signal before compressing it. Some of the newer compressors also have a built-in enhancer feature to restore brightness lost during heavy compression. Those I've tried work well on acoustic guitar and help maintain an edge to the sound, even when a lot of compression is being used.

# REVERB

To achieve a natural guitar sound, it shouldn't be necessary to do much more than add a suitable amount of reverb to the recorded part, and in the case of mono recordings, a stereo reverb can be used to give the sound a sense of space and width which it wouldn't otherwise possess. If the basic sound is sufficiently live but is lacking in width, you could appropriately add a short room reverb or early reflections pattern, which will create a sense of space and identity without making the sound muddy. You might also find that a bright reverb setting will add life to the sound in a way that EQ can't.

● TIP ●

If a longer reverb is required, don't just solo the guitar and then pick a flattering setting, because you'll find that everything sounds different once the rest of the mix is up and running. Far better to set up a rough mix first and then add the reverb.

## ● TIP ●

Rolling some bass off the reverb returns can help to keep the sound clear when a lot of reverb is added, but take care when doing this that the remaining reverb doesn't sound too edgy and thin. There is a tendency to add too much reverb to instruments in a mix, and the professional engineer has come to understand that less is often more. Music relies on contrasts in level, and though reverb does create a sense of space, it also fills the valuable spaces between the notes. On an interesting psychoacoustic note, reverb also creates the illusion of distance, so if you're after an up-front, in-your-face acoustic guitar sound, don't pick a long reverb time. Instead pick a short room, plate or early reflections setting and be sparing in how much you add to the dry signal.

# OTHER EFFECTS

In the context of pop music, a gentle chorus effect works well on the acoustic guitar, giving it an enhanced sense of presence and depth but without making it sound too unnatural or processed. A shallow, mild flange achieves a similar effect — but it isn't always necessary to resort to electronic effects. Take the example of chorus; the effect is designed to create the illusion of two or more instruments playing together, but using multitrack tape, you can do it for real by playing the same part twice on two different tape tracks. If you can't afford the space to leave them on separate tracks, you can always bounce them down onto one afterwards.

## ● TECHNIQUE ●

To achieve more of a 'detuned' chorus effect, you could detune the guitar slightly when you do the second take, but a far easier approach is to make use of your tape machine's varispeed control:

• Instead of recording one part at the normal speed and one at a slightly altered speed, try recording both parts with the varispeed on — one take with the tape running slightly fast, and the other with it running slightly slow.

• When the recording is replayed at the normal speed, this will place the average pitch somewhere between the two, which is more likely to sound in tune with the rest of the track. On the other hand, if you record one part at the normal pitch and then add a second part that is a few cents sharp, the average of the two will still appear slightly sharp.

• A shift of less than one percent in each direction should be sufficient, but do a few trial takes and find what settings give the most appropriate chorus depth. It's also worth noting down the settings for future use.

• The two tracks can then be panned to the two sides of the mix, unless you've had to bounce them, in which case a subtle stereo reverb will help recreate the lost sense of space.

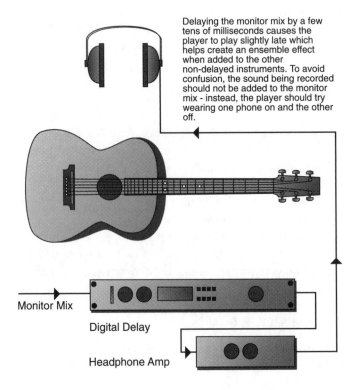

Delaying the monitor mix by a few tens of milliseconds causes the player to play slightly late which helps create an ensemble effect when added to the other non-delayed instruments. To avoid confusion, the sound being recorded should not be added to the monitor mix - instead, the player should try wearing one phone on and the other off.

Monitor Mix

Digital Delay

Headphone Amp

**Figure 8.4: Delaying the Monitoring for Natural Ensemble Effect.**

• It is possible to further exaggerate the chorus effect by delaying one of the guitar parts by a few tens of milliseconds; this is particularly effective if the two tracks can be kept separate for left/right panning. Rather than use a delay unit to create the effect while mixing, it is possible to use a delay unit to delay the headphone feed slightly when recording the second part. In other words, the guitarist is being forced into playing late because he's hearing the backing track after it's been delayed. Figure 8.4 shows this method of delayed monitoring.

If you think about it, this approach is bound to produce better results than using a DDL in the mix because the recorded sound hasn't been processed at all — which means that the quality of the delay line is quite unimportant. Even a budget delay pedal can be used and it won't affect the recording.

# ELECTRIC GUITARS

The electric guitar sound is the result of a unique symbiosis as, unlike other instruments, it relies on its amplification/loudspeaker system to enhance the sound in a creative way rather than simply to make it louder. Because there are so many different types of guitar and guitar amplifier, and so many playing styles, the range of sounds that can be coaxed from this instrument is vast and varied. The method of recording the instrument adds a further variable, and this potential for creating radically different individual sounds undoubtedly accounts for the continuing popularity of the electric guitar in all forms of contemporary popular music. As the sound is produced via a loudspeaker rather than directly from the instrument, it is useful to examine the guitar amplifier further.

## GUITAR AMPLIFIERS

Guitar amps are usually fitted with 10-inch or 12-inch speakers, often in multiples, mounted in cabinets which may be sealed or open-backed. The distinctive overdrive sound is caused by harmonic distortion added in the amplifier, but if fed through a full-range monitor speaker system the result is invariably buzzy and unpleasant. Guitar speakers are built with a deliberately poor frequency response, and this has the effect of filtering out the less musical harmonics, resulting in a sound which still has plenty of edge but doesn't sound buzzy or nasty. Furthermore, many guitar speakers are specifically designed to add distortion at high sound levels.

Open backed cabinets tend to have a fatter sound than closed ones and are often referred to as having a bass thump. That's because the speaker doesn't have a cushion of air to damp it, so low frequency sounds caused by the player's hands hitting the strings cause the speaker cone to move a considerable distance, with an audible thump. This characteristic also affects the more musical sounds of the instrument to quite a large extent, especially on the lower notes. Different players will argue on whether the open or closed-back cabinet sounds best, but both are quite easy to record.

Most rock guitar players still express a preference for valve amplifiers, as these have a sound quality that is difficult to emulate using solid-state circuitry. Valve circuits, with their transformer output stages, can reproduce transient peaks well in excess of their average rated power handling capacity, while their distortion characteristics when overdriven are considered more 'musical' than those of solid-state designs. The vast majority of guitar amplifiers would be considered technically disastrous from a hi-fi point of view, but the high orders of even harmonic distortion they produce have become synonymous with rock guitar sounds worldwide.

# THE GUITAR

The basic design of the electric guitar has changed little since it was invented — indeed, one of the most popular guitars today is the Fender Stratocaster (or one of its many copies), which was one of the first production electric guitars ever. The electrical principle of the guitar pickup is fairly straightforward and isn't too far removed from the magnetic microphone principle, except that the guitar string takes the place of the diaphragm. The string vibrates within a magnetic field generated by a permanent magnet, causing a signal voltage to be induced in a coil of wire wound around the magnets. It works very well, but as the pickup coil behaves exactly like the coil of a transformer, it also picks up stray magnetic fields from transformers and mains wiring, resulting in a background hum.

# HUMBUCKERS

It is possible to cancel out most of the hum by using a pickup with not one but two coils, one wound in the opposite direction to the other. This is the humbucking principle, which was originally devised to cancel the hum generated in loudspeakers in the days when their magnets were energised from the mains current.

A well designed humbucker has almost perfect immunity to hum pickup, but because of the different coil impedance and the spaced magnetic pole-pieces, they invariably have a significantly different tonal characteristic than the simple single-coil pickup.

Unfortunately, the guitars that are currently popular tend to feature single-coil pickups, and these can be a nightmare in the studio because nearly every piece of equipment radiates mains hum to some degree. It is possible to rotate the instrument to find a position of least hum, but this imposes restrictions on the player and rarely leads to perfect cancellation. Furthermore, now that computer monitors are commonplace in studios, the problem is worsened, as these radiate a high level of buzz which will interfere with the operation of a single coil pickup at distances of ten feet or more.

One solution is to use one of the newer mini-humbuckers which come as standard on some instruments and are available as replacements for standard instruments. These locate the two sets of magnets very close together, in an attempt to combine the noise rejection capabilities of a humbucking pickup with the tonal qualities of a single-coil model. Different manufacturers meet the challenge with differing degrees of success, though the better ones come very close indeed.

# ACTIVE PICKUPS

Another approach is the so-called active pickup, which usually comprises a low-impedance pickup followed by a battery-powered electronic buffer. These still suffer from interference, though to a lesser extent than a standard pickup, and they offer the advantage that they can be DI'd without the need for a DI matching box if a clean sound is sought. Active models do, however, produce a degree of background noise due to the amplifier circuitry and, when boosted by the extra gain of an overdriven amplifier or effects pedal, the noise level can become obtrusive.

# SETTING UP

Obviously it is up to the musician to ensure that his or her instrument is properly maintained, but the reality is that many guitar players turn up at the studio with an instrument that is inadequately set up and frequently unrecordable. Professionals are unlikely to fall into this trap, but amateur players coming into the studio for the first time can easily be let down by their instrument. However, there are a few things you can do to help ensure a good result.

• Old, worn strings can turn an expensive guitar into an unresponsive, dull and thoroughly uninspiring instrument, so if you know you have a session coming up where the players are inexperienced, ask them to check that their strings are OK, and if not, to replace them a day or two before the recording so as to give them time to settle in. Changing strings directly before a session is merely inviting tuning problems.

• Action and intonation problems can defeat the most talented player, and here a little first aid can be administered by an engineer with a little guitar experience. Though this is, again, not the engineer's responsibility, he is inevitably the one who gets the blame when a session goes badly, whatever the true cause. Furthermore, if he can demonstrate an ability to sort out minor problems with guitars and drum kits, he's more likely to win the respect of the artists, which will help the session go more smoothly and possibly win repeat business.

• Ideally, the guitar's strings should be as low as possible without buzzing, and the correct neck shape to allow this is not dead straight but slightly concave. If you hold a guitar string down on the first and last frets simultaneously, you should be able to see a small space between the middle of the string and the frets it passes over. If it touches all the way down the neck, it is either too straight, or worse still, a touch convex. Slackening the truss rod an eighth of a turn at a time should correct this problem. A twisted or warped neck will also cause problems with the action of the guitar, but this is beyond the scope of first aid and requires the attention of an experienced guitar technician.

• Bad intonation is probably the easiest fault to fix and is caused, mainly, by incorrectly positioned bridge saddles. Using an electronic tuner, compare the pitch of the string fretted at the twelfth fret and the harmonic struck at the same position. If the fretted note is sharper than the harmonic, then the bridge saddle needs to be moved to lengthen the string slightly until the two pitches are the same. Conversely, if the fretted note is flatter than the harmonic, move the bridge saddle slightly towards the neck and try again.

• Another less well-known source of intonation error is insufficiently deep nut slots. Aside from making the guitar harder to play, this forces fretted notes to be slightly sharp, as the string is stretched by a small amount when fretted. Owners of such guitars frequently distrust electronic tuners because whenever they tune their open strings, the fretted notes are sharp! Unfortunately, most production guitars suffer from this fault to a greater or lesser extent. A junior hacksaw blade is normally fine enough for deepening nut slots, but only take off a little material at a time, refit the string into the slot, and check the action.

• One final tip which can help keep tuning stable is to keep a roll of plumbers' PTFE tape in your spares kit and slide a piece beneath the strings where they cross the nut. The tape will be stretched down into the slots where it acts as a very efficient lubricant to prevent the strings sticking when notes are bent or a tremolo unit used. This is, obviously, unnecessary when using a locking nut system. The tape is thin enough not to affect the action or sustain, but it does help ensure that a bent note returns to its previous pitch when released.

# GUITAR NOISE

Noise is a particular problem with guitars, not just because of the propensity of the pickups to act as aerials for interference, but also because guitar amplifiers tend to be noisy. This isn't down to bad circuit design but is more a function of the tonal voicing of the amplifiers and the high levels of gain needed to produce overdrive sounds. If an attempt is going to be made to remove some of the noise by electronic means, it may be best to leave this until the mixing stage so that an incorrectly set gate or noise filter doesn't ruin a good take.

A dynamic noise filter such as the Symetrix 511A, Drawmer DF320, Rocktron Hush or dbx Silencer can be a powerful ally when cleaning up noisy guitar tracks, and these are generally far more successful than conventional gates. Also known as single-ended noise reduction units, these devices work by reducing the audio bandwidth as the sound level falls; the filter action is so rapid that attack transients pass through with very little change. As any natural sound decays, the higher harmonics decay most rapidly so no significant tonal change is noticed as the filter closes. The filter action is further aided by the fact that electric guitars have a relatively low upper frequency limit anyway — most of their energy is below 3kHz. Because these filters only tackle high frequency noise, many models have an integral expander, which shuts down the audio path once the signal level has fallen below a threshold set by the user.

# NOISE FILTERS

Recently, digital noise filtering systems have become available which track the mains frequency and then apply a series of very narrow notch filters to remove both the fundamental and the harmonics that make up the buzz. Because of the precision available with digital filtering, even quite severe buzzes can be removed with little or no subjective effect on the wanted part of the sound.

High frequency hiss is taken care of by means of a multi-band expander which, subjectively, produces similar benefits to those offered by an analogue dynamic filter. At the time of writing, these units are still relatively costly, but in a studio specialising in electric guitar work, they might still be a worthwhile investment.

In the absence of a dynamic filter, a gate may be used to clean up the pauses between notes or phrases, but as electric guitars can sustain for a long time, there may be few periods of true silence where the gate can be effective. In any event, the gate release time needs to be set long enough to allow the guitar to decay naturally without being cut short.

## ● TIP ●

Whether you use a gate or a noise filter, it is sensible to use them to process the guitar sound before any delay or reverb effects are added. This way the reverb or delay will decay naturally and will help cover up any slight truncation of the original sound caused by the gate or filter action. Any attempt to filter or gate a sound that contains added reverb is almost certain to change the reverb decay characteristics quite noticeably.

# GATE FILTERS

There is another technique which can be used for cleaning up electric guitar tracks, which relies on the limited bandwidth of guitar amplifiers. Rolling off some EQ above 3kHz should, in theory, remove high-frequency hiss and noise, but allow the guitar sound to pass with little subjective change. In practice, however, the slope characteristics of conventional equalisers restricts their effectiveness in this application because the response is simply not sharp enough. In other words, if the EQ is set to remove the high end noise, the chances are that it will have a significant effect on the wanted sound too.

A solution presents itself in the form of the side-chain filters included in many studio gates, including the popular Drawmer DS201. These are variable frequency filters with a 12dB per octave characteristic designed to process the side-chain input with a view to reducing the risk of false triggering. By selecting the Key Listen mode, it is possible to place these filters in the audio path, enabling the unit to be used as a filter rather than as a gate. And in the fight against noise, the sharp filter response is a powerful ally.

By setting the upper cutoff frequency to between 2.5kHz and 3.5kHz, it is possible to significantly improve the signal-to-noise ratio of a typical electric guitar sound without dulling it noticeably. If an even sharper filter response is required, the two channels of the gate can be wired in series, and with both switched to Key Listen mode, a 24dB per octave filter can be created, simply by setting the upper frequency controls to similar values.

In this application, the sound is usually treated after being recorded to tape, to eliminate the risk of irretrievable overprocessing; the gates are connected to the console via the appropriate channel insert points. As you may have noticed, this technique is very similar to that described in the chapter on Acoustic Guitars for removing finger noise and squeaks; it can also be surprisingly effective at reducing distortion on tape caused by over-recording of clean electric guitar parts.

# MICROPHONES

When miking up a guitar amp, it is important to realise that the speaker cabinet should be treated as an instrument in its own right. Much of the sound comes direct from the speakers but there's also a lot of sound emitted from the back and sides of the box, especially in the case of an open-backed cabinet. The sound is different close to the speakers than it is further away in the room, which gives several miking options, including close miking; ambient miking at a distance; and a combined approach with two or more mics set at different distances.

Most British recording engineers choose fairly unsophisticated cardioid, dynamic microphones to record electric guitar, as neither sensitivity nor high frequency extension is a priority, due to the fundamental nature of the electric guitar sound. In other words, guitar amplification systems aren't short on volume and produce very little in the way of true high frequencies.

American engineers, on the other hand, often choose a capacitor microphone for the job, which undoubtedly contributes to the American rock sound. This is not so fat as the English sound and has more top, to the point where a British engineer or producer might consider it too buzzy. A mic with a presence peak will help a sound cut through a mix, but a sound that's already quite abrasive may sound smoother if a fairly flat mic is used. As with vocals, it's down to matching the choice of microphone to the sound you're recording.

# SETUP

To get the sound of a live stack, the textbook approach is to set up a full stack in a big studio, play it loud, and then mic it from several feet with an additional close mic to enhance the bite. The more distant mic captures the direct sound from the speakers plus room reflections, including any phase cancellation effects caused by multiple drivers. Sound is also reflected from the floor, which creates further comb filtering when it arrives at the microphone via different paths.

In other words, the distant mic hears the performance much as an audience would. You can omit the close mic but the sound then tends to be indistinct and distant-sounding, even after considerable EQ'ing.

# CLOSE MIKING

A more common approach, especially in smaller studios, is to close-mic a smaller amp, such as a single speaker, open-backed combo. The mic is initially positioned very close to the speaker grille and is pointed directly at the centre of the speaker cone. If a less bright sound is sought, it can be moved slightly to one side, which will give a warmer result. Again, an ambient mic may also be used, positioned several feet away. Figure 9.1 shows a guitar combo being recored via a single microphone.

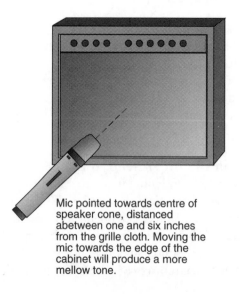

Mic pointed towards centre of speaker cone, distanced abetween one and six inches from the grille cloth. Moving the mic towards the edge of the cabinet will produce a more mellow tone.

Figure 9.1: Close-miking a Guitar Combo

An even warmer sound may be achieved by miking the rear of the cabinet; indeed, there's no reason not to mic both the front and rear of the cabinet simultaneously if it gives a sound you like. The phase of the rear mic should, strictly speaking, be inverted so that its output is in-phase with that of the front mic, but do try both phase positions, as what is technically correct doesn't always give the best sound.

If you want to try an ambience mic, place it several feet from the cabinet and add this to the close miked sound, either summed in mono or with one mic panned left and the other right. The ambient mic may be pointed directly at the guitar amplifier or, alternatively, aimed at a reflective surface within the room. Check the sounds individually and you'll soon notice the weighty power of the distant mic compared with the incisive edge of the close-miked sound. For a brighter ambient sound, use a capacitor mic as the distant mic. By combining these two mics in different proportions, a wide range of sounds can be achieved.

## ● TIP ●

If the guitar is played in the control room with the amp itself in the studio, a capacitor microphone may be used to pick up the direct sound from the guitar strings. In isolation, the miked strings will sound very thin, but when mixed in, they will add definition to the notes, rather like an exciter. Again, this is a matter of preference — some engineers and producers use the technique a lot, while others would never bother to do it. A similar effect can be achieved by splitting the guitar output and feeding some of it direct to the console via a DI box.

# PROCESSING

Most engineers would agree that adding effects at the mixing stage allows greater creative flexibility, but for a guitarist, the effect may be so much a part of his sound that he can't play the part properly without it. Obviously the right overdrive effect must be set up prior to recording, but effects like chorus, echo and wah wah can also be very important to the performance. Ultimately, the performance is what really counts, so many producers believe that if the player really wants to use his own effects live as he plays, then it's best to let him.

Having put that viewpoint, if some of the effects are too noisy for serious recording and they can't be cleaned up, with dynamic noise filters for example, consider patching them in to allow the player to monitor the desired effects while playing, but record the signal unprocessed. That way you can simulate his effects with high quality studio processors when you come to mix, with the added benefit that the effects can be in stereo, they can be fine-tuned and their level can be changed.

# DIRECT INJECT

As an alternative to miking up guitar amplifiers, there's a variety of DI recording techniques available, some of which are very effective and can save a lot of studio time, as well as allowing for greater separation between instruments being recorded simultaneously. It is almost standard practice to DI bass guitars for the majority of pop recording, and even where the amplifier is miked up, some proportion of DI'd sound is often added.

Many players have had bad experiences with DI guitar techniques, to the point that they may even refuse to try them. It's true that they seldom sound exactly the same as a miked-up amplifier, but modern recording preamps and speaker simulators can work exceptionally well. It's true, though, that simply plugging a guitar into an overdrive pedal and the output of the pedal into the desk will produce a disgusting sound.

There are very genuine problems that stand in the way of a good DI'd electric guitar, not the least being that the output impedance of a passive guitar pickup is too high for a mixer's mic or line input. This results in an electrical mismatch, causing loading on the pickups which adversely affects the sustain and tone of the instrument.

Any active DI box will solve the impedance matching problem, but the tone is unlikely to be right. In a guitar amplifier, the frequency response isn't flat but is 'voiced' to sound good; in addition, the guitar speaker completely changes the character of the sound. A basic rhythm sound can be achieved by using a DI box and then applying some corrective or creative EQ, but a dedicated guitar processor will give better results.

# GUITAR PROCESSORS

Direct recording guitar preamps started with the Rockman, which combined compression, delay, chorus, equalisation and overdrive to give a workable clean or dirty guitar sound straight into the mixing desk. The designers appreciated the effect that the speaker has on the overdrive sound and included filtering to simulate this. Though the sound wasn't much like a real miked guitar amp, it was probably the first time a genuinely usable DI'd guitar sound could be obtained.

Since then, many advances have been made, using a variety of technologies. Some designers have chosen to go back to valves in order to capture the authentic tube sound, some have built digital circuits to simulate the same effects, and others employ solid-state, analogue circuitry to do the job.

Many of the newer units are quite sophisticated and offer MIDI-programmable digital multi-effects as well as the more obvious overdrive, EQ and compression. The quality of design has improved over the years and some of the latest units really do come very close to the sound of a miked-up cab. Even so, guitar players always tend to complain that the sound isn't the same as what they hear when standing in front of a loud stack at a gig — though that's hardly surprising, since studios seldom monitor at that kind of level.

The only fair way to judge such a guitar processor is to see if it gives the same kind of sound over the studio monitors that you'd expect to hear from a conventionally miked guitar amp on a record. At the time of writing, the best-sounding recording guitar preamps are those using analogue circuitry to create the overdrive effect, but it is only a matter of time before digital technology beats the problem.

# RECORDING PREAMPS

Relatively inexpensive recording guitar preamps which have no internal effects and no programmability are available. These are often the most cost-effective way of doing the job, as they are very quick to set up and can be processed via any studio effects unit.

# SPEAKER EMULATORS

A more basic approach to DI'd guitar is to use a conventional guitar amplifier, but to plug in a speaker simulator instead of the usual speaker. A typical speaker simulator comprises a reactive dummy load, allowing the amplifier to work normally, followed by circuitry that approximates the filtering effect of a guitar loudspeaker. Apart from the dummy load which is, of necessity, passive, the circuitry may either be passive or active and the output appears as either a mic or line level signal that can be plugged directly into a mixing console. Most models can handle up to 100 Watts of input power, which means that the majority of guitar amps can be run flat out to get the best overdrive sound. Figure 9.2 shows how a speaker emulator is connected.

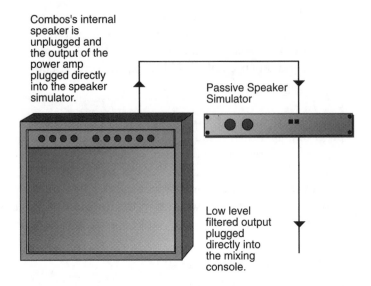

Combos's internal speaker is unplugged and the output of the power amp plugged directly into the speaker simulator.

Passive Speaker Simulator

Low level filtered output plugged directly into the mixing console.

**Figure 9.2 Using a Speaker Emulator**

Some include switchable filters, enabling them to simulate open or closed-backed speaker cabinets, and the difference in sound between different models is surprisingly great. As a rule, valve amplifiers produce a nicer overdrive sound when used with speaker simulators than do solid-state amplifiers, but in any event, speaker simulators can come very close to the sound of a miked-up amplifier. All that's missing is ambience, which can be applied with a studio reverb processor. Some electronic reverb is an advantage, even if the guitar amp has a built-in spring reverb, because few guitar amplifiers have a stereo output. Adding even a small amount of stereo digital reverb really opens up the sound and creates the impression of that it was recorded in a real space.

● TIP ●

Some engineers have been known to use a guitar sound on tape to drive a guitar amplifier, which is then miked up and re-recorded onto a spare tape track prior to mixing. This means that the original sound can be modified by the character of the amplifier, additional overdrive can be added and different EQ settings tried. It's also possible to mic up the amp in a room with a flattering acoustic which can contribute to the sound. Concrete stair-wells, corridors and basements have all been used at one time or another, and the way in which a basic sound can be changed by this method is little short of dramatic.

# EQUALISATION

The electric guitar sound is not natural, so there are no hard and fast rules as to how it should sound. Invariably, some EQ will be necessary to fine-tune the sound and it is quite acceptable to add EQ during recording as well as when mixing. However, don't go overboard with EQ while recording, because few console equalisers are good enough to 'undo' a previous EQ treatment, even if you happen to remember the exact settings used.

Final EQ settings should always be decided in the context of the entire mix — sounds optimised in isolation seldom work properly when everything else is playing. Here are a few guidelines:

• Cut applied at between 100Hz and 250Hz can help sort out a boomy or boxy sound; boost in the same range can fatten a thin sound.

• Cabinet clunk can be accentuated by boosting at around 75-90Hz, though it can be argued that there's little point adding EQ boost much below 100Hz on a conventional electric guitar, as the fundamental of the lowest note is in the order of 80Hz. All you'll do is bring up the boom of the cabinet or the room resonances which is, generally, not what you want.

• Bite can be added to the sound anywhere between 2kHz and 6kHz, depending on the effect you're after. The electric guitar isn't a natural instrument, so the only rule is to get the sound you want. Don't add any really high end boost unless the guitar is DI'd; nothing much over 4kHz comes out of a guitar speaker, so boosting higher than this would simply bring up the background noise for no reason.

• Two similar sounding electric guitars can be separated by adding bite at different frequencies — at 3kHz on one guitar and around 4kHz on the other, for example. It also helps to choose two different types of guitar if the parts are both busy — perhaps one single-coil model and one with humbuckers.

• Single-coil guitars cut through a mix without taking up too much space, so they may be the best choice in a busy mix. Humbucking pickups create a thicker sound, which can help when aiming for a full sound from a small rock band such as a three-piece lead, bass and drums outfit.

# SIGNAL PROCESSING

Aside from optimising the EQ, what else can you do to a guitar sound? The answer to that question really depends on whether you merely wish to enhance the sound or make it significantly different; in extreme cases, the guitar can be so heavily treated that it is no longer recognised as a guitar at all.

Multi-effects processors are relatively cheap, and most allow the user to create reverb, delay, chorus, phasing, flanging, vibrato, pitch shifting and so on; more up-market models offer extras such as panning, exciters, complex equalisers, compressors, gates and auto-wah. The list of possible effects is endless but, as in the worlds of art and music composition, it is often what you leave out that makes more difference than what you put in.

# REVERB

If you're after a fairly straight rock sound, then the basic overdrive sound, however achieved, need only be treated with a little EQ and reverb to make it sound right — choosing the right type of reverb is the only problem. For a raunchy, live sound, a short reverb with a fairly bright character is ideal, and the shorter the reverb decay, the more of it you can add into your mix without making the mix sound cluttered. If the original amplifier sound had reverb added, you may even find an early reflection or ambience program works best, as this will add brightness and interest as well as opening up the stereo spread, but without changing the essential character of the original sound too much.

More abstract musical forms may demand a longer, more flowing reverb and these can be combined with repeat multi-echo effects to create a sense of vastness. Further interest can be added by feeding the effects signal through a chorus or flange unit before it gets to the reverb unit. There are no hard and fast rules, but in general terms, the less busy the guitar part, the more reverb you can add before you run into problems. For a more in-depth discussion of the effects of reverb, read the chapter dedicated to reverb treatments.

# COMPRESSION

Compressors are commonly used on guitar tracks of all types to increase sustain and to keep an even level. In this application, compressors with programme-dependent attack and release times are very helpful, as they will automatically adapt to the different sounds produced by different playing styles. Even a heavily overdriven guitar sound can be made to appear more powerful if compressed, as its average energy level is increased. Of course, manual compressors may also be used, in which case the attack time of the compressor may be increased slightly to give individual notes more attack if desired. Optimum release time depends on playing speed, but around half a second is usually adequate.

Using a faster release time in combination with a high degree of compression can cause audible level pumping, but this artifact may be used creatively to enhance the feeling of power. As a rule, a medium compression ratio of between 3:1 and 5:1 is adequate, with the threshold set to give between 8 and 15dB of gain reduction on the loudest notes.

It must always be borne in mind that 10dB of compression also means a 10dB deterioration in the signal-to-noise ratio during the quieter sections where noise is most likely to be obtrusive, so tracks containing guitar solos are best kept closed down until the moment before their entry. This may be done manually, but is more easily handled by an automated mute system. Remember that guitar amplifiers produce more noise than almost any other instrument (especially during heavy overdrive), which means that special care must be taken if the end recording is not to be compromised.

# GENERAL MIC TECHNIQUES

There are well-established microphone techniques for all the more common musical instruments, but the musical world is a large place, and there is an abundance of ethnic instruments for which no standard miking methods exist. Nevertheless, there are a couple of simple rules that can be applied to virtually every instrument ever conceived, and which give acceptable results every time.

Most instruments produce sound from more than one place — take the acoustic guitar; some sound comes out of the sound hole due to air vibration inside the body, the wooden panels making up the body resonate, the strings themselves produce sound, and the neck and headstock vibrate. What we identify as a good acoustic guitar sound is in fact a combination of all these separate sounds. The same is true of all acoustic instruments, and even in the case of an electric instrument such as an amplified guitar, it could be argued that the cabinet vibrates and contributes to the sound directly produced by the loudspeaker.

## MIC DISTANCE

Miking distance presents a problem, because if we bring the microphone too close to the instrument, we start to focus on just one part of it, which means that we are no longer capturing the composite sound of the whole instrument. It is tempting to put the microphone close to the part of the instrument that seems to be making the most sound, such as the bell of a trumpet, the sound hole of a guitar or the head of a drum, and though it is occasionally possible to obtain usable results in this way, what we actually get is not really representative of the whole instrument.

On the other side of the coin, placing the microphone too far away may capture the necessary components of the sound but could also pick up other unwanted sounds or room ambience effects. It is always easier to record an instrument if it is played in a sympathetic acoustic environment, and most western instruments need a little reverberation because they were designed to be played indoors. The same is not necessarily true of ethnic instruments, as many are only ever played out of doors, and thus need a less reflective environment.

# UNIVERSAL RULE

As acoustic instruments vary enormously in loudness and frequency content, I'd tend to choose a capacitor microphone in order to be confident of having a high enough degree of sensitivity and the ability to capture the full audio spectrum. Most instruments sound reasonably accurate to the person playing them, which gives us one fallback position straight away; if all else fails, put a mic close to the player's ears. As I mentioned in an earlier chapter, I've used this technique to good effect when working with acoustic guitars, where a cardioid mic 'looking' over the player's right shoulder will often produce a very natural and well-balanced sound

The other method I've evolved is based on rules normally applied to the stereo miking of ensembles. When working with stereo, it is common practice to create an equilateral triangle with the musicians forming one side of the triangle and the stereo mic array occupying the point opposite. This ensures that all the instruments in the ensemble are roughly the same distance from the mics, yet the mics are close enough to exclude external sounds to a useful degree.

# SINGLE INSTRUMENTS

A typical drum kit is around five feet in width, so a single mic placed five feet in front of the kit will give a usable result. Of course, few people would record the drum kit with a single mic, but it serves to illustrate the principle.

This rule may be extended slightly to accommodate single instruments; it is necessary only to measure the longest dimension of the instrument and then place a cardioid pattern mic at that distance from the instrument and pointing towards its centre. For example, a drum kit is normally miked from between four and five feet, while a piano might be miked at between five and eight feet. This is only a 'rule of thumb', and if it is desirable to capture a little more of the room ambience, then the mic can be moved a little further away until the desired balance is achieved. Even so, check the mic position which results from using this method against the standard mic positions for known instruments and you'll be surprised at how closely they correlate. Virtually all the wind instrument mic positions can be worked out in this way. Likewise, the acoustic guitar can be recorded using a single mic at a distance of around three feet.

# THE 5:1 RULE

A further consideration arises when several instruments are being recorded together, as it may be necessary to compromise the individual microphone positions in order to minimise leakage or spill between the instruments. Using Cardioid pattern mics, it is recommended that the mics be separated by a distance at least five times as great as the distance between the microphones and the instruments they are trained upon. This principle is illustrated in Figure 10.1. A slight improvement in unwanted leakage can be achieved by using a tighter microphone pattern, such as a Hypercardioid or Supercardioid, but it could also be argued that Omnis will produce just as good a result. Admittedly there may be more spill, but because of the improved off-axis response of Omni mics, the spill will at least be recorded faithfully.

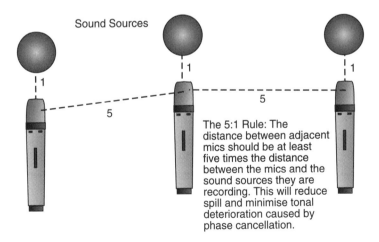

Sound Sources

The 5:1 Rule: The distance between adjacent mics should be at least five times the distance between the mics and the sound sources they are recording. This will reduce spill and minimise tonal deterioration caused by phase cancellation.

Figure 10.1: The 5:1 Rule

Cardioids will produce slightly better separation, but their inferior off-axis response means that what spill is picked up may be tonally inaccurate, leading to a less accurate representation of the performance when the outputs from all the mics are mixed. There are Cardioids with excellent off-axis response, but these tend to be rather specialised and very expensive.

# STEREO

When attempting stereo recordings of large ensembles, the classic approach is to use a stereo mic pair, usually M&S or XY (coincident) mounted in front of the performers, as stated earlier. In a venue with suitable acoustics, this can produce excellent results, with the outputs from the mics being recorded directly to DAT or similar stereo recording device. Realistically, though, the balance is unlikely to to be exactly right, and though individual performers can be moved around to compensate to some extent, most engineers resort to using spot microphones to reinforce the weaker sections. Working with a small folk duo or string quartet, this may not be a problem, but in situations such as orchestral recording sessions, where much greater microphone distances are involved, the time delay between the sound reaching the spot mics and the main stereo mics becomes significant.

# DELAY CORRECTION

The time delay problem can be corrected by using a high quality delay line to delay the spot mic outputs by exactly the right amount, so that the signals arriving from both sets of mics are brought back into phase with each other. As sound travels at roughly 300 metres per second, this isn't too difficult to calculate, and the spot mics (suitably panned) can then be added in with the main stereo mics before being recorded onto the stereo machine. Alternatively, the performance can be recorded onto multitrack tape for subsequent mixing. Figure 10.2 shows how the delay is connected.

To do this properly requires a separate digital delay for each spot mic, but in all but the most serious classical recording situations, this might be considered a touch extravagant. It is normally sufficient to delay all the spot mics by the same amount; this is easily achieved by creating a stereo subgroup of the spot mic signals (either while recording or during mixing) and then using a good quality stereo DDL to delay the subgrouped signal by the required amount.

It is essential that the spot mics are panned to the correct positions in the stereo soundstage so that they corroborate the image produced by the main stereo mic array. The delay unit may be connected to the subgroup insert points, and if the business of adding delay can be left until the mixing stage, this gives the added flexibility of being able to 'fine tune' the delay time by ear for the best subjective result.

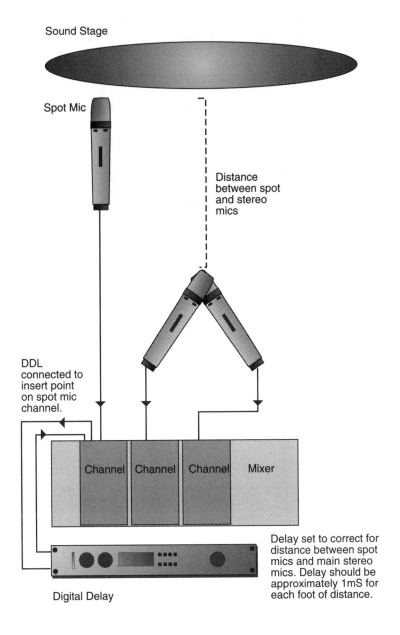

Figure 10.2: Delaying a Spot Mic

# ESOTERICA

There is some disagreement as to whether the sound from spot mics should be delayed until it is exactly in phase or whether subjectively better results are produced if the spot mics are slightly over-delayed. The logic behind over-delaying the spot mics is that the sound from them blends in with the early reflections picked up by the main stereo mics. This has the effect of changing their subjective level but without the need the timing to be precisely accurate.

It must be stressed that these are very high-brow considerations and are the subject of debate between engineers at different leading classical record companies. But it strikes me that if a compromise must be made, and all the spot mics have to be processed by a single stereo delay line, over-delaying the sound very slightly, rather than under-delaying it, might achieve a better result — bearing in mind that it is impossible to give all the spot mics exactly the right delay time using a common delay line.

# AT4033

## STUDIO CONDENSER MICROPHONE

*"Audio Technica is still in its infancy in the professional market, and not having encountered it before, the 4033 Transformerless Capacitor Studio Microphone came as a very pleasant surprise. Its styling is distinctive and elegant, the finish is excellent, and the cat's cradle, again supplied as standard, is simple and effective and balances the microphone very well. Everything about the microphone looks and feels sturdy and professional.*

*Once again the facilities are simple; the only switches are for the high pass filter and the pad, and the polar pattern is cardioid.*

AT4033
shown with
optional shock
mount AT8441

*But the biggest surprise was the sound. On everything I tried – including a Steinway grand –*

Reprinted from

**STUDIO SOUND**
AND BROADCAST ENGINEERING
February 1992

*the output was virtually indistinguishable from that of the 414 – open, transparent and clean, quiet and free of colouration. The main difference was in the sensitivity – the 4033 is few dB more sensitive than the 414.*

*If this is an example of what Audio Technica has to offer, I await further developments with interest. A variable-pattern microphone with the sound of the 4033 would be a very useful addition to the arsenal indeed. As it stands, I can't imagine it will be long before this microphone is a much more familiar sight."*

**Other Models in the Pure Condenser Series include**

| | | | |
|---|---|---|---|
| AT 4031 | Fixed Charged Condenser | AT 4051 | Complete Set (4051E + 4900-48) |
| AT 4049-ELE | Omnidirectional Element | AT 4071 | Shot Gun (395mm long) |
| AT 4051-ELE | Unidirectional Element | AT 4073 | Shot Gun (232mm long) |
| AT 4053-ELE | Hyper Cardioid Element | AT 4900-48 | Pre Amplifier |
| | | AT 4462 | Complete Field Production Mixer |

## ⚆ audio-technica ®

☐ INNOVATION   ☐ PRECISION   ☐ INTEGRITY

Technica House, Royal London Industrial Estate, Old Lane, Leeds LS11 8AG Tel: 0532 771441 Fax: 0532 704836

---

# Road TOUGH

**ATM   ARTIST SERIES**

**G**reat stage and studio sound starts with the microphone and today more musicians and sound engineers find their greatest sound starts with with the A-T Artist Series. It's a rugged group that's engineered to take the stresses of live performance yet deliver audio quality that only A-T's ultra-precise manufacturing and stateside R&D can deliver.

**W**ith a choice of both dynamic and condenser models there's a solution to even the most difficult of pick-up problems, and they're rapidly becoming the first choice of many major artists on both sides of the Atlantic. Check out just what the ATM range can do for you at your local music dealer or call us direct for a colour information pack.

VOCAL

▲ **ATM41HE**
DYNAMIC   *HI-ENERGY*

Close working, field proven hand held cardioid tailored to punch through accompaniment with a gently rising curve from 2 kHz to 5 kHz. Outstanding high gain-before-feedback properties. ATM41HE epitomises the 'road tough' of all ATM models with 3 layer metal mesh ball and superb isolation from handling and shock noise.

**ATM25** DYNAMIC ▶

Tough hypercardioid microphone with the ability to 'focus' on desired sound location for clean response in high SPL surroundings. Big, warm low frequency response with excellent presence for bass drums, toms, snares, acoustic bass, piano or any high output low frequency instrument. Full sound also for close-up vocals and dialogue.

## ⚆ audio-technica ®

☐ INNOVATION   ☐ PRECISION   ☐ INTEGRITY

Technica House, Royal London Industrial Estate, Old Lane, Leeds LS11 8AG Tel: 0532 771441 Fax: 0532 704836

# REVERB

Reverberation is undoubtedly the most important studio effect at our disposal, and no book on engineering or production would be complete without a section devoted to this subject. In pop music production, and indeed in some classical recording situations, reverberation tends to be added using digital reverberation simulators rather than relying on the natural acoustics of the studio or venue.

Digital reverberation units were originally very costly, due to the complexity of their circuitry and the research which went into them, but as new circuit technology was developed and as the principles of artificial reverberation became better established, inexpensive units became commonplace. Nowadays, a basic digital reverberation unit can cost less than a couple of hundred pounds.

The more expensive professional studio reverb units tend to have a better technical specification in terms of noise, audio bandwidth and distortion, and they also produce a more realistic effect. But, though budget units are technically inferior, they still offer surprisingly good reverb simulations and are generally quiet enough, if used with care, to make good master quality recordings. Some models offer a choice of preset reverberation treatments, while others allow every detail of the effect to be programmed. It is, admittedly, useful to be able to vary the more important parameters which make up the reverberation effect, but it is arguable whether the very detailed programming possible on some models is worthwhile. A basic unit offering a choice of over 100 preset reverb treatments (as many now do) will cover most eventualities; such models make ideal second reverb units.

# VITAL STATISTICS

When a sound impulse is fed into a reverb unit, there is a short delay before any reverberant sound is heard; this is known as the reverb 'pre-delay', and is often used to increase the impression of room size ,but can also be useful in separating the reverb slightly from the dry sound, especially on vocals, to increase vocal clarity.

Directly after the pre-delay come the so-called 'early reflections', which are really closely spaced, discrete echoes representing the first reflections from the room boundaries. These discrete reflections quickly built up into a dense, reverberant pattern which further increases in density as its level decays. In a real room, these early reflections help us to localise sounds, and in a digital reverberation simulator, they help create the illusion of space around the sound. Figure 11.1 shows how reverberation develops and decays following a percussive sound.

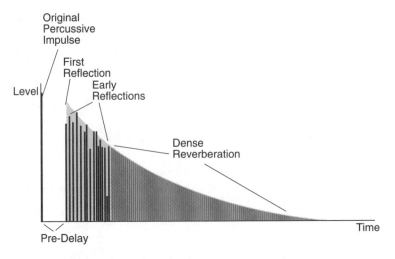

**Figure 11.1 Anatomy of Reverberation.**

# EARLY REFLECTIONS

Herein lies one major difference between real rooms and artificial reverberators: in a real room, every instrument in an ensemble produces a different early reflection pattern because the performers are occupying different positions relative to the room boundaries. As a consequence, the early reflections from the different instruments tend to blend, creating a more dense, more complex pattern than would be produced if all created the same early reflections pattern.

Artificial reverb devices produce a fixed pattern of early reflections which has the effect of placing every instrument in our imaginary room in the same position. This isn't always a problem, especially when producing pop music, as artistic considerations come before the need for authenticity. But in classical or other 'acoustic' work, it helps to turn down the early reflection level if the reverb unit is programmable, or to pick a hall setting with a slow reverb build-up if the unit offers a choice of presets. Not only does this prevent the 'everything in one place' effect, it also sounds more natural, as most digital reverberation units produce early reflection patterns that are far more obtrusive than those found in real concert halls.

# MONO INTO STEREO

Reverb units usually take a mono sound source and create a pseudo-stereo output by producing different reverberation patterns for the left and right channels. This is a perfectly viable approach and closely simulates what happens when a single sound source (which can be considered as mono) is heard in a reflective room — different reverberant patterns arrive at the left and right ears of the listener, creating the impression of space. Those units which have stereo inputs invariably sum the two channels to mono for processing, leaving only the dry portion of the sound in stereo. The reverberant sound is generated from the summed mono signal and processed to provide stereo (left and right) outputs. Some units can be programmed to operate as separate mono reverb processors, but these are relatively uncommon.

# REAL LIFE

During a real musical performance, all the instruments would normally play in the same room and so be influenced by the same natural acoustic environment. It follows that in order to simulate this using artificial reverberation, all the instruments in the mix should be treated with the same type of reverberation. In the production of pop music, however, we are under no such constraints, as a natural result is not necessarily the most artistically pleasing result. Consequently, it is common practice to use several different reverb settings on the same mix; for example, the vocals might have a medium length, warm-sounding reverb while the snare drum might be treated with a short, bright plate or even a gated setting. Other instruments could be treated with other reverb types or be left completely dry. Furthermore, the relative level of reverb to dry sound is likely to be different in each case. The choice of settings for individual instruments or parts is a purely artistic one, but there are some points to take into consideration which might make this choice more logical.

# PSYCHOACOUSTICS

In nature, reverberation is used by our ears to determine something about our immediate environment. If we hear a sound with a lot of reverberation, we assume that it is quite distant, because nearby sounds will contain far more of the direct portion of the sound and less reflected sound. This is true both in and out of doors, though outdoor reverb is only evident in places where there are large reflective surfaces such as buildings, cliffs or densely-growing trees. Furthermore, bright reverbs suggest hard surfaces, while duller or warmer reverbs characterise softer environments such as concert halls.

It can be deduced from these facts that if the level of reverberation following a sound is increased, the sound can be made to seem more distant, and this provides a way of creating a front-to-back perspective in a mix, as opposed to the simple left/right positioning offered by pan pots. Also bear in mind that high frequencies are absorbed by the air, so distant sounds tend to be less bright than nearby sounds.

## ● TIP ●

This applies to both the direct and reverberant sound, which means that a sound may be placed in the far distance by using a very high level of reverberant sound with a low level of direct sound and a degree of HF cut. Conversely, the illusion of proximity can be created by placing a relatively bright, dry sound against a backdrop of less bright, more reverberant sounds; this explains why highly reverberant lead vocals need to be mixed at a high level to prevent them receding into the background.

# SMALL ROOMS

Small rooms tend to have pronounced early reflection patterns with a fairly rapid reverb decay. Such treatments can be used to create an intimate club atmosphere — it is possible, using very short reverberation decay times, with a relatively high level of reverb compared to the dry sound, to bring a sound alive without making it seem processed in any way at all. That's because we are simulating the type of acoustic that we're used to living and working in — one which we recognise as normal and take for granted. Some reverb units contain specific ambience or early reflections programs, and these are very useful for creating space without apparent reverb. They are also useful for processing tape tracks that have been recorded with a mono effect and which need to be given a sense of width.

● TIP ●

For example, a vocal recorded with a medium reverb can be processed using an early reflections setting to create the illusion of depth and stereo width. This is extremely useful for 4- and 8-track users who invariably have to bounce tracks together and add some effects as they record.

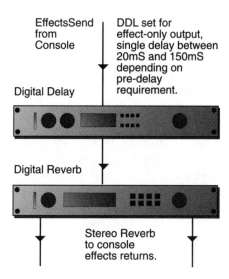

Figure 11.2: Adding Pre-Delay to Reverb

# FURTHER EFFECTS

Reverberation used alone is a very powerful effect, but it can also be combined with delay to make things more interesting.

• If you are using a digital reverb with no programmable facilities, you can add pre-delay simply by patching a DDL into the reverb input, using a single repeat at between 30 and 300ms, depending on the effect required. Figure 11.2 shows how this is patched up.

• Multi-tapped delays can be used to create very spacious reverb effects, especially if the delay is patched before the reverb unit.

• Setting longer, multiple echoes gives a very rich echo effect because each individual echo is surrounded by its own halo of reverb.

• Modulating the delay very slightly creates a kind of chorus echo which can work beautifully on guitar or synthesizer.

Multi-effects units don't always allow you to connect the effects in the order you would prefer. This is significant because the order in which effects are connected makes a profound difference to the end result.

# AUTOPANNED REVERB

• Processing a reverb signal via an autopanner, to sweep it from side to side at a rate of one sweep every couple of seconds or so creates a nice sense of movement without sounding too obvious or gimmicky.

• A mono-in/stereo-out autopanner must be fed with a mono reverb signal which can be obtained from the reverb's mono output, if the unit has one, or by combining the two channels using a mixer. Panning this signal from side to side at the rate of half a second or so per sweep creates a distinct side-to-side movement, and if the pan time can be made a multiple of the song tempo, the result can be very subtle. This works particularly well when trying to make backing vocals more interesting or for treating instruments in New Age or ambient music productions.

• Alternatively, a stereo panner can be used to treat both the reverb's left and right outputs, causing the left and right signals, in effect, to cross over and back again as the pan progresses.

## ● TIP ●

It is also worth experimenting with processing the send to the reverb unit as follows:

• Applying a small pitch detune to the reverb send can thicken the sound, especially if the reverb level is high in the mix; this may be used to good effect on parts such as backing vocals or synthesized strings.

• Similarly, applying chorus or mild flange to the reverb input helps add movement and spread to the sound, while the random nature of the reverb breaks up the cyclic nature of the chorus or flange.

# MULTI-EFFECTS PROCESSORS

The hardware required to produce additional studio effects is little different from that used to generate reverb, and in recent years, digital multi-effects units costing little more than straight reverb devices have appeared. Depending on their cost and sophistication, these units may be preset or programmable, and may allow anything from four to 20 effects to be used in combination at the same time. There is usually a limitation to which effects can be used simultaneously and in what order they can be used, the permutations often being grouped into so-called 'algorithms'. These algorithms are, in effect, pre-assigned configurations of effects, where the user can change the parameters of the various effects and store the modified composite effect as a patch for later recall.

Most multi-effects units offer reverb, delay and all the modulated delay effects such as chorus, phasing, flanging and vibrato as standard. More sophisticated models may provide pitch shifting, exciters, compressors, gates and equalisers; guitar-specific models often include overdrive and speaker simulation. These days, it is common practice to use guitar multi-effects units to process synthesizers or samplers to produce overdriven synth guitar sounds or distorted organ simulations.

While the same reverb is often used on several instruments or voices in a mix, this is not really true of complex multiple effects patches. These tend to be created with a specific musical part in mind, are often confined to a single vocal or instrumental part, and may only ever be used in one song.

It is becoming increasingly popular to include real-time MIDI control over key parameters within an effect. This allows a performer to change, for example, reverb decay time or pitch shift amount from a MIDI pedal unit. By the same token, these same parameters may be controlled from a MIDI sequencer, which opens up new avenues for automated effects processing. In this application, some units work better than others — on some the parameter being changed will vary smoothly, while with others, the change can be heard as a series of fine steps. Obviously, the smoother the change, the better.

# DYNAMIC CONTROL

The term 'dynamic control' is generally held to apply to any automatic process which changes the gain of an audio signal. In the context of outboard equipment, the term refers to compressors and gates, though it could equally cover mixer automation and autopanners. Gates and compressors were originally designed for corrective purposes, but they also have a creative role in the studio, and few modern recordings are made without the help of these devices.

## COMPRESSOR

A compressor is a device which reduces the dynamic range of an audio signal — in other words, it reduces the difference between the loudest and quietest parts of a piece of music. Compression is invariably necessary when recording vocals, as singers vary in level a great deal, depending on the notes they are singing and on their phrasing. Certain instruments, such as bass, electric and acoustic guitars, also benefit from the use of a compressor to help produce a smooth, even level. The compressor really plays a vital role in pop music production, where dynamics need to be quite strictly controlled, and it also increases the average signal level of a recording — which, when applied to music, helps produce a full and punchy sound. In non-musical applications, such as in the processing of broadcast speech, compression is used to ensure intelligibility at all times.

All conventional compressors work on some form of threshold system and are arranged such that signals exceeding the threshold are processed while those falling below the threshold pass through unchanged. This threshold may be set by the user, either by varying the threshold level relative to the input signal or, conversely, by varying the input signal level relative to a fixed threshold. A further stage of gain, called 'make-up' gain is then provided after processing, to allow the user to restore or 'make up' any gain lost in the processing.

# RATIO

When a signal exceeds the threshold set by the user, its level is automatically reduced, the amount depending on the 'ratio' setting. On many compressors, the ratio is variable: the higher the ratio, the more severe the degree of compression. (High ratios produce an effect known as 'limiting', where the input signal is prevented from ever exceeding the threshold.) The best way to understand the effect of a compressor ratio is by giving an example: if a compression ratio of 5:1 is set, an input signal exceeding the threshold by 5dB will cause only a 1dB increase in level at the output. The concept of threshold and ratio are illustrated in the graph in Figure 12.1.

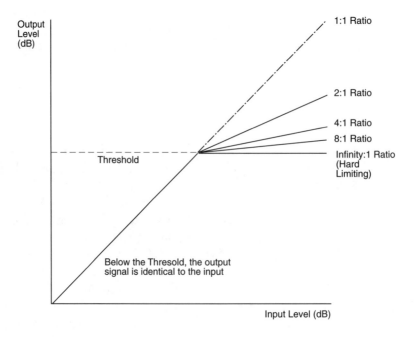

Figure 12.1: Compressor Threshold and Ratio

# SOFT KNEE

A standard compressor has a well-defined threshold — if the input signal is just below the threshold, no compression takes place, but if it is just over, then the full compression ratio is applied. An alternative approach is the so-called 'soft-knee' compressor where the threshold level is 'blurred' over a range of 10dB or so. This type of compressor is less able to exercise really positive gain control than fixed ratio or 'hard-knee' types, but its real advantage is that it is less obtrusive in use, making it suitable for compressing complete mixes or for treating instrumental or vocal sounds that need to retain a natural quality. Figure 2 shows how the Soft Knee appears on the Threshold/Ratio graph.

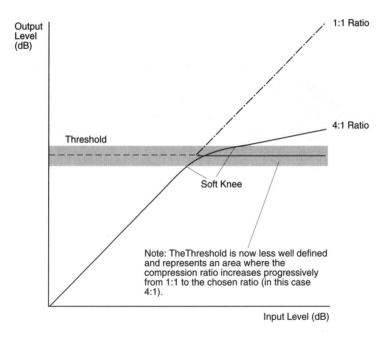

**Figure 12.2: Soft Knee Graph**

Soft-knee compressors give a more progressive kind of level control, because the compression ratio gradually increases up to the value set by the user rather than being applied abruptly. Hard-knee compressors are better where a more firm degree of control is needed or for making deliberate modifications to the sound of percussive or picked instrumental sounds.

# ATTACK

The term 'attack', in the context of compressors, does not refer to the attack of the sound being processed but to the reaction time of the gain control circuitry within the compressor. The attack time control determines how long the compressor takes to respond once the input signal exceeds the threshold. If the attack is set fast, the signal is brought under control very quickly, whereas a slower attack time might allow the input signal to overshoot the threshold before gain reduction is applied. Allowing deliberate overshoot to occur in this way is a popular way of emphasising the attack characteristics of instruments such as guitars or drums; the slower the attack of the compressor, the more pronounced the attack of the sound being treated.

# RELEASE

Release sets the time taken by the compressor to restore the gain to normal once the input signal has fallen back below the threshold. If the release time is set too short, the gain returns to its normal level too quickly, resulting in an audible surge in volume, often referred to as 'gain pumping'. On the other hand, if the release time is set too long, the compressor may still be applying some gain reduction when the next sound comes along — if this is a quiet sound, it will still be suppressed and the benefit of compression will be lost. Long release times can be useful when trying to even out long-term changes in levels, such as the differences in level of different songs on a radio broadcast. However, in music mixing applications, a typical release time is in the order of half a second.

# AUTO MODE

Optimising the attack and release settings of a compressor is not difficult when the dynamics of the signal being processed are consistent, but if the dynamics are consistently varying, as is the case with most complete mixes, slap bass parts and some vocal lines, then the ideal settings are less obvious. In such situations, it is often better to use a compressor which has an auto attack/release feature.

When the auto mode is selected, the compressor analyses the dynamics of the incoming signal and varies its attack and release times 'on the fly' to maintain maximum control with the minimum of side effects. For complex mixes or signals with varying or unpredictable dynamics, the auto setting is usually most effective.

# PROBLEMS WITH COMPRESSORS

Compressors are not without their negative aspects. For every dB of compression we apply, we also bring up the background noise by 1dB. This might not be obvious at first because, as I've said, a compressor only affects signals exceeding its threshold, and even then, it turns the sound level down, not up. However, the reason for the increase in noise is obvious if you think about it. If we use a compressor to reduce the highest signal peaks by, say, 10dB, we're likely to use the make-up gain control to restore the peak level of the signal to its original value. This means applying 10dB of gain to the whole signal, with the result that any noise present in the signal will also be boosted by 10dB. This will be most apparent when there is no wanted signal to hide the noise, as is the case with low level signals that don't exceed the threshold.

Excessive noise can be alleviated to some extent by using a gate or expander before the compressor, to ensure that breaks and pauses are completely silent; many compressors now come with an inbuilt expander for this very reason. However, this is a corrective measure and, as such, is less satisfactory than the preventative measure of ensuring that the original signal is as free of noise as is possible. In practice, an expander used to clean up a well-recorded signal with a low noise content produces very good results.

# WHERE AND WHEN

Most engineers tend to compress their signals while recording and then again during mixing. There are good reasons for this, the main one being that compressing a signal while recording it makes the best use of the tape's dynamic range and, at the same time, helps to prevent unexpected signal peaks from overloading the tape machine. Because any processing applied during recording is irreversible, it is normal to use rather less compression than might ultimately be needed, so that a little more can be added at the mixing stage if required. It is at this latter stage that the expander or gate is best applied to clean up the pauses. If the gate setting is incorrect, the tape can always be run again, but if a mistake is made during recording, an otherwise perfect take may be ruined.

# COMPRESSOR SOUND

Much of what I've explained so far is common knowledge in recording circles, but what may be less obvious is why different models of compressor can sound so different to each other. Part of the difference can be attributed to the side-chain detector circuit — that part of the system which analyses the dynamics of the incoming signal. There are two distinct types in use: peak detecting and RMS detecting. A peak detecting circuit, as its name suggests, will respond to peaks in the input signal regardless of how short they are, while the RMS detector averages the signal level over a short period of time.

The latter approach is more akin to the workings of the human ear and so tends to give a more natural type of dynamic control, but it has a disadvantage in that short signal peaks can get through undetected. Of course, short peaks may also get through any type of compressor unchecked, unless the fastest attack time is set, which is why, in some critical applications, a fast peak limiter is also required.

A good example of this is digital recording, where signals larger than the maximum permitted level must be avoided, or serious audible distortion will result. It is possible to patch a separate limiter after the compressor, but in critical applications such as digital mastering or broadcast, it may be desirable to use a compressor with a built-in peak limiter.

The limiter threshold is invariably set higher than the compressor threshold and such limiters are very fast acting, thus preventing any overshoot. In practice, most employ a clipping circuit which physically arrests any signal trying to exceed the limiter threshold until the necessary gain correction has been applied. Though this kind of limiter action is pretty drastic, the sound it produces can be useful in a creative way, especially on rock music.

# SIDE EFFECTS

Most of the energy in a typical music signal resides in the lower frequencies, which means that the bass drum, bass guitar and, to a lesser extent, the snare drum control most of what the compressor is doing. This shows up one real weakness of compressors, which is that any high frequency sounds occurring at the same time as a low frequency sound will be turned down as the compressor responds to the input signal level. For example, a quiet hi-hat beat occurring at the same time as a bass drum beat will be reduced in level even though it isn't too loud.

The usual way around this is to set a longer attack time on the compressor to allow the attack of the beat to get through unchecked; even so, if a lot of compression is applied to a complex mix, the sound can become dull as the high frequency detail is overruled by the low frequency peaks .

Some of the early valve compressors seemed to suffer less from this problem than apparently more sophisticated later designs, and here's one of the reasons — most valve compressors introduce a significant amount of even harmonic distortion, which increases as gain reduction is being applied. This has the effect of brightening the sound, very much like an exciter, which helps to compensate for the over-reduction in level of high frequencies.  A little even-order harmonic distortion can actually make a signal sound brighter and cleaner than it really is — and valve compressors were adding this distortion quite unintentionally.

Some early FET-based designs also introduced a similar kind of distortion, which is why FET compressors can sound very similar to valve models. More recent designs have attempted to recreate this serendipitous combination of effects by building in a degree of  harmonic distortion or dynamic equalisation, which provides a subtle treble boost related to the amount of gain reduction taking place. This can work very well in maintaining a detailed and relatively transparent sound, even when heavy compression is taking place.

# DUCKING

Though compressors are used, in the main, to smooth out large fluctuations in signal level, they may also be used to allow one signal to control the level of another. This technique is generally referred to as ducking and is frequently used by radio DJs to allow the level of background music to be controlled by the level of the voice-over. As the DJ starts to speak, the level of the background music drops, but whenever there is a pause in the speech, the background music will return to its normal level, at a a rate determined by the setting of the compressor's release control.

Such techniques are only possible if the compressor being used has side-chain access. Normally the side-chain of a compressor is fed from its own input signal, but if it is fed from an external source instead, the dynamics of that external source will control the gain reduction process. In our DJ example, if music is fed into the main compressor input and the DJ's voice is fed into the side-chain or external input, whenever the DJ's voice exceeds the threshold level, gain reduction will be applied to the music.

The amount of gain reduction will depend on the compression ratio that has been set; many engineers prefer to use a gate with a dedicated ducking facility in preference to a compressor because the results are more predictable.

Apart from the obvious application just described, ducking can be very useful when mixing pop or rock music.

## ● TIP ●

Loud, relentless rhythm guitar or pad keyboard parts can be forced down in level to allow the vocals to punch through. The amount of ducking needed to make this work is surprisingly small — a drop in level of just 2 or 3dB is often sufficient to avoid conflict, and the slight gain pumping effect caused by the gain change can add to the sense of power. It is important not to overdo the effect, though, as once the gain changes start to become noticeable, they cease to be pleasant.

Apart from controlling one instrument level with a voice or other instrument (such as solo guitar), ducking may also be used to control the output level from an effects unit. Reverb or delay are very powerful effects, but if too much is used in a busy mix, the result can be very cluttered. Nevertheless, the same mix might have sudden breaks or stops where a high level of reverb or delay is necessary. The answer is to use, say, the drum part to feed the external side-chain input of the compressor and feed the reverb or delay outputs through the compressor's main input. Now, whenever the drums stop, the effect level will return to normal, but when the drums are playing, ducking will take place and the level of the effect will be reduced. Figure 12.3 shows how a ducker might be used in the context of using a voice-over to control the level of background music.

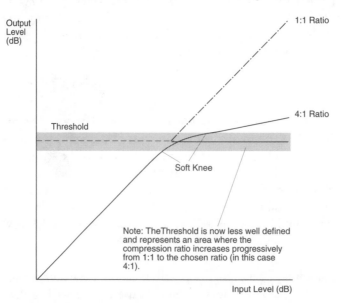

Figure 12.3: Using a Compressor as a Ducker

# COMPRESSOR DISTORTION

We have already touched upon valve and FET distortion, which can work to our advantage by brightening heavily compressed sounds, but there are other, less pleasant distortion mechanisms to be aware of. Normally, a compressor's side-chain follows the envelope of the signal being fed into it, but if the attack and release times are set to their fastest positions, it is possible that the compressor will attempt to respond not to the envelope of the input signal but to individual cycles of the input waveform.

This is particularly significant when the input signal is from a bass instrument, as the individual cycles are relatively long. If tracking of the individual waveform cycles is allowed to occur, very bad distortion is audible as the cycles are compressed 'out of shape'. The way to get around the problem is either to increase the release time of the compressor or, if your model allows it, increase the compressor's hold time. The hold facility is a simple time delay that prevents the compressor from going into its release cycle until a certain time has elapsed after the input signal has fallen below the threshold. If the hold time is set longer than the lowest audio frequency likely to be encountered, the compressor will never be able to release quickly enough to distort individual cycles. A hold time of around 50mS should cover all eventualities, and some manufacturers build a fixed hold time of this order into their compressors to make them, in effect, undistortable. Such a short hold time is unlikely to restrict the flexibility of

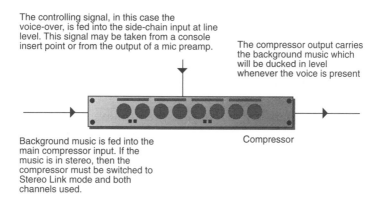

The controlling signal, in this case the voice-over, is fed into the side-chain input at line level. This signal may be taken from a console insert point or from the output of a mic preamp.

The compressor output carries the background music which will be ducked in level whenever the voice is present

Background music is fed into the main compressor input. If the music is in stereo, then the compressor must be switched to Stereo Link mode and both channels used.

Compressor

Note: The compressor Attack time determines how quickly the compressor will react when the voice signal is present. The compressor Release time determines how long the background music takes to rise back to its normal level once the voice stops.

**Figure 12.4: Compressor Distortion**

the compressor in any way and there is a very good argument for including a fixed hold time of around 50mS in all compressor designs. Figure 12.4 illustrates the effect of compressor distortion when fast attack and release times are used with no hold time.

# DE-ESSING

A typical compressor reacts equally to all input signals, whether they are bass sounds or high pitched instruments. For routine gain reduction applications, this is exactly what is required, but sometimes, it is desirable to have the compressor react more strongly to some frequencies than to others. The prime example is in de-essing, where we need to remove or reduce the sibilant content of a vocal signal. Sibilance is caused by breath passing around the lips and teeth of the singer and manifests itself as a very high-pitched whistle which can be very distracting and is further exacerbated by high frequency EQ, heavy compression or digital reverberation.

## ● TECHNIQUE ●

• If an equaliser is inserted into the side-chain signal path of a compressor, the equaliser can be used to determine which section of the audio spectrum is compressed the most.

• Sibilance normally occurs in the 5 to 10kHz region of the audio spectrum, so if the equaliser is tuned to the offending frequency and set to give, say 10dB of boost, then compression will occur at this frequency at a level 10dB lower than the rest of the audio spectrum.

• Both graphic and parametric equalisers can be used in this application, the parametric giving more control. The equaliser can be set up by listening to the equaliser output and then tuning the frequency control until the sibilant part of the input signal is most pronounced.

• By careful setting of the threshold and ratio controls, the sibilant sounds can be pushed down in level quite dramatically without significantly affecting the wanted sounds. However, if the amount of processing is too high, there will be a noticeable drop in gain whenever a sibilant sound occurs and this can be almost as annoying as the sibilance itself. Figure 12.5 shows how a conventional compressor may be used as a de-esser.

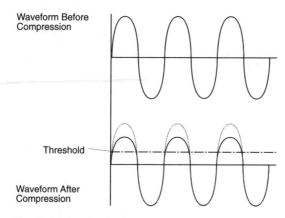

Waveform Before
Compression

Threshold

Waveform After
Compression

Note how the positive half cycle of the wave is 'squashed' as it
exceeds the threshold level. This problem is most evident on low
frequency sounds such as bass instruments and only happens
when very fast attack and release times are used on a
compressor that doesn't have a hold facility. Some designs have a
built-in hold time which is invisible to the user.

**Figure 12.5: De-essing with a Compressor**

# DEDICATED DE-ESSERS

A better approach is to use one of the more sophisticated, dedicated de-essers. Using a compressor as above results in the gain of the whole signal being reduced whenever a sibilant sound occurs. Ideally, we would reduce only the level of those frequencies that make up sibilance. Some of the more refined, dedicated de-essers do just this by using either a shelf or notch filter to reduce the gain in the 5-10kHz region whenever a sibilant sound is detected. This allows more processing to be applied without any undesirable side-effects becoming noticeable. Prevention is, however, far better than cure, and if using a different microphone or changing the microphone position can help reduce the sibilance at source, this should be done.

# GATES AND EXPANDERS

Gates were first devised to solve a problem in the film industry, where dialogue was often recorded under less than ideal conditions due to the need to keep the microphone out of shot. Their purpose is to shut down the signal path when the signal falls below a threshold set by the user; normally, this threshold will be set just above the ambient noise floor. When the gate is open, both the wanted signal and the unwanted noise pass through, the noise (hopefully) being masked by the signal. During pauses in the wanted signal the gate closes, and in doing so shuts off the background noise which would otherwise be clearly audible in the absence of any signal large enough to mask it.

Gates have undergone a process of refinement over the past couple of decade, and modern models can be quite sophisticated. Like the compressor, they now have attack and release controls which determine how quickly they respond, enabling them to be used to process most types of sound without undue difficulty. The fastest attack settings are used to allow percussive or highly transient sounds to pass through cleanly, while slower attack settings enable the gate to open more smoothly when processing signals which themselves have longer attack times, such as bowed strings.

The variable release time of a gate is also vital in that it enables the gate to close gradually when sounds with a slow decay are being processed. Examples of such sounds are plucked strings, some synthesized sounds, and sounds that have a long reverberant 'tail'. As with the compressor, problems can arise if the fastest attack and release times are set, as the gate triggers on each individual cycle of the input, producing a badly distorted, gritty sound. The solution is the same as for the compressor — many newer gates have a hold feature or a built-in hold time. In the absence of a hold facility, it is necessary to extend the release time until the problem disappears. The envelope structure of a typical gate is shown in Fifure 13.1.

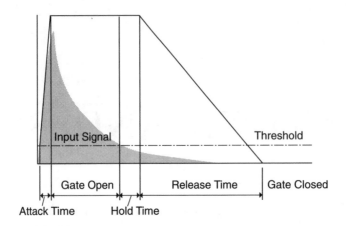

**Figure 13.1: Typical Gate Envelope.**

### ● TECHNIQUE ●

The hold facility may also be used in a creative way to produce hard 'gated' reverb or ambience sounds. If the reverberant sound is fed into the gate and then triggered externally using a mic located close to the drum, the gate can be used to impose an envelope on the reverberant sound. A fast release time combined with half a second or so of hold time produces the familiar gated drum sound when used to treat percussion.

## SIDE CHAIN FILTERS

A feature which is common on newer gates is side-chain filtering. This usually takes the form of a pair of shelving equalisers, one high-pass and one low-pass, connected in series with the side-chain circuitry. By varying the filter settings, it is possible to make the gate respond only to a selected band of frequencies, which helps exclude unwanted sounds in situations where spill is likely to cause false triggering.

An example of a situation in which filters can be helpful is when miking a drum kit, where sounds from all the drums spill into all the mics to a greater or lesser extent. By making the gate selective, it is possible to reduce the risk of, say, the hi-hat triggering the snare gate.

By setting the filters to minimise the amount of hi-hat spill fed to the side chain, while at the same time maximising the amount of snare signal, a greater degree of separation can be obtained.

This can only be achieved by listening to the filter output while adjusting the controls when 'key listen' is selected during setting up. It is important to realise that the filters are only connected in series with the side-chain signal path and do not affect the main input in any way. The only exception to this rule is when the filters are deliberately used as an equaliser by leaving the gate set to the 'key listen' mode.

# GATING WHILE MIXING

Gates are very important in multitrack recording, even when the recordings appear to be relatively free of noise. In a multitrack situation, the noise from all the tracks adds up cumulatively, so if a track can be gated into silence when nothing is playing, the finished mix can be made considerably cleaner. For example, the vocalist will not be singing during instrumental breaks and solos, so it makes sense to gate the vocal track in order to mute any tape noise from that track, as well as breath noise and any spill from the headphones that might otherwise be audible during pauses in the singing.

It is also desirable to gate electric guitars, as they have a relatively poor noise performance, especially when used for overdriven or heavily distorted lead guitar sounds. Using a gate will remove the hum, hiss and buzz generated by a guitar amplifier, and can significantly improve the clarity of the final recording.

Gating is best carried out after the signal has been recorded rather than during recording, for the obvious reason that an incorrectly set gate at the recording stage can ruin a take beyond any hope of salvage. Nevertheless, sometimes it is necessary to gate while recording — for example, in situations where several signals have to be mixed onto one tape track and only one of these is to be gated.

In this instance, it is wise to set the gate attenuation control to give only as much attenuation as is really necessary and to err on the side of caution when setting the threshold. It is better to put up with a little unwanted spill than to to suffer a signal with vital sections cut out of it by an overzealous gate!

# ALTERNATIVE FILTER APPLICATIONS

The side-chain filters used in gates necessarily have a very sharp response — usually 12dB per octave. This makes them far more selective than most conventional equalisers, and in some circumstances, the filters in a spare gate can be used to supplement the basic desk EQ. To do this it is only necessary to leave the gate switched to 'side-chain listen'; the gate will be bypassed and the filters placed in-line with the signal path.

## ● TIP ●

The low-pass filter can work wonders in removing high frequency noise from an electric guitar track without significantly changing the character of the basic guitar sound, while the high-pass filter can be used to remove low frequency hums and rumbles as well as to 'thin out' rhythm guitar or backing vocal parts. In very desperate circumstances, the low-pass filter can even be used to reduce the effects of overload distortion on recordings of rhythm guitar and other dynamic sounds, where a little tooo much enthusiasm on the part of the player can drive the tape machine or mixing console into clipping.

# EXTERNAL CONTROL

Gates can be externally triggered via their side-chain access points, allowing the level of one signal to be controlled by another. An 'External' switch is usually provided to enable the side-chain input, though some models may simply be fitted with a side-chain access jack wired in the same way as a console insert point. Used normally, this facility enables the signal routed through the gate to be turned on and off by the signal fed into the side chain. For example:

## ● TIP ●

• A sustained sound fed through the gate could be turned on and off by a drum beat fed into the side-chain input. The rate at which it turns on and off depends on the attack and release settings, but it does provide a novel way to synchronise a sustained sound with a percussive one. Figure 13.2 shows how this might be set up.

• Bass synth sounds can be gated so that they appear only when a bass drum is present.

• Synthesizer chords can be gated from a rhythm pattern to create a synchronised arpeggio effect.

• A popular trick is to use the bass drum in a track to trigger the gate while passing the bass guitar track through the gate. The attenuation range control may then be set to reduce or even remove any bass guitar notes not falling directly on top of bass drum beats which can help to tighten up an otherwise sloppy track. The gate release time control is set to allow the bass guitar notes to decay at an appropriate rate.

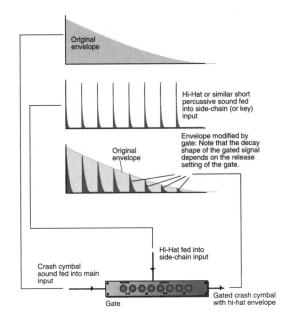

**Figure 13.2: Gating a Decaying Sound with a Percussive Sound**

# GATE DUCKING

If the gate has a Duck facility, it can be used as a ducker in exactly the same way as a compressor. The attenuation control of the gate can be used to determine how much the signal level drops once the side-chain input signal (a voice, for example) exceeds the threshold, and as this control is calibrated directly in dBs, it is much easier to set up a precise ducking effect using one of these gates than it is using a compressor. Again, the gate's attack and release times determine how fast the ducked signal will fades out and in again in response to the side-chain input.

# GATE PANNING

The side-chain access facility of a gate also means it can be used to produce a limited range of panning effects.

## ● TECHNIQUE ●

• If the signal to be panned is fed into both channels of a two-channel gate, the side-chain inputs could alternately be triggered with percussive sounds from a drum machine.

• By setting the attack and release times of the gate to fairly long values and panning the two outputs hard left and right in the mix, the signal will appear to move back and forth between the speakers as first one channel is triggered and then the other. Figure 13.3 shows how this is done.

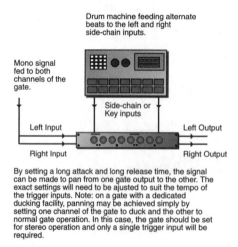

Drum machine feeding alternate beats to the left and right side-chain inputs.

Mono signal fed to both channels of the gate.

Side-chain or Key inputs

Left Input          Left Output

Right Input         Right Output

By setting a long attack and long release time, the signal can be made to pan from one gate output to the other. The exact settings will need to be ajusted to suit the tempo of the trigger inputs. Note: on a gate with a dedicated ducking facility, panning may be achieved simply by setting one channel of the gate to duck and the other to normal gate operation. In this case, the gate should be set for stereo operation and only a single trigger input will be required.

**Figure 13.3 Panning with a Gate.**

• If the gate has a ducking function, the process is simplified further; one channel is set to gate, the other to duck, and the two channels linked for stereo operation. Now feeding a single pulse or drum sound into one side-chain input will cause the signal to pan and then return.

• If the tempo of the drum machine is synchronised to that of the music by means of a tape time code track or similar, the pan timing is accurately synchronised to the tempo of the music. Furthermore, the pan triggers don't have to be evenly spaced but can follow a suitable rhythm, allowing more complex effects to be created.

• This basic triggered pan setup can be further modified to produce a passable rotary speaker simulation, simply by feeding the two gate outputs into two equalisers, each set to give a noticeably different sound as shown in Figure 13.4.

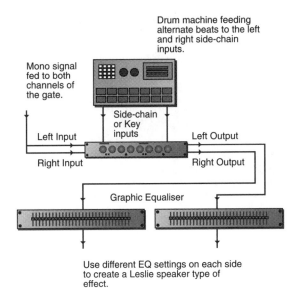

Figure 13.4: Leslie Simulation using Panned EQ

# EXPANDERS

Though they perform a similar task to gates, expanders are easier to understand if you think of them as compressors in reverse. Compressors reduce the gain of a signal once it exceeds the threshold, while expanders apply gain reduction to signals falling below the threshold. Whereas a gate will close completely when the signal falls below its threshold, the expander reduces the gain of below-threshold signals by a user-definable ratio, just like the compressor. For example, if the expansion ratio is set to 1:2, for every 1dB the signal falls below the threshold, the output will fall by 2dB. This produces a more progressive and more subtle muting effect than can be achieved using gates, but because the action of a gate is smoothed considerably by its attack and release controls, both gates and expanders behave in a subjectively very similar way when used to clean up sounds. The smaller the expansion ratio, the more subtle the gain reduction effect; a high expansion ratio will make the expander behave in exactly the same way as a gate. Expanders are often incorporated into compressor designs because they are less critical to set up than gates, yet still provide a worthwhile reduction in noise during pauses in the signal.

# MINIMUM SIGNAL PATH

In the studio, we rely on the mixing desk and patchbay to such a extent that we often forget about alternative methods of routing signals to tape while recording. In this era of high quality digital or analogue/Dolby S recording, engineers are becoming more quality conscious, and in some circumstances, passing an electrical signal through an entire mixing console just to get it onto tape isn't the best way to do the job. No matter how well the mixer is designed, some signal degradation must take place, and the more circuitry the signal has to pass through, the worse the degradation will be. Take the example of a single microphone signal that needs to be amplified and then routed to a single track on the tape machine: sending it through the console might be the easiest method, but it certainly isn't the best in terms of quality. Think about all the circuitry, switches and controls in a typical mixer channel, and then add that to the routing switches and the group output electronics; it's hardly surprising that the signal suffers.

## MIC PREAMPS

A more purist approach to recording vocals is to use a separate, high quality microphone preamplifier plugged directly into the tape machine. This is known as the 'minimum signal path' approach, and the more discerning engineer may choose to record important parts such as lead vocals in exactly this way. If the vocal needs compressing on the way to tape, a compressor may be patched between the mic amp and tape machine, or a compressor with a built-in mic amp may be used instead. Aside from avoiding unnecessary circuitry in the mixer itself, it is possible to bypass the patchbay too by plugging directly into the back of the tape machine. Although patchbays contain no active circuitry, contact corrosion and dirt can add considerably to the noise and distortion present in a signal passing through the patchbay. Figure 14.1 shows a practical approach to recording vocals without going via the mixing console.

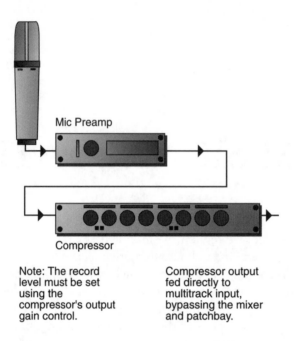

Mic Preamp

Compressor

Note: The record level must be set using the compressor's output gain control.

Compressor output fed directly to multitrack input, bypassing the mixer and patchbay.

**Figure 14.1: Minimum Signal Path for Recording Vocals**

# DI BOXES

Line level signals can also be recorded direct to tape, preferably via a DI box, which will match the impedance of the source to that of the tape machine and may also offer some form of level control, allowing the recording level to be optimised. Line level signals include the outputs from guitar preamps and speaker simulators, as well as active guitars, basses and some electronic instruments. Passive guitars have high impedance pickups which, in theory, means that an active DI box will give the best matching. Even so, a good passive (transformer) DI box can give surprisingly good results and may produce a more natural sound than an active model. The lower input impedance may also reduce the effect of interference on the signal, giving a cleaner result.

Guitar speaker simulators and preamps designed specifically for direct recording are very effective these days; whereas a few years ago nobody would have dreamt of using anything other than a mic to record a guitar, the direct approach is currently very popular, even on serious guitar album projects. The advantages of this way of working are immediately obvious — the sound the performer hears over the monitors is the same sound that is going to tape, and perhaps more importantly, there is complete isolation between the guitar and any other instrument being recorded at the same time. Acoustic spill problems are completely eliminated, making the guitar as easy to record as the electronic keyboard synthesizer.

# RHYTHM GUITAR

Clean rhythm sounds can be recorded directly to tape using a simple DI box, though some EQ is usually necessary to simulate the way in which guitar amplifiers are voiced.

### ● TECHNIQUE ●

• A significant amount of upper mid boost is generally needed, and if this may be achieved using something like an upper-mid sweep equaliser tuned to between 3 and 6kHz, the necessary brightness can be produced with less of a noise penalty than would be the case if the high shelving EQ were used.

• It can be advantageous to over-boost the upper mid and then back off the high frequency shelving control a little to compensate. This will result in a reduction in high frequency noise without unduly dulling the guitar sound.

• A popular approach to recording rhythm guitar is to feed the guitar, via a DI box, into a suitable compressor, and then directly to tape. A suitable compressor is really any model that sounds good, though valve compressors are often chosen for their warm, smooth sound. In general, if a compressor sounds good on vocals, it will work well with guitars.

# OVERDRIVEN GUITAR

Recording overdriven guitar is less straightforward, and if an overdrive pedal is patched directly into a tape recorder, the result will be quite unlike that produced by miking an amplifier. The reason for this was touched upon in my chapter on recording guitars, and is mainly to do with the way in which a guitar speaker and its enclosure modify the electric guitar's sound. Guitar speakers generally use a large driver with no separate mid-range units or tweeters, which gives them a severely restricted frequency response. Indeed, if full-range speakers were used, the overdrive sound would be most raspy and unpleasant. The cabinet design also affects the way in which the speaker behaves, and an analysis of the speaker and cabinet combination reveals a complex low-pass filter response. If this is emulated using electronic filters, it is possible to take the output from an overdriven guitar preamp or pedal, process it via the filter and record it directly.

The result is surprisingly close to the sound produced by a close-miked amplifier but it isn't exactly the same. That's because most 'speaker simulator' units fail to duplicate the complex distortions that occur when a loudspeaker is overdriven and they also fail to take into account the characteristics or positioning of the microphone normally used to record the guitar amp.

Even so, a little extra work with EQ and a little added artificial reverb or ambience at the mixing stage can render the differences very small indeed. Indeed, over the past decade, the popular rock guitar sound has changed significantly, making it more difficult to judge the authenticity of any electronic simulation. Speaker simulator circuitry is becoming more common in guitar preamps and guitar multi-effects units, though the results that can be achieved vary drastically from model to model.

## SPEAKER SIMULATOR

The other popular form of speaker simulator is, in effect, a combined filter and power soak which is used to replace the speaker in a conventional guitar amplifier. Supplied as add-on boxes, these are available in both active and passive versions and produce either a line level or mic level output from amplifiers rated up to 100 Watts or so. Some have virtually no controls, while others may have voicing switches and equalisation enabling them to simulate many different types of guitar speaker system. Used with a good valve amplifier, these produce what many feel is a more authentic, basic tone than solid-state preamps and effects units, though any effects must be added separately.

The line output type of speaker simulator may be connected directly to a tape machine, but the type with a mic level output need to be recorded via a separate mic preamp or via the mic input of the mixing console. It can be argued that an overdriven guitar sound is so noisy and distorted that there is little to be gained in bypassing the mixer completely, but ultimately, the decision must be taken by the individual engineer. It is certainly worth making a test recording, both direct and via the desk, to see how significant the difference really is. It is common practice to use a compressor after the speaker simulator. Figure 14.2 shows how a speaker simulator is connected.

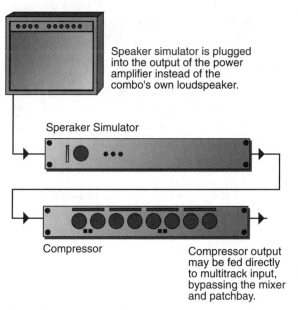

Speaker simulator is plugged into the output of the power amplifier instead of the combo's own loudspeaker.

Speraker Simulator

Compressor

Compressor output may be fed directly to multitrack input, bypassing the mixer and patchbay.

Note: Though the use of a compressor is not mandatory, its inclusion generally produces a more appealing sound by creating a more even tone and enhancing the natural sustain of the guitar.

**Figure 14.2: Using a Speaker Simulator**

# ACTIVE GUITARS

Active guitars and basses may be plugged directly into the mixing console without any impedance matching problems, but some form of speaker simulation is still necessary when working with overdriven guitar sounds, and basses generally need to be compressed. In my own experience, active guitars tend to be noisier than guitars with passive pickups.

# KEYBOARDS

Keyboard instruments, samplers, drum machines and synth modules can be recorded directly, but most have relatively low output levels, ranging from -20 to -10dBv. This means that it may be possible to plug them directly into a semi-pro machine operating at -10dBv, but the vast majority will have insufficient output to produce a healthy recording level when used with professional tape machines. Furthermore, some instruments have no proper output level controls, especially drum machines with multiple outputs.

Again, the answer is to use an active DI box, which will improve the impedance matching and provide the additional gain needed. As with the electric guitar, it is up to the individual to decide whether it is worth going to the trouble of recording direct or whether recording via the mixer is adequate. The majority of synthesizers still have a disappointing audio specification and it is arguable whether the trip through a mixing console would make the situation significantly worse. As more recordings are now being made with all the MIDI sound sources played live into the mix from a suitably synchronised sequencer, this question may never arise.

The only keyboard system that must be miked rather than DI'd is the Leslie cabinet where it is common to use separate mics on the horns and the bass rotor. If possible use a stereo mic arrangement on the rotary horns.

# MIXER NOISE

Even if recordings are made through the mixing console, there are ways to ensure that the signal remains as clean as possible. For example, if a mixer has direct channel outputs or even insert points, a signal could be taken directly from the mixer channel and routed to the tape recorder; this would bypass the routing switches, the pan control and the group output electronics. Of course, this is only viable when one channel is being recorded to one tape track — if two or more channels have to be mixed together, then there is little choice but to use the desk's normal routing system.

Having said this, there are steps that can be taken to minimise the amount of noise added to the signal on its way to tape. Most consoles have an EQ bypass button, and if no EQ is being added at the recording stage, switching the EQ out of circuit will shorten the signal path slightly.

# MUTING AND ROUTING

Most people instinctively mute any mixer channels that are not being routed and nearly all will set the faders at zero, but this, perhaps surprisingly, doesn't entirely prevent the channel from contributing noise to the mix.

### ● TIP ●

When recording, make sure that any unused channels are not only muted but also that they are not routed to any of the group outputs — in other words, ensure that all their routing buttons are up. Even if unused channels are muted and all the gain controls turned down, they will contribute noise to any mix buss to which they are routed simply by virtue of being connected to the buss via their routing switches.

This is more important when you come to mix, as any unused channel with its Left/Right routing button down will be contributing unnecessary noise to the final mix. To prove this to yourself, route all your mixer channels to the main stereo output and turn all the channel faders right down. If you have channel mute buttons, set these to their mute positions. Now, turn up the monitor level control until you can hear the console hiss through the monitors. Without changing anything else, go along the console switching the Left/Right routing buttons to their up positions and I guarantee you'll be surprised by the drop in hiss. The more channels you have on your desk, the greater will be the benefit of careful routing.

# MONITOR SECTION

The other danger area is the monitor section of the desk which, on some models, is routed directly to the Left/Right buss with no means of disconnecting it. On some consoles, the monitor mutes actually disconnect the monitor channels from the mix buss but on others, especially budget desks with MIDI muting, they mute the signal but still leave the monitor routed. There's not much you can do about this, other than be aware of the problem. Repeating the previous noise test using the monitor mute buttons will tell you whether they are simply mutes or whether they do switch the monitors off the mix buss — if the noise goes down as you mute the monitors, you're in luck — the mute switches are really routing buttons.

The same rules apply to auxiliary sends, and many an innocent effects unit has been blamed for being noisy when in fact the mixer has been to blame. Few mixing desks offer the facility to switch individual aux sends off their respective aux busses when they are not being used, but there are several mixers that allow their aux sends to be routed to a choice of aux send busses. This is particularly common in the mid-price market, where a console may have eight aux busses but only four aux send controls which can be switched between them.

## ● TIP ●

Unless all the aux send busses are in use, one useful trick is to route any unused sends to unused effects busses. For example, if you can route aux 1 and 2 as a pair to either aux busses 1,2 or 3,4 you could designate aux busses 3,4 as being unused and route any unused sends there. This obviously restricts the number of available aux sends, but there are many occasions when a specific effect is required on only one mixer channel, in which case the effects unit can be fed from the direct channel output or insert send point. There's no reason why an effect shouldn't be patched in via the channel insert point, but as most modern effects have stereo outputs, some other method must generally be sought if the effect is to be kept in stereo.

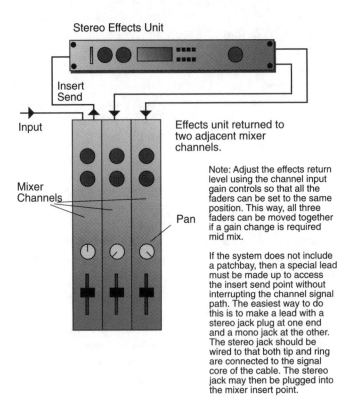

Stereo Effects Unit

Insert
Send

Input

Mixer
Channels

Pan

Effects unit returned to
two adjacent mixer
channels.

Note: Adjust the effects return
level using the channel input
gain controls so that all the
faders can be set to the same
position. This way, all three
faders can be moved together
if a gain change is required
mid mix.

If the system does not include
a patchbay, then a special lead
must be made up to access
the insert send point without
interrupting the channel signal
path. The easiest way to do
this is to make a lead with a
stereo jack plug at one end
and a mono jack at the other.
The stereo jack should be
wired to that both tip and ring
are connected to the signal
core of the cable. The stereo
jack may then be plugged into
the mixer insert point.

**Figure 14.3: Using the Insert Point as an FX Send**

# DIRECT OUTPUTS

Using the channel's direct output as an effects send has the advantage that the send level will be controlled by the channel fader, but unless significant gain changes are planned during the mix, it is possible to get away with using the insert send. Indeed, if the effects returns can be arranged to come up on an adjacent channel, it should be possible to move the faders together, which gets around the problem of using the insert send point. Figure 14.3 shows how this is set up.

An equally viable solution is to use the insert send or direct output from the channel carrying the signal to feed the mono input of the effects unit, exactly as before, but this time the channel is not routed to the mix. Its only purpose is to provide an input feed to the effects unit.

• The two effect outputs are connected to the inputs of two spare channels.

• The effect/dry balance can then be set using the mix control on the effects unit, and the two channels can be panned left and right to create a stereo effect.

• With most effects units, using the mono input will position the dry portion of the sound in the centre of the mix with the stereo effect outputs left and right.

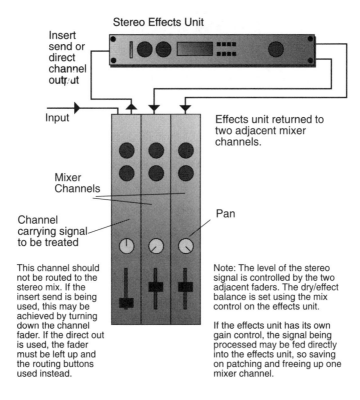

Stereo Effects Unit

Insert send or direct channel output

Input

Effects unit returned to two adjacent mixer channels.

Mixer Channels

Channel carrying signal to be treated

Pan

This channel should not be routed to the stereo mix. If the insert send is being used, this may be achieved by turning down the channel fader. If the direct out is used, the fader must be left up and the routing buttons used instead.

Note: The level of the stereo signal is controlled by the two adjacent faders. The dry/effect balance is set using the mix control on the effects unit.

If the effects unit has its own gain control, the signal being processed may be fed directly into the effects unit, so saving on patching and freeing up one mixer channel.

**Figure 14.4: Alternative Effects Patch**

This variation is shown in Figure 14.4, the only restriction being that the dry portion of the sound will always be panned to the centre of the mix. If the effects unit has its own input level control, and most have, then an even simpler approach is to patch the required signal or tape track directly into the effects unit and feed the output of the effects unit into two mixer channels.

# GAIN STRUCTURE

Finally, all this effort will go to waste if the gain structure of the mixer isn't set up properly.

• The channel input trims should be set up using the meters in conjunction with the PFL or Solo buttons.

• The mix should be arranged so that the average fader position is around the three-quarters full position.

• Set the aux send controls so that the highest one is almost full up and use the aux send master or the input gain on the effects unit to get the right signal going into the effects processor.

• Don't forget to optimise the level trim on any channels being used to carry effects returns, and turn any unused sends right down.

• Always be suspicious if you have output level controls (or effects unit input controls) set at minimum. If you use one control to knock the signal level down and the next one in line to build it up again, you're setting up the ideal conditions for unwanted noise. Try to arrange everything so that all gain controls are set in 'sensible' positions.

The measures outlined above may appear unnecessarily complicated, but the few extra moments taken to set up the console properly will yield a significant difference in signal quality. Eliminating noise at source is infinitely more satisfactory than trying to remove it with gates or dynamic filters at a later stage.

# TEAM SPIRIT

Now there's a Soundcraft mixer that goes beyond MIDI muting, that works the way you work, in harmony with MIDI, sequencers and computers.

## HARDWARE
### By Soundcraft

Take the best-selling Spirit Studio – six auxiliary sends, 4-band swept EQ, eight groups and superb audio performance.

Add VCA fader automation: the result is Spirit Auto, the ultimate creative tool. Designed by musicians, for musicians, at a price you won't believe.

## SOFTWARE
### By Steinberg and JL Cooper

Mixing with Spirit Auto becomes even more powerful and intuitive when you team it up with high quality custom-written software, taking it beyond the range of many big studio systems. The Spirit Automation Software package from Steinberg provides graphical on-screen editing with cut and paste of mix data – just like using your sequencer package. The automation software runs concurrently with Cubase, too, allowing you to mix "live" sequenced data. Softmix by JL Cooper offers a similar interface with offline editing and a host of features for the Apple Mac. Spirit Auto will also work with any sequencer software for Atari, Apple Mac or IBM PC.

For small studios, pre-production suites, and even audio post-production, you need the perfect mix of hardware and software.

You need Team Spirit.

Soundcraft Electronics Ltd.,
Cranborne House,
Cranborne Industrial Estate,
Cranborne Rd, Potters Bar,
Herts EN6 3JN, England.
Tel: 0707 665000. Fax: 0707 660482.

## SPIRIT
### By Soundcraft

H A Harman International Company

# MIXING

Watching a really skilled engineer at work can be an intimidating experience — the real experts can move along the desk pushing up the faders one at a time, having an almost perfectly balanced mix by the time they reach the end. Somehow they have an instinct for balance, and what they achieve seemingly by magic, we have to arrive at by hard work.

It helps before starting the mix to organise logical groups of sounds into subgroups, which means that the mix can be handled with fewer faders. Most recordings have the drums spread over several tape tracks, and life is far easier if these are routed to a pair of adjacent group faders to form a stereo subgroup. Similarly, backing vocals can be assigned to subgroups along with any other sections that seem logical.

## BALANCE

If the basic tracks have been recorded properly, it should be possible to set up a reasonable initial balance without resorting to EQ. Effects need not be added right from the outset, but it helps to have the necessary effects units patched in and ready for use, and some vocal reverb helps paint the picture. Switch the EQ to bypass on all channels where it isn't being used and ensure that any unused mixer channels are not only muted but also unrouted — in other words, all the routing buttons should be in their 'up' position. This will prevent the channel from contributing to the mix buss noise of the console, and will help achieve a quieter final mix. All unused aux sends should be set at zero level, and the loudest sends should be between three quarters and full up. Again, this helps to reduce noise. All console inputs should be trimmed using the PFL metering system if your console allows trim on mixdown. Likewise, all the effects units should be checked for correct input levels. If it is possible to route unused sends to an aux buss that isn't being used, this can reduce mix noise considerably, while any effect intended to process a single channel will produce the best audio quality if connected via the channel insert point.

Having attended to these basic niceties, my own way of working is to sort out the drum and bass balance first, but this should not be refined too much, as the apparent balance will change once the rest of the instruments and voices are in the mix. Once the rhythm section is sounding good, the remaining faders can be brought up one at a time until a reasonable overall balance has been achieved. It's only when all the instruments are in place that you should start to worry about the finer points of EQ and balance, because things sound so different when they are heard in isolation.

Of course, some engineers and producers insist that the only possible way to work is to put all the faders up to start with and then adjust for a balance. Don't be put off by this, though, because I've spoken to many well-regarded engineers and producers who admit that they don't have this natural gift for balance — they have to work just as hard as the rest of us!

# STEREO POSITIONS

Once a reasonable balance has been achieved, you can start to work on the effects being used and the stereo positioning of the different sounds. Bass drums, bass guitars and bass synths are invariably panned to the centre to anchor the mix and to spread the load of these high energy frequencies over both speakers. Similarly, lead vocals are usually positioned centre stage because that's where we expect the vocalist to be.

The position of backing vocals is less rigid, and can be split so that some are left and some are right; they can be left in the centre, or they can all be grouped in one position off-centre. I like to hear different backing vocal lines coming in from different sides, but this decision is purely artistic — there is no absolute right and wrong. If recorded vocals exhibit any sibilance problems, a de-esser should be patched in before proceeding.

Once the mix is almost there, it can be very helpful to listen to the balance from an adjacent room with the adjoining door left open. Although I can find no logical explanation for the phenomenon, any slight balance problems really show up when a mix is auditioned in this way, and most engineers and producers who've discovered this way of checking a mix use it regularly. Figure 15.1 shows a typical panning arrangement for a pop song.

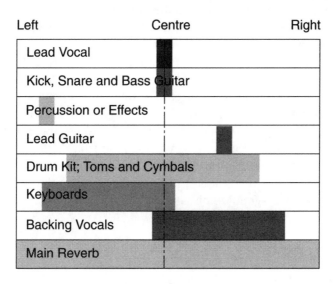

**Figure 15.1: Typical Stereo Panning Scenario**

# LEVEL CORRECTION

A good mix will almost 'fly' itself, but some parts invariably need level corrections throughout the mix. Obvious examples are instrumental solos and changes in effects levels, but even on vocals with heavy compression, it may still be necessary to adjust the odd vocal phrase by a dB or so to make it sit properly. If the mix is being conducted manually, responsibility for the various fader adjustments can be devolved amongst the various band members. The level settings should be clearly marked with wax pencil and each person should have a note of the various tape counter positions at which levels have to be changed. Of course, if an automated mixing system is available, these changes can be handled quite automatically.

If a track requires a fade-out ending, this may be performed manually or with an autofader. Fades are seldom shorter than 15 seconds and may be as long as 30, so it is important to ensure that there is enough recorded material to cover the duration of the fade. If you know in advance that the album is going to be compiled using a hard disk editing system, it might be wiser to leave the fades until the final editing stage, where they can be controlled more precisely and will fade into true silence.

I've already covered some of the console settings that affect noise, but we also have to consider noise that is part of the recorded sound. We have breath noise from singers, hum and hiss from guitars and digital background noise from synths, samplers and drum machines. If sequenced MIDI instruments are being used, it is often possible to program level changes via MIDI, but we have to be careful, as some instruments put out a more or less constant level of unwanted noise, regardless of the level of the voice currently playing. We should always strive to use these machines as close to their maximum volume setting as is practical, as this will usually give the best signal-to-noise ratio. Likewise, it is possible to mute instruments via the sequencer, but this just stops the sequenced parts from playing and doesn't affect the background noise in any way.

# GATES AND MUTES

Gates or expanders are very effective in cleaning up electronic instruments, though care must be taken to match the release time of the gate to the sound being processed. In some cases, it may be possible to use a pair of gates over a stereo subgroup; this offers the advantage that fewer gates are needed. It must be remembered, though, that gates can only keep the noise down during pauses and can do nothing when signal is present.

Perhaps the most dramatic effect of MIDI muting or gating can be noticed right at the beginning of the song where perfect silence reigns until the first note is played. It shouldn't be necessary to mute every short silence, but it is a good idea to mute the vocal track during instrumental solos or bridge sections, and to mute the lead guitar track both before and after the solo.

MIDI console muting can be very useful for dealing with source noise, and though it may take a little time to set up, the results are usually well worth the trouble. It is necessary to go through each tape track and set up the mute points individually, but once they're right, they'll be right every time you run the mix. If you can arrange muting and unmuting on a beat, it may help to disguise any discontinuity or change in noise level.

The mutes on most MIDI desks are very quiet in operation, but I know that on some models there is an audible click if many mutes are switched at the same time. If this is the case, it should be possible to work around the problem by using the mutes on the subgroups or master output faders rather than attempting to switch all the channels at once.

# NOISE FILTERS

In the event that some of your sound sources are noticeably noisy even when being played, it might be desirable to use a single-ended noise reduction unit to minimise the noise. These are dynamic filter units which filter out higher frequencies as sounds decay; used carefully, they can bring about a dramatic decrease in noise without affecting the sound of the wanted signal. However, they do tend to affect the tail end of long reverbs so it is probably prudent to assign all the noisy sounds to a stereo subgroup and process just this. This leaves the higher quality sounds and effects returns unprocessed, which will give a more natural result.

# MIX PROCESSING

Producers tend to be divided when it comes to applying further processing to the overall stereo mix. The more puritanical might say that there is no need to process the mix once you've got it right, while others will insist on putting it through their favourite compressor, equaliser or exciter. There can be no definitive right or wrong answer to this question; in pop music production, the end always justifies the means (so long as it is within budget!). However, we can explore some of the implications inherent in post-mix processing.

# OVERALL COMPRESSION

Compressing a complete mix reduces the difference between the quietest parts of the mix and the loudest. If the highest levels peak at around the same value as they did before compression, then it follows that average level must be higher, and this is reflected in a subjective increase in musical energy. However, a sound will only appear to be loud if it has a quieter sound to contrast with, so there is a danger of making a piece of music sound quieter by compressing it too much.

When compressing a mix, the attack time of the compressor is usually extended slightly to allow transient sounds such as drums to punch through with more power, though the best setting can only be determined by ear, as every piece of music is different. It is also true that some compressors perform disappointingly when used on complete mixes, whereas others produce results that appear to be little short of magic. As a very general rule, soft-knee compressors produce the most subtle results — but do you always want to be subtle? Sadly, the compressors that work best in this application also seem to cost the most!

# OVERALL EQ

Equalising the whole mix might seem a little reckless, but some equalisers seem to improve the sound noticeably, even when very subtle settings are used. Music can be made to appear louder by cutting the mid-range slightly, as this emulates the response curve of the human ear. It may also be necessary to equalise a mix if it has been made in a studio with an inaccurate monitor system. Indeed, there are so many inaccurate control rooms around that when a master tape is sent to the cutting room to be prepared for record or CD mastering, it is very common for the engineer to apply a degree of corrective EQ at that stage.

Cutting rooms don't always have the nicest sounding equalisers, so if the producer has access to a good monitoring system (and many take their own with them), it may be preferable to make any changes at this stage, where they can be controlled and evaluated on an artistic rather than a purely technical basis.

# EXCITERS

It is not uncommon to treat a whole mix with an exciter or a dynamic equaliser. These tend to emphasise certain parts of the frequency spectrum in a way that is related to the dynamics of the signal, so that transient sounds are given more definition. This increases the perceived sense of loudness, which helps a record stand out from the competition on the radio or on the dance floor. The exciter actually synthesises harmonics based on the existing programme material and so may be more suitable for dealing with a mix that is insufficiently bright.

The dynamic equaliser creates no new harmonics but, in effect, redistributes what is already there and so may give a smoother sound. Dynamic equalisers can also be used to add power at the bass end, whereas most exciters simply work at the very high frequency end of the audio spectrum. Newer models, however, increasingly address the bottom end of the frequency spectrum by offering some type of bass enhancement.

# MONITORING ALTERNATIVES

Before a final mix is approved, it should be checked on different speaker systems, including car systems and domestic hi-fi. Large studio monitoring systems can be very misleading and it is essential to test the mix at a moderate listening level on a small pair of speakers. Avoid the temptation to mix at too high a volume, as this will only serve to adversely affect your hearing judgement. Ultimately, the best test is to listen to your mix at the same level as you would expect the end user to listen at.

# THE MASTER

DAT has become a standard mastering medium, even though it is still, strictly speaking, only a semi-pro or domestic format. If there is a choice, make the master at a sampling frequency of 44.1 kHz, as this will save the need to have the sample rate converted when making a CD master.

With any form of digital recording, you must keep a very close eye on recording levels, because there is no leeway above 0VU — the sound immediately clips and distortion is usually audible. Try to arrange your levels so that the peaks reach between -3 and -6VU on the DAT machine's meters; this should provide an adequate margin of safety while still giving a good signal-to-noise performance.

Once the master tape has been recorded, it must be backed up, particularly if it is on DAT as, contrary to some expectations, DAT isn't 100% reliable. To back up a DAT to another DAT, make a clone by connecting the machines via their digital audio links. It is safest to leave at least 10 seconds of unrecorded tape at the beginning of a DAT cassette — if trouble is going to occur, it usually occurs here — and the backup should be clearly marked and stored in a safe place.

It is also worth backing up DAT masters to open reel tape. Interestingly, in many cases, the analogue copy sounds subjectively better than the DAT! This is undoubtedly due to the many small imperfections of analogue recording that contribute to its alleged warm, comfortable sound.

# LABELLING

All session tapes should be clearly labelled, as should any unused mixes and out-takes you wish to keep. Include information such as:

- The track format
- The tape speed
- The noise reduction system used
- Track titles
- Track start times and end times
- Track durations.

If you're not working in your own studio, ask the engineer to put a set of calibration tones at the start of any analogue masters or backups. Though calibration tones shouldn't be necessary with DAT, tape duplicators and mastering houses like to have a 1kHz tone recorded at the start of a tape, usually around 20 seconds in duration, at a level of -10VU. The actual level is less important than writing on the box what the level is!

If the master tape is intended for album production, the individual tracks must spaced apart by the required duration of silence. With analogue tape, this is achieved by splicing lengths of plastic leader tape or blank recording tape between the individual songs, the actual length depending very much on how the previous song ends and on how the next one starts. For example, the space required after a song with a fade-out ending might need to be only a couple of seconds; on the other hand, if one songs ends with a bang and the next starts equally as abruptly, anything up to five seconds might be needed. There are no hard and fast rules about this, but you can instinctively feel if a gap is more than half a second too short or too long.

# TRACK SPACING

Spacing songs on a DAT tape is far less easy than doing the same job with analogue tape, because DATs can't stop and start in the same instant way as analogue machines. Using two DAT machines, it is possible to make a reasonable job of compiling an album simply by using the pause button on the second machine to start and stop it, but it is difficult to time gaps to an accuracy of better than one second. It is far better to use a hard disk editing system, where the gaps can be timed to millisecond accuracy and where unwanted noise before and after songs can be cut out with surgical precision. With such systems, it is usually possible to handle precision fade-outs and fade-ins, level changes and occasionally, digital equalisation. Some also offer digital time or pitch compression, but in my experience, this is seldom satisfactory.

# STEREO WIDTH TRICKS

When it comes to stereo, most of what we do in the recording studio is out-and-out fraud! In real life, our hearing systems establish the direction of a sound source by evaluating a multitude of parameters including phase, amplitude and spectral content; in the studio we cheat and use pan pots. True, there are proper stereo miking techniques that capture many of the nuances of a real-life soundfield, but when it comes to producing pop music, we are inclined to rely on pan pots to change the balance between the left and right speakers, effects with synthesised stereo outputs, and electronic musical instruments whose stereo outputs are artificially created by routing different mixes of signal to the left and right outputs.

Even so, there are some simple but effective processing techniques that can be used to create the illusion of stereo, even when the signal being treated is mono. In multitrack recording, such processing is very useful, especially when working with 4 or 8-track where parts often have to be bounced into mono to conserve track space.

# ALL IN THE MIND

Sophisticated though the human hearing system is, it would appear that it is far easier to fool than, for example, our vision. Digital reverberators create the illusion of stereo simply by using different sets of delay taps on the left and right channels, giving rise to two sets of reverberation patterns, which, although similar in their overall parameters, differ in their fine detail in essentially random ways. It seems that our hearing systems are so keen to make sense of the world around us that they eagerly accept this random information and use it to construct an imaginary, auditory world in which the processed sound exists.

This provides us with one very simple way to turn a mono sound into something that sounds like stereo — add reverb to it. The trouble is that we might want the sound to appear to be in stereo, but we don't want to add any noticeable amount of reverb. In that case, choose a reverb setting that provides an early reflections pattern but without the following reverb. Such settings add a relatively small number of closely-spaced reflections to the sound with different patterns in the left and right channels. The result is that the sound takes on a sense of space but with no apparent reverberation.

● TIP ●

A similar effect can be achieved using a less sophisticated reverb unit by selecting a very short, bright reverb setting (around half a second decay or even less) and then increasing the mix of reverb until the sound takes on the required extra dimension. If the reverb time is set short enough, the effect is not dissimilar from that created by an early reflections pattern setting, though with some of the cheaper reverb units, short settings might tend to sound a touch 'ringy', especially if percussive sounds are involved.

# DELAY

There are lots of tricks you can try with a simple delay unit that have the effect of widening the stereo image, but you must be aware that most of these are not completely mono compatible, so keep pressing the mono button on your mixer or power amplifier to see if what you've done has unacceptable side-effects when listening in mono. This is particularly important for broadcast material, as there are still many people listening to mono radios and mono TV sets, but insisting on absolute mono compatibility does place severe restrictions on what you can do — after all, real life isn't actually mono compatible when you come to think about it!

Here's the simplest trick:

● TECHNIQUE ●

• Pan your mono signal to one side of the stereo field and pan a delayed version of the same sound, at the same level, to the other side. The delay should be very short so as not to produce an obvious echo — between 2mS and 20mS will work.

You'll notice something very interesting when you try this — even though the level of signal in both speakers is equal, the sound will appear to be coming from the speaker that's receiving the undelayed sound. At the same time, it will sound wider that a straight mono source. The reason for this is tied up with the way in which our brains process sound; if a sound comes from our left, it will reach the left ear before it reaches the right ear, and this small time difference is one way the brain works out direction. In recording, this is known as the precedence effect. Figure 15.2 shows a simple way to set up this process using a basic DDL and a mixer with channel insert points. The DDL should be set to between 2mS and 20mS delay time with no modulation and no feedback. The mix control should be set to give only the delayed sound and none of the direct sound. On a manual unit, this usually means the fully clockwise setting of the mix control.

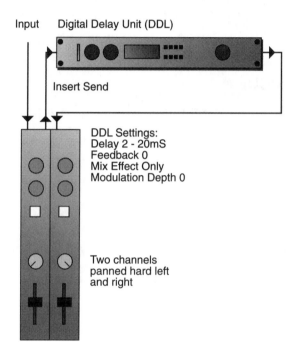

Input     Digital Delay Unit (DDL)

Insert Send

DDL Settings:
Delay 2 - 20mS
Feedback 0
Mix Effect Only
Modulation Depth 0

Two channels
panned hard left
and right

Figure 15.2: Delay Panning

Another effect which can be produced using the same setup is stereo chorus. This is something I discovered back in my serious gigging days at a time when stereo chorus units didn't exist. I used to have two guitar amps, one fed from the straight guitar sound and the other fed through a mono chorus pedal. Straight away I noticed this combination created the illusion of movement between the speakers, and from the normal listening position, it wasn't easy to tell which speaker was producing the straight sound and which one had been put though a chorus. When I got into home recording, I took this technique into the studio and found it incredibly useful for creating really wide, dynamic chorus effects for guitar and synthesizer. Even though stereo chorus units then started to become available, I don't think any of them ever sounded wider than my simple setup. Furthermore, if you have a mixer that has plenty of line input gain, you can set up this effect using a standard pedal chorus unit rather than tying up your multieffects unit for the job. And, by feeding the effect from a post-fade aux send, you can add different amounts of chorus to different instruments in a mix. The only limitation here is that to get the full effect of the stereo spread, all the sounds being processed should be panned more or less to one side of the mix and the output from the chorus unit to the other. To achieve a suitable chorus setting:

## ● TECHNIQUE ●

• The DDL should be set with a delay time between 10 and 50mS with a modulation rate of between 1Hz and 5Hz.

• The modulation depth is then brought up slowly until the required chorus effect is created.

• The mix control should be set at 50% delayed sound, 50% direct sound — which is generally the centre position on a manual unit.

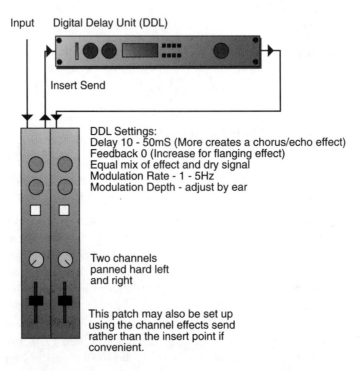

Input     Digital Delay Unit (DDL)

Insert Send

DDL Settings:
Delay 10 - 50mS (More creates a chorus/echo effect)
Feedback 0 (Increase for flanging effect)
Equal mix of effect and dry signal
Modulation Rate - 1 - 5Hz
Modulation Depth - adjust by ear

Two channels
panned hard left
and right

This patch may also be set up
using the channel effects send
rather than the insert point if
convenient.

**Figure 15.3: Pseudo Stereo Chorus**

True chorus uses no feedback, but some feedback may be added to create an effect somewhere between chorus and flanging if preferred. As a rule, when setting up modulated delay effects, the longer the delay time, the less modulation depth is required.

An interesting variation on this effect is:

● TECHNIQUE ●

• Pan the dry sound to the centre.

• Pan the chorused sound to one side

• Pan the same chorused sound processed via a channel with the phase button depressed to the other side.

This also gives a wide stereo spread, but if the sound is subsequently summed to mono, though the original sound survives intact, all the chorus effect is cancelled out. This is obviously undesirable for serious recording which might be used for radio or TV airplay.

# USING EQUALISERS

One effective but decidedly artificial method for making mono appear to be in stereo was devised back in the early days of stereo recording, when old mono records were frequently reprocessed to sound wider in stereo. This particular technique used a stereo graphic equaliser setup, the input signal being split to feed both channels of the equaliser. The idea was to set the two equalisers differently so they'd emphasise different parts of the mix, which could then be panned left and right.

The method outlined in Figure 15.4 is a refinement of this idea and has the additional benefit that it can be accomplished with a single-channel equaliser while being completely mono-compatible. In general, the more bands the better, but you can get a useful result from just about any graphic equaliser. The patch may be set up either using a Y lead to split the output from the graphic equaliser or by using the channel insert sends as shown.

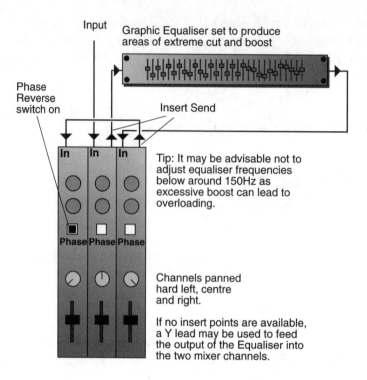

Input    Graphic Equaliser set to produce
         areas of extreme cut and boost

Phase
Reverse
switch on

Insert Send

In    In    In

Tip: It may be advisable not to
adjust equaliser frequencies
below around 150Hz as
excessive boost can lead to
overloading.

Phase Phase Phase

Channels panned
hard left, centre
and right.

If no insert points are available,
a Y lead may be used to feed
the output of the Equaliser into
the two mixer channels.

**Figure 15.4: Pseudo Stereo Using EQ**

Here's how:

## ● TECHNIQUE ●

• Feed the original signal directly to a mixer channel and pan it dead centre.

• Take a feed from that channel's insert send and feed it into the graphic equaliser.

• Split the output of the equaliser into two using a Y-lead, and feed into two more mixer channels, one panned hard left and the other right; the phase invert button is depressed on one of these two channels — it doesn't matter which one.

• To create the stereo effect, the equaliser needs to be set to produce a number of bumps and dips in the audio spectrum, and though just about any setting will produce a useful result (for example, setting the faders alternately up and down), it is more productive to try to identify specific areas of the spectrum where certain things are going on — guitars, keyboard pads and so on, and then home in on these.

How does it work? Assuming that the channel panned to the right is the one with the phase button down, the left signal will be a sum of the direct signal (centre) and the equalised signal (left). The right hand signal, on the other hand, will be the difference between the direct signal and the equalised signal because of the action of the phase invert button. This means that what constitutes an EQ peak in the left channel will manifest itself as an equal and opposite dip in the right channel and vice versa.

The neat thing about working in this way is that if the signal is heard in mono, the contribution of the equaliser cancels itself out and so you're left with just the original mono signal. However, don't assume that the process is 100% mono compatible because the subjective level appears to drop when the left and right components are cancelled out. How serious this is depends on how much of the equalised sound is added to the direct sound.

It is important to get the level of the two channels fed from the equaliser as similar as possible. The easiest way to do this is to mute the direct signal using the channel mute and listen to just the two channels fed from the equaliser. If these are, temporarily, panned to the centre, the signal will cancel completely when both are exactly equal in level. Once this has been verified, they can be panned back to their respective sides and the direct signal turned back on.

The result of this processing trick is quite interesting, in that the stereo image does take on an extra dimension, but you can't actually pick out where the sounds are supposed to be coming from. It's rather like reverberation in that respect — the illusion of space is created, but no real directional information is provided. Though it's no substitute for true stereo recording, this trick and others like it make it possible to produce a wide and interesting stereo image when working on four-track, where several musical parts have to be bounced into mono.

# FEEL THE WIDTH

Here's a simple but nevertheless effective technique for making the stereo spread appear to be wider than the spacing of the stereo loudspeakers, though it's no substitue fro true 3D sound.

● TIP ●

This particular trick has been used in ghetto blasters for many years and simply involves taking some of the right hand signal and feeding it, out of phase, to the left hand channel, and vice versa. The phase effects introduced in this way appear to push the sound out beyond the boundaries of the speakers, but if too much of the out-of-phase signal is added, the stereo positioning actually appears to swap sides. For this reason, it is vital to make sure that the unprocessed stereo signal remains the loudest part of the mix. Too much out-of-phase component also makes the mix sound 'phasey', and though different people perceive this in different ways, I find it physically uncomfortable; try it yourself by setting an equal mix of direct and out-of-phase sound and standing exactly between the speakers.

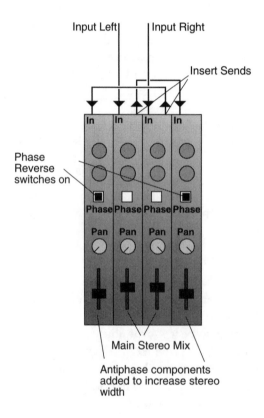

**Figure 15.5: Stereo Width Expansion**

Ideally, you need to mix the out-of-phase sounds low enough to avoid this effect. Though it's no substitute for Roland's RSS 3D sound system or Q-Sound processing, this simple trick can be usefully applied to individual subgroups within a mix or to stereo effects returns to add an extra dimension to a mix. And, because the added components are equal and opposite, they cancel completely when the signal is summed to mono, so the only changes will be changes in perceived level. Figure 15.5 shows how the stereo width expansion trick works.

# DIFFICULT MIXES

If you can't get a mix sounding right, check the following points:

• Try to get an initial rough mix without using EQ or effects and then work from there. Also check that the mix sounds OK in mono.

• Is there too much going on at once? Do you need all those parts, and if so, can some of them afford to be lower in the mix?

• Are mid-range sounds cluttering up the mix or overlapping with the bass sounds? If so, try using EQ to thin out the sounds. They might sound odd in isolation but they are more likely to sound right in the context of the whole mix. For example, shave some bottom end off a pad synth part or acoustic guitar rhythm line to clean up the low-mid region of the mix.

• If you are still having difficulty, balance up the drum and bass sounds first and then add the vocals and main instruments. You will probably find that the mix sounds 90% there with just the drums, bass, chords and a vocal line.

• If you are working with a sequencer, try alternative pad or keyboard sounds if the sounds you have chosen appear to be taking up too much space.

• Use effects sparingly — add reverb where it sounds good, not simply where you feel it ought to be. Very often the restrained use of effects produces the best result.

• Pan the instruments and effects to their desired positions.

• There may be some benefit in adding a little compression to the complete mix, though this shouldn't be considered compulsory. A compressor with an auto attack/release feature may cope best with the shifting dynamics of a real mix, and a soft-knee expander will usually provide the most transparent results.

• Valve compressors often give the most flattering sound, and many top engineers like to pass the mix through their favourite valve compressor more for the benefit of the valve coloration than for the compression.

• Subtle use of an enhancer such as an Aural Exciter will also help separate the individual sounds and emphasise detail.

# HARD DISK EDITING

If you don't own a hard disk editing system, it's unlikely that you'll need to know too much about using them, as most hired systems come with operators, but it still helps to know what such a system can and can't do. There are two musical areas in which hard disk editors really make life easy: one is in the compiling of albums from individual tracks, and the other is when editing a song to change its arrangement. It is also possible to use hard disk recorders to provide audio tracks for certain MIDI sequencing packages, the recorded data being manipulated and edited from within the sequencer program.

Musical data is recorded directly onto a hard disk unit via interface hardware that comes either as an add-on for a personal computer or as part of a dedicated hardware editing system. In other respects, the hard disk is exactly the same type as is used for routine computer work, except that it needs to have a fairly large capacity if whole albums are to be compiled on it. As a rule of thumb, stereo material sampled at 44.1kHz (the same as CD) occupies around 10 Mbytes of disk space for each recorded minute. It follows that to put an album together, you'll need in excess of 600 Mbytes of disk space available.

Material is transferred onto disk in real time, either from DAT via the digital input or as a conventional analogue, stereo signal. If the transfer is digital, then the recording is an exact clone of the original and there is no need to worry about recording levels. However, metering is usually provided for level setting when the analogue inputs are used.

There is just one area of concern when transferring from DAT in the digital domain; any errors caused by interference picking up on the cable can give rise to seemingly inexplicable clicks or glitches on the finished master. It is therefore imperative that good quality cable and connectors are used and that the cable is kept as short as possible. It is also wise to use a mains filtering system to avoid mains-borne interference causing data corruption.

# RANDOM ACCESS

Unlike recordings made onto tape, hard disk recordings can be accessed very rapidly without the need to rewind. Even sections of recording that are, say, half an hour apart can be accessed in an instant, and with the addition of a little buffer memory to accommodate the join, it is possible to select sections from anywhere on the disk and replay these in any order with absolutely no break between them.

This so-called random access is fundamental to hard disk editing, and it makes possible editing procedures that are quite unthinkable by conventional means. Furthermore, the original recorded data need never be erased or altered — the editing is non-destructive.

The way in which a hard disk editing unit handles data will be more readily appreciated by those who have had some experience with MIDI sequencers. A sequencer allows a composition to be built up by combining various sections or patterns into some kind of order, and there is no restriction on how many times the same pattern can be used. For example, a chorus section can be recorded as a pattern and then called up whenever a chorus is required. Hard disk editing allows us to do exactly the same with audio data. Songs can be divided into sections such as verses, choruses, intros, links, bridges, solos and so on, and then rearranged to produce a longer or more interesting version of the song.

# ALBUM COMPILING

When compiling an album, the required songs are recorded into the system either via the analogue inputs or via a direct digital SPDIF link from a DAT machine. Editing is accomplished by dividing the recording into marked sections which can then be compiled into a playlist. Indeed, many so-called extended remixes are accomplished using these techniques. A typical remix application is shown in Figure 16.1.

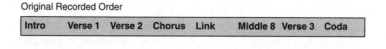

Original Recorded Order

| Intro | Verse 1 | Verse 2 | Chorus | Link | Middle 8 | Verse 3 | Coda |
|-------|---------|---------|--------|------|----------|---------|------|

Recording marked into sections or regions

| Intro | Verse 1 | Verse 2 | Chorus | Link | Middle 8 | Verse 3 | Coda |
|-------|---------|---------|--------|------|----------|---------|------|

Regions replayed in a different order according to a playlist compiled by the user

| PLAYLIST |
|----------|
| Intro |
| Verse 1 |
| Chorus |
| Verse 2 |
| Chorus |
| Link |
| Middle 8 |
| Chorus |
| Verse 3 |
| Chorus |
| Chorus |
| Chorus |
| Coda |

## Figure 16.1: Random Access Editing

Many systems allow cue points to be set 'on the fly', making it very easy to mark a song at exactly the right place. The edit points can subsequently be fine-tuned to perfection. This degree of precision is very useful when it comes to removing unwanted sounds that occur before the start of a song, such as count-in beats or the noise of fingers on guitar strings.

The individual songs simply have their start and end points marked, and are then arranged in the correct order with the required gap between each. Most systems provide some form of visual display which shows the actual audio waveform of the material being worked on; this makes it easier to locate the starts and ends of songs. It is normally possible to audition the transition between one song and the next, and if the gap is too short or too long, it can easily be modified. Fade-outs at the end of songs can be handled automatically by marking the start and end of the fade, while some systems allow the respective levels of different marked sections to be adjusted and may provide some form of digital equalisation. These latter two facilities can be invaluable when compiling songs from different recording sessions to go on the same album. With a little effort, their levels and tonal balances can be matched to give a more cohesive result. However, not all hard disk editing systems have all the aforementioned features.

Album compilation is pretty routine stuff to a digital editing system, but it does offer far greater precision than manual editing methods and, once the songs have been marked and named, it is easy to compile several alternative running orders, as might be necessary when producing masters for CD, vinyl and cassette releases of the same album.

# REARRANGING

It is when editing individual songs that the real power of a digital hard disk editor becomes apparent. Providing the recorded material is accurately marked off into sections, these sections can be strung together without the slightest trace of a glitch between them. A straight butt joint between sections is normally quite satisfactory, but the better editors offer crossfading between sections for occasions where this is more appropriate. It is normally best to choose edit points that coincide with drum beats, as these make timing easy to handle and tend to hide any discontinuities that might occur when joining two sections which weren't originally consecutive.

# CORRECTIVE MEASURES

Some of the better computer-based systems allow the operator to zoom right in on a tiny section of the musical waveform, where flaws such as interference clicks can be identified quite easily. These can usually be 'drawn out' using an on-screen drawing tool to replace the damaged section with something smoother or, alternatively, a similar section can be copied from elsewhere in the song and pasted in the place of the damaged piece. This is not always as easy as it seems, but an experienced operator should be able to cope with most eventualities.

The equalisation provided by such systems is often quite powerful, and may be applied to specific marked sections if desired. I recall one editing session on a piece of piano music, where one chord in the song contained an additional wrong note. This was at a lower level than the rest of the chord, but it was still clearly audible. Rather than re-record the piece, we established the pitch of the rogue note and looked up its frequency, which we then set into the parametric EQ. This was tuned to give a bandwidth of around one semitone, and the marked section at the start of the chord was subjected to cut at this frequency. This trick made the wrong note much less noticeable, so the EQ process was repeated an octave higher to remove some of the harmonics. This was so successful that further treatment was considered unnecessary.

As hard disk drives and the new, faster breed of magneto-optical drives continue to fall in price, sophisticated stereo (and multitrack) recording systems will become available at a cost which makes them attractive to the home user as well as the audio professional. Indeed, magnetic disk-based systems are already available at low enough costs to be viable for the enthusiast, though it would be a mistake to think that disk will replace tape overnight.

Tape has the overriding advantage of low cost, and while disk-based systems are faster and more flexible, they suffer from the major drawback that work has to be backed up, usually to tape, in order to free up the disk for the next project. Backing up is very time consuming and even the faster systems are not significantly faster than real time when backing up stereo recordings. For multitrack recording, the problem is compounded - working in real time, one hour of 16-track recording would take eight hours to back up and a further eight hours to reload (time based on eight stereo pairs). Until inexpensive, removable disk media become available, tape and disk will tend to be used alongside each other so that the strengths of each format may be utilised to the full.

# 3D SOUND

Over the past couple of years, several devices which claim to create the illusion of three-dimensional sound from a standard two-speaker stereo system have come onto the market. The term 'three dimensional' indicates that sounds in the mix can be made to appear to originate from a location outside the boundaries of the loudspeakers. Some processors, Roland's RSS (Roland Sound Space) processor in particular, are able, under certain circumstances, to create the illusion that the sound source actually moves behind the listener. Bearing in mind that all the sounds must emanate from two speakers in front of the listener, how is this possible?

## 3D HEARING

To understand how 3D sound systems work, it is necessary to know a little about how the human hearing system handles the directionality of sounds. Indeed, a little understanding of this subject helps us to position sounds in the normal stereo soundfield, so even if you have no intention of using a 3D processor, this section will be of value. Even so, I feel it's inevitable that low cost 3D sound processors will soon be a common feature of even small recording studios.

Just as our two eyes give us stereoscopic vision by presenting two simultaneous viewpoints of the world, our two ears do the same for sound. Only if a sound is directly ahead of us or directly behind us (or somewhere on an imaginary line joining the two points) do both ears register the same sound. The speed of sound being finite, it stands to reason that a sound originating directly from our right will arrive first at the right ear and then, some short time later, at the left ear. This time difference is noted by the brain and is just one of the means used to determine direction.

The sound arriving at the right ear will be unobstructed, while the sound arriving at the left ear will be masked by the head itself. This masking serves to reduce the level of the sound and also to modify its spectral content — high frequencies are attenuated more, whereas low frequencies remain relatively unaffected because their wavelength is significantly greater than the dimensions of the head. So far then, the human brain has three parameters to work on when analysing the input from a pair of ears: the time delay between the sound reaching first one and then the other ear; the difference in sound level occurring between the two ears; and the tonal change caused by the masking effect of the head. In contrast, a conventional pan pot only simulates one of these parameters: the level difference between the left and right ears.

# FRONT OR BACK?

Useful though the above explanation is, it doesn't tell us how we can discriminate between a sound that's directly in front of us or directly behind us, because in both cases, the signals arriving at both ears are identical. Similarly, if the sound originates at any point on the imaginary line drawn between these two extremes — such as directly over the head — the ears will still hear the same thing.

This is a more complex mechanism to comprehend, and it is thought that small, involuntary head movements help us to compare the signals arriving at both ears in the same way that we might move our heads to establish visual parallax between two objects that are otherwise ambiguous. How important this mechanism is has not been confirmed, but there is another point to consider which is far easier to quantify.

Ears are not just biological microphones stuck onto the side of the head, but are recessed and surrounded by the flaps of skin that we recognise as ears — more correctly termed 'pinnae'. This skin masks the inner ear from incoming sounds to a greater or lesser extent depending on the direction of the sound; measurements show that the effect of this masking is mainly spectral. In other words, the tonal property of the sound is changed in some way depending on its direction.

# DUMMY HEAD

When Roland developed their 3D sound system, they took the logical approach of using a dummy head, complete with pinnae, to analyse sounds originating at different positions around the head. The inter-aural level changes, time delays and spectral filtering effects were all noted and then used to control a set of computer controlled filters, delays and level shifters which, in theory, would recreate the original sounds as perceived by a typical pair of ears. Indeed, they went further, making numerous measurements using volunteers with small microphones fitted into their ears to obtain a true average set of values.

The system so far, theoretically at any rate, allows a mono sound to be processed so that when monitored over good headphones, it can be positioned anywhere in front of, behind or above the listener using a couple of 360 degree pan pots, one for the horizontal plane and one for the vertical. However, such a system won't work effectively on loudspeakers, because when we listen to a conventional stereo system, some of the sound from the left speaker enters the right ear and vice versa.

This crosstalk completely undermines the validity of the effect, so Roland went a stage further and measured this crosstalk in a typical listening room, then used the data to generate a crosstalk cancelling signal. In other words, what you shouldn't be hearing in the left ear (from the right speaker) is synthesized and then reversed in phase before being added to the normal left signal, and vice versa for the right. Now, if you're listening to a properly set up stereo system in a decent listening room from a point equidistant between the two speakers, it should be possible to perceive the processed sound coming from wherever the system positioned it.

There are an awful lot of 'ifs' in this explanation, and the fact is that none of the 3D sound systems work perfectly for all material or on all stereo setups. Most will enable sounds to be placed noticeably outside the speaker boundaries, and the result is very convincing, but any attempt to place the sound behind the listener depends for its success on several factors, not the least being the kind of sound being processed. In practice, the illusion of sound coming from behind the listener tends to break down unless the sound is moving — if it is panned from one side at the front, round the back of the listener's head and then back to the front opposite side, the result can be very convincing indeed, but any attempt to place a stationary sound behind the listener tends to fail. To confuse matters, different listeners respond to these effects in different ways.

# MONO COMPATIBILITY

While it would appear that all these systems offer a useful means of widening the available stereo image, and some can be used in a gimmicky way to move sounds or effects right around the listener's head, their real downfall is their lack of mono compatibility. This is inevitable, as real life can't be considered mono compatible, but as long as mono TV sound and mono radio receivers are with us, it has to be a cause for concern. The main problems are the phase and timbral changes that occur when the left and right signals are summed; the further the sound is panned by the 3D system outside the speakers, the more noticeable the side-effects become.

At the time of writing, more work is being done to improve the mono compatibility of these systems and to make their  effects less dependent of the listener's position relative to the loudspeakers. Whether 3D systems will ever become fully effective is questionable at this stage, but the techniques that make these effects possible are already being employed in various pieces of studio equipment. Stereo sound samples are already being prepared via 3D sound systems, while the basic principles are being applied to widening the subjective sound of digital reverbs and other stereo effect processors.

Currently, 3D sound processors are expensive items and are limited in the number of channels that can be processed at any one time. However, their use requires no special skill, as the horizontal and vertical pan pots can be used quite intuitively, while the control movements (on some models) may be output as MIDI data and stored on a conventional MIDI sequencer, enabling some degree of automation. Whatever the limitations imposed by current processors of this type, their real beauty is that recordings need no decoding or special equipment at the user's end, and while, in its present state, 3D sound may be no substitute for true quadraphonic sound, it can be used to add interest to pop records and to enhance the special effects used in video movie soundtracks.

# STEREO EFFECTS

Having learned how the human hearing system perceives sound direction, it is possible to employ a little studio trickery to exploit these effects without having to buy special equipment. For example, we now know that to make a sound really appear as though it is coming from one side or the other, we not only have to change the relative left/right balance, but we also need to delay one of the signals slightly. The time taken for sound to travel around the human head is a little under 1mS, so it is useful to experiment with a DDL as shown in figure 17.1. Here the signal is being panned to make it appear as though it is coming from the right hand side while a lower level, delayed version is panned to the left. This creates a more solid directional image than using the pan pot alone, though it isn't perfect because no account has been taken of the crosstalk between the speakers. The effect can be made slightly more authentic by rolling some of the top off the delayed signal to simulate the effect of head masking. The delayed signal only needs to be 3dB or so lower in level than the undelayed signal, and varying the delay time slightly varies the perceived sound location to some extent.

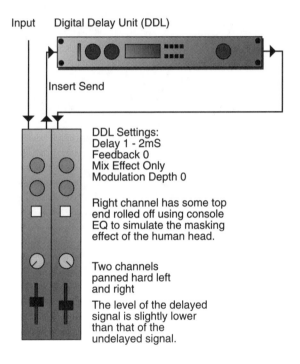

Input    Digital Delay Unit (DDL)

Insert Send

DDL Settings:
Delay 1 - 2mS
Feedback 0
Mix Effect Only
Modulation Depth 0

Right channel has some top end rolled off using console EQ to simulate the masking effect of the human head.

Two channels panned hard left and right

The level of the delayed signal is slightly lower than that of the undelayed signal.

Figure 17.1: Stereo Positioning Using a DDL

This principle is being unwittingly employed when a sound is split and a direct version of the sound panned to one extreme while a chorused or flanged version is panned to the other. The sense of depth and movement is due to the shifting delays between the processed signal and the unprocessed signal, making this a very powerful processing technique, even though the chorus/flanger need only be a mono unit. Variations on this effect are used extensively to enrich synthesized string and pad keyboard sounds or to create pseudo-stereo guitar chorus effects. These specific techniques are described in more depth in chapter 15: Mixing.

# HEADPHONES

Have you ever wondered why people don't just mix all their music on headphones? After all, it would reduce the amount of environmental noise considerably and would completely eliminate the need for acoustically treated control rooms. It sounds like the ideal solution, but unfortunately, headphones behave rather differently to loudspeakers in several key areas, and, as most music is optimised for loudspeaker playback, relying solely on headphones can be very misleading.

When stereophonic music is heard over a conventional pair of loudspeakers, our natural hearing mechanism positions the soundstage in front of us, whereas with headphones, there is little or no front-to-back information, which makes the sound appear to originate from either inside or above the listener's head. The problem of accurate stereo imaging is further compounded by the fact that when listening via loudspeakers (or, indeed, to a sound in real life) some of the sound from the left loudspeaker enters the right ear, and vice versa. With headphones, there is a very high degree of separation between the signals presented to the two ears, which produces an artificially enhanced sensation of stereo imaging. While this makes it difficult to predict the effect of the same musical mix over loudspeakers, it can be helpful in checking that all the sounds are where they were intended to be, and that any stereo effects sound properly balanced.

A more serious shortcoming of headphones is that different people will hear a different tonal balance, even though they are using the same model of headphone. This is particularly true at the low end of the audio spectrum, where factors such as the distance between the diaphragm and the ear and the effectiveness of the cushion seal will influence the amount of bass that the listener perceives. You can try this for yourself by listening via headphones and then pushing them closer to your ears; you should notice a dramatic increase in bass because the headphone diaphragm has moved closer to your ear and the proximity effect is causing a significant degree of bass lift.

The problem of maintaining an effective seal between the headphone and the area of head around the ear can be avoided by making the headphones acoustically open. In other words, instead of the headphone being in the form of a sealed enclosure which fits over the ears, the transducer is mounted in an acoustically transparent basket and spaced away from the head by means of padded cushions. Such open designs have the added advantage that the sound is less coloured than when confined by a sealed cavity, but the down side is that external sound is free to leak in and some of the sound from the headphones will leak out. This is not a problem when monitoring while mixing, but it can be troublesome when a performer is using such headphones to listen to a backing track or click track, as some of the spill from the headphones may leak back into the performer's microphone.

Though the sound quality of open headphones can be excellent and inconsistencies due to ineffective sealing can be largely eliminated, there is still some inconsistency in bass perception, caused by variation in the diaphragm/ear distance, which is dependent on the physical makeup of each individual ear. Where such headphones excel is in their ability to discriminate fine detail within a musical mix, and traces of distortion which can go unnoticed during loudspeaker listening are more likely to be picked up. Ideally, a mix should be checked on both headphones and loudspeakers, though for the home recordists working in a noise-sensitive environment, it is possible to do a considerable amount of work using headphones, resorting to loudspeakers only to check crucial stages of a mix for overall tonal balance.

# NO AUDIO TAPE HAS EVER RATED SUCH INCREDIBLE RESPONSE

"After using 996 for over 12 months, I remain very impressed with it's consistency and performance. 996's low noise floor makes it ideal for most applications, even without noise reduction, and its high level capability copes with almost anything we throw at it without any saturation".
-**Callum Malcolm, engineer and producer. Castle Sound Studios.**

"The performance is excellent. You can push it very high indeed, yet it still retains the clarity needed for CD's, combining the best of analogue warmth with a good crisp quality - real competition for digital".
-**Craig Leon, producer.**

"I've been using 3M 996 tape at 30ips without noise reduction, and it sound terrific. It's analogue like analgue ought to be - with digital, all you can do is get the level right but 996 gives you far more control over getting the sound right. It's the only tape I use now."
-**Chris Kimsey, producers**

"3M 996 knocks the spots off previous-generation analogue. Recording multi-track at 30ips, with noise reduction,996 lets me achieve the kind of warmth that's very hard to get with digital. And the results are as super-quiet as digital, you just don't know it's there - what you put on you get back".
-**Hugh Padgham, producer**

Clarity, punch, excitement. 3M 996 Audio Mastering Tape elicits a dynamic response from producers and engineers. It provides the analogue performance they've always wanted the ablility to record as hot as +9dB, with a maximum output of +14dB. A very low noise floor, achieved by a signal-to-noise ratio of 79.5dB and class-leading print-through of 56.5dB. 3M 996 captures every subtley, delivering every note just as it went down. The highest level of response.

3M United Kingdom PLC,
Professional Audio/Video Group, 3M House,
Bracknell, Berkshire RG12 1JU. Tel: (0344) 858614 Fax: (0344) 858493

# MASTERING

One of the less glamorous but nevertheless essential tasks in any studio is to ensure that all tapes are properly labelled — to do otherwise risks at best confusion, and at worst, the erasure of an irreplaceable recording. There is now a standard tape labelling system put forward by the APRS (Association of Professional Recording Studios) which sets out to reduce the potential for error and which I shall describe briefly. This covers both multitrack and stereo master tapes, copies, clones and DAT. Colour coded labels are available via the APRS but simply writing the correct term on the box is a good start.

In all cases, tapes should be labelled with format details: in the case of analogue recordings, the tape speed, track format, noise reduction, EQ and, of course, the title and date of the recording are essential. Digital tapes should be labelled with sample rate and details of the type of machine used to make the recording. Open-reel tapes are traditionally stored 'tail out', as this reduces the degree of 'print-through' when the tapes are stored for a long time. The tapes must be rewound before playing.

## SESSION TAPE

The first tape created during a project is a Session Tape; this is usually a multitrack tape and comprises the first-generation recordings made during a session. In other words, it is the working tape on which material is recorded and overdubbed — consequently it may contain out-takes as well as wanted material. There may be several Session Tapes created during an album project. Session Tapes may be of any format and may be analogue or digital; indeed, in the case of direct-to-stereo recording, the original recording is still known as the Session Tape. All relevant data should be recorded on the tape box or inlay card. The APRS label is solid blue and bears the words SESSION TAPE.

## ORIGINAL MASTER

When a multitrack tape is first mixed to stereo, the result is the Original Master tape. It is the earliest generation of the final stereo recording. This is not necessarily the tape used for production, as it may later be necessary to add EQ or to edit the material. The APRS label is solid red with the legend ORIGINAL MASTER.

## PRODUCTION MASTER

The Production Master is usually an edited copy of the Original Master where the tracks have been placed in the correct running order and with correct spacing between the tracks. Often the Production Master will be equalised, and as different versions may be required for different release formats, the Production Master should be marked with the desired format: CD; Cassette; Vinyl; DCC or MiniDisk. The standard APRS label is solid green with the legend PRODUCTION MASTER. The label also includes space for release format details.

For digital formats such as CD, DCC or MiniDisk, the Production Master will have to be transferred to Sony U-Matic format at the mastering stage. Test tones should not be recorded onto tapes destined for digital formats. Many production masters are now made on DAT cassettes; a sampling rate of 44.1kHz is preferred if the machine allows it.

## PRODUCTION MASTER COPY/CLONE

This is copied from the Production Master to allow distribution of the tape for manufacturing purposes without having to release the original Production Master. A tape copied in the analogue domain from either a digital or analogue source is known as a Copy while a digital clone of a digital original is known as a Clone.

In theory, a clone will be identical to the original in all ways. The APRS label is bright orange with the words PRODUCTION MASTER COPY CLONE printed on it. The appropriate Copy or Clone box should be ticked and the label should include all information relating to the Production Master

### SAFETY COPY CLONE

This is strictly a backup copy or clone of another tape; the original from which it is taken should be clearly marked on the label. The label is bright pink and is legended SAFETY COPY CLONE. The appropriate Copy or Clone box should be ticked and the label should include all information relating to the original.

### NOT FOR PRODUCTION

Description of any tape in any format which must not be used as a source for media manufacture. The label is yellow and bears the words NOT FOR PRODUCTION.

### PQ ENCODED MASTER TAPE

This is the final U-Matic tape ready for the manufacture of a digital media release such as CD, DCC or MD and includes the coding information pertaining to number of tracks, playing time, table of contents and so on. Each of these release formats requires the PQ Encoded Master to be prepared in a specific way, so it is essential that the media is identified on the label. The label is grey and is labelled PQ ENCODED TAPE MASTER. Tick boxes are provided for the various release media formats and whether the tape is an original or a clone.

### MEDIA VERSION

A copy or clone made for a specific purpose, such as radio broadcast or film/video soundtrack work. If the tape is recorded with timecode, this should be noted on the label. The label is yellow and marked MEDIA VERSION, with tick boxes for Radio, TV, Film or Video.

## TAPE COPYING

When copying a tape, it is necessary to know the maximum recorded level on that tape. (This is not the case when making a digital clone, as the copy will be the same as the master tape in all respects). Recordings are normally preceded by test tones, and the reference level of those tones should be marked on the tape box. Correctly recorded tones will be recorded with a burst in the left channel only at the start of the tones section, so it should be possible to check that you haven't got the right and left channels transposed. It is also wise to do a few spot checks throughout the tape to ensure that the test tones do in fact relate to the recorded level.

If the tape has been produced as a Production Master for CD (or other digital format) manufacture, there will be no test tones, in which case it may be necessary to play the material and establish at what level the peaks have been recorded.

# TEST TONES

The standard format for test tones is five seconds of 1kHz tone on the left channel only, followed by around 30 seconds of the same tone on both channels. The tone should be recorded at 0VU and the level noted on the box. It also helps alignment in the case of the tape being replayed on another machine if a 100Hz, 0VU tone is recorded, followed by a 10kHz tone, the latter often being recorded at around -10dB and the level again being noted.

In the case of digital tapes such as DAT, it is usual for them to be recorded so that the peak levels come to around 2dB below the maximum meter reading or FS (Full Scale). It is always a good idea to record a couple of minutes of silence onto the start of the tape, as the very start of a tape is more prone to errors. If continuous test tones are required for calibration, a nominal level of -14dBFS (1kHz) is considered acceptable and this should be noted on the label. At the end of the copy, there should be at least 30 seconds of recorded silence before the tape is stopped.

# RECORD TAPE AND CD MANUFACTURE

With the advent of Minidisk (MD) and Digital Compact Cassette (DCC), there are now five potential record release formats - and that doesn't include film or video soundtracks. The main formats at the time of writing remain Compact Disk (CD) and the analogue Compact Cassette, though vinyl is still a viable option, especially for specialist dance and club music.

The purpose of this chapter is to present an overview of the various processes that take place between completing a mix in the studio and the manufacture of a record from that recording.

Once the Session Tape, (usually analogue or digital multitrack), has been mixed down to stereo, the resulting tape is designated the Original Master, and it is from this tape that a Production Master must be made. In all probability, the Original Master (or Masters) will contain out-takes, odd spuriae such as count-ins, and the material will probably be recorded in the wrong order with incorrect gap lengths between the songs. It may also be necessary to adjust the relative levels of some of the tracks and it is not uncommon to add further equalisation.

# WORKING WITH DAT

When mixing to DAT, it is important to record as close as possible to the digital peak shown on the recorder's meters and to use the 44.1kHz sampling rate setting if available. When working with a DAT machine that has a fixed 48kHz sampling rate, don't worry - if you're planning to make CDs, the company who produce the CD Master tape for you should be able to handle this. However, never mix the two sample rates on one tape (or set of tapes) - you could end up with part of your album playing back at the wrong speed!

When making DAT Production Masters, always set start ID function to On. Normally, playing a song cued using an ID recorded with the Auto ID is to risk clipping the first note because Auto ID must sense the presence of the programme material before writing the ID. Because of this, it is wise to manually move all IDs back by half a second or so.

Avoid recording music on the first or last minute of tape and always record silence before and after the programme material - digital tapes contain subcode information and it is important that this starts before the recording and continues for a while after it. Don't simply run the tape in play mode to create a gap as this will leave a section of tape with no subcode.

# HARD DISK EDITING

While it is possible to make up a Production Master by compiling from one tape machine to another, a more precise option is to use a hard-disk editing system. These have the advantage that individual tracks can be 'topped and tailed' to ensure that they are clean up until the moment the first note sounds and that all count-ins and other unwanted material are removed. The edited material is then copied from the hard disk system to a stereo tape machine, ideally DAT, as the transfer can be made in the digital domain. This new tape is the Production Master. Digital formats such as DAT offer the advantage that the material can be cloned rather than copied making it possible to create backups and compiled Production Masters with no quality loss.

# PRODUCTION MASTER

When making the Production Master, a decision must be made as to whether the release will be on vinyl, cassette or disk. If it is to be on cassette, there must be a gap between the two sides and the playing times of the two sides must be calculated so as to be as equal as possible. As a rule, side one is made slightly longer than side two so that when the tape is turned over at the end of side one, side two is ready to play.

Careful listening is required to ascertain whether any of the tracks need adjusting in either level or EQ. The gaps between songs should also be auditioned, and though most are around four seconds, the actual length must be determined by ear; if the preceding songs fades out, then a shorter gap may be required than if the song finishes abruptly. Essentially, if the gap feels right, it is right.

A full listing of the songs by title, start time (Start IDs) and playing time must accompany the Production master and this sheet should include full details of the recording format such as sampling rate and, ideally, the type and model of machine that was used.

When compiling to open-reel analogue, the gaps are created by splicing either blank tape or leader tape between the songs. The length of blank tape required can be calculated from the running speed of the recorder.

The total time on a cassette can be a lot longer than on CD — most CDs offer a maximum recording time of 74 minutes. However, most commercial CDs are under 60 minutes in duration so this should present no problems. In the case of other formats, including vinyl, consult the manufacturer before producing the Production Master tape to find out the maximum playing time that can be accommodated.

# WHAT COMES NEXT

If you're planning to release your material only on analogue cassette, then a copy or clone of the Production master may be all you need. Of course you also have to think about artwork, but that will be covered shortly. Under no circumstances send away your only master tape; always keep a cloned backup in a safe place.

Unfortunately the Production Master isn't the end of the line if you're aiming for a CD release — there are two more stages to negotiate: the CD Master tape and the Glass Master. Similarly, if you're going to add either MiniDisk or DCC to your release formats, you'll need to speak to the manufacturers as to their requirements. At the time of writing, these formats are still very new, so direct contact with the manufacturers is recommended. The main difference between MD and DCC and the established formats is that both newcomers use a form of data compression to reduce the amount of digital data to around one fifth of that of a conventional CD or DAT tape. Furthermore, both formats have the ability to store text, which can be used to display such things as the song titles on those machines equipped with display windows.

# CD MASTERING

For CD mastering, the Production Master tape will be arranged with no gap between the two sides of the album and a total playing time, including gaps, of less than 74 minutes. The factory will require a fully prepared CD Master Tape, which is most often handled by a specialist mastering facility and involves cloning or copying the Production Master to a U-Matic Tape. This is PCM encoded, timecoded and has the necessary PQ (Pause and Cue) code information added. This information is used to create the Table of Contents (or TOC) on the finished CD so that a CD player can locate the tracks. A track title and times sheet will also be produced at this time for use by the CD manufacturers, usually by the company that produces the CD Master tape.

Some mastering facilities can make a Reference CD from the CD Tape Master. This is relatively inexpensive, and the small outlay is worth it for the peace of mind in knowing that the finished product will turn out as you expected it. If a proper reference CD is unavailable, a one-off CDR disk is better than nothing, though the track start times may not accurately reflect those on the finished product.

While on the subject, the falling cost of low-volume CDR duplication may eventually make this a viable alternative to conventional manufacture for small quantity runs of 50 discs or less. These may be made directly from a Production Master tape, saving the cost of having a CD Master tape produced.

# GLASS MASTERS

At the CD plant, the CD Tape Master has to be played into a Glass Mastering Machine which uses all the special coding on the tape to determine timing and Table of Contents. After the data has been transferred to the Glass Master (so called because a glass disk is used to carry the photosensitive surface which is imprinted with digital data from a modulated laser), the Glass Master is plated with nickel to make a mechanical stamper, similar in concept to that used to stamp out vinyl records.

During manufacture, the reflective part of the CD is stamped out of aluminium and then sandwiched between layers of transparent plastic which protect it and give it rigidity. Labels are printed directly onto the pressed CD using a special, quick-drying ink, and may be in single or multiple colours. The manufacturer should be consulted as to what form the original artwork should take.

After manufacture, the discs are automatically loaded into jewel cases along with an inlay card and booklet. These must be provided by the client prior to manufacture. Few CD pressing plants handle their own inlay card printing, but most will be able to recommend a company that can do this for you or arrange printing on your behalf. However, if you don't arrange the printing yourself, there are going to be at least two other businesses in the chain which increases the possibility of error.

# BROKERS

An alternative approach to CD production is to negotiate a package price with a broker who will handle all the aspects of record or CD production, including the various mastering stages, printing and packaging. However, don't assume that everything will proceed smoothly — check at every stage if at all possible. Also check at the outset that there no hidden costs; companies quoting attractive prices for CD manufacture often don't include essential services such as producing the CD Master Tape, Glass Mastering and printed material — these are all priced as extras. Realistically, a minimum practical production run of CDs is 500, with 1000 or more being even more cost effective.

Try to find a broker recommended by someone you know if at all possible because, as in all areas of business, there is a vast difference in quality between the best and worst companies offering what is ostensibly the same service.

# VINYL

Vinyl records are produced using metal stampers which, in turn, start life as a pair of Lacquer Masters, one for each side of the record. These are cut from blanks using a record cutting lathe and then taken to the record manufacturing plant where the stampers are made. The stampers (or Factory Masters) are formed onto the lacquers using an electro-plating process.

The actual record labels are printed on paper using special heat-resistant inks; most record plants have the facility to arrange manufacture. Fixing of the labels is achieved during the pressing process, and once the records have been trimmed of waste material and inspected, they are placed in sleeves. Inner sleeves are often optional, so discuss sleeve requirements with the factory when discussing cost. As with CDs, the minimum practical quantity for manufacture is several hundred.

# COMPACT CASSETTE

**High Speed Copying:** Cassettes may be made from a Production Master tape, ideally in DAT format. In the case of high speed copying, the Production Master will normally be copied onto a special analogue machine designed to work at high speed. The recording is made onto cassette tape stored on large reels (or 'pancakes'), which is wound into empty cassette shells after recording. This procedure offers the advantage that the tape can be cut exactly to length, and the copying process is not compromised by the mechanics of the cassette shells.

As a rule, both sides of the tape are copied at the same time, and unless you state otherwise, the recordings will be made using Dolby B noise reduction. Depending on your budget, there is a choice of standard Fe tape or Type II tape, also known as Chrome equivalent. Standard cassette shells are available in black or white.

Solid state memory stores have replaced high speed tape for mastering purposes in some duplicating plants, and in theory, these produce less degradation in audio quality. Essentially the whole album is loaded into a large digital memory in real time and then clocked out at the high speed during the copying process.

**Real-time Copying:** Real-time copies may be made directly from a DAT source; the destination cassettes are usually pre-loaded with tape. This gives less flexibility as regards playing time, but has the advantage that low production runs are economically viable.

**High Speed Cassette to Cassette Copying:** The least satisfactory method of cassette duplication is the high speed system which works from a cassette master and records onto pre-loaded blank cassettes. The tape guides in cassette shells don't work well at high speeds, which leads to inconsistent recording quality. The fact that the Production Master must be copied to cassette also introduces another generation of quality loss into the duplication process.

**Labelling:** Cassettes may use printed paper labels or the printing may be done directly onto the cassette shell. This latter process must be done during the duplication process and is only cost effective for runs of several hundred tapes or more due to the cost of making the special printing plates. As a rule, paper labels give more scope in the use of colour and design.

**Packaging:** Cassettes are normally delivered in transparent library boxes and the folded inlay cards are generally printed separately. For small runs, these may be inserted by hand. In the case of very small runs, it may be worth using a colour photocopy bureau to copy the original artwork.

# Good Housekeeping

## Favourite
## Chicken
## Recipes

**250** Tried, tested, trusted recipes ★ Delicious results

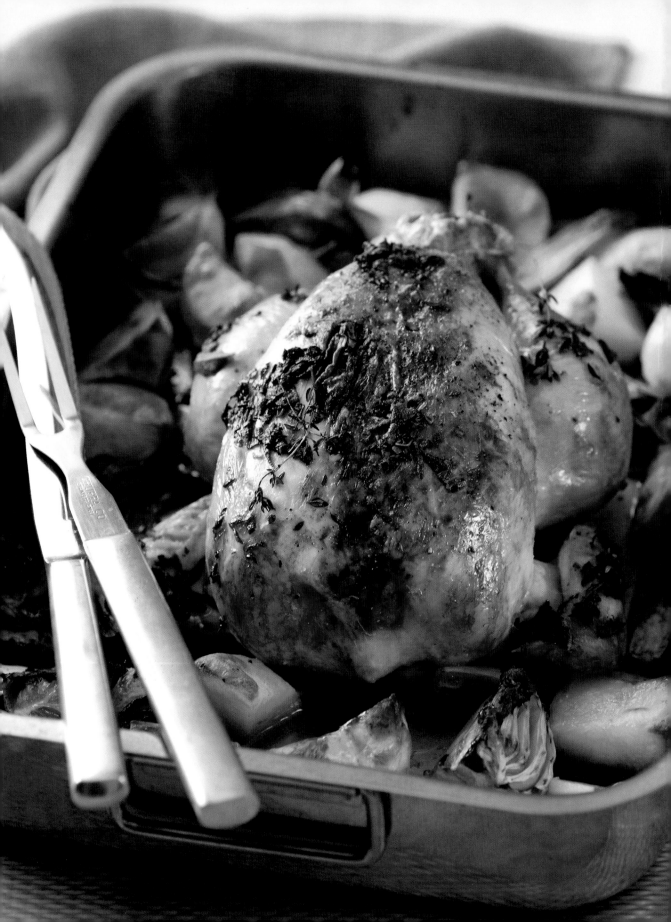

# Good Housekeeping
# Favourite
# Chicken
# Recipes

**250** Tried, tested, trusted recipes ★ Delicious results

Compiled by Barbara Dixon

COLLINS & BROWN

First published in the United Kingdom in 2011 by
Collins & Brown
10 Southcombe Street
London
W14 0RA

An imprint of Anova Books Company Ltd

The Good Housekeeping website is
www.allaboutyou.com/goodhousekeeping

10 9 8 7 6 5 4 3 2 1

ISBN 978-1-84340-604-4

A catalogue record for this book is available from
the British Library.

Repro by Dot Gradations Ltd UK
Printed by Times Offset Malaysia

This book can be ordered direct from the publisher at
www.anovabooks.com

Recipes in this book are taken from the Good Housekeeping recipe
library and may have been reproduced in previous publications.

Picture Credits:
Neil Barclay (pages 13, 27, 41, 49, 56, 59, 61, 64, 65, 78, 79, 97,
141, 142, 153, 162, 165, 167, 172, 176, 182, 185, 189, 198 and
214); Martin Brigdale (pages 16, 127, 148, 151, 193, 209, 211,
216, 218, 227, 243 and 253); Nicki Dowey (pages 11, 14, 17,
19,20, 21, 24, 25, 28, 29, 31, 34, 37, 38, 42, 44, 45, 50, 51, 52,
55, 58, 62, 67, 72, 73, 82, 85, 86, 88, 91, 92, 95, 96, 99, 102,
108, 118, 121, 122, 123, 124, 128, 129, 130, 132, 133, 135,
136, 138, 143, 147, 149, 152, 155, 159, 160, 168, 173, 180,
184, 190, 192, 194, 203, 204, 206, 207, 220, 226, 229, 231,
232, 235, 237, 238, 239, 240, 242, 244, 246, 248, 249, 257,
259, 261 and 262); Will Heap (pages 22 and 101); Craig
Robertson (Basics photography and pages 40, 46, 68, 75, 76, 87,
93, 98, 107, 109, 110, 111, 114, 119, 144, 166, 177, 179, 181,
187, 188, 201, 202, 210, 212, 215, 217, 230, 234, 250, 252,
258); Clive Streeter (page 161); Lucinda Symons (pages 12, 35, 81,
83, 112, 113, 139, 174, 199, 221, 223 and 254)
Home Economists: Anna Burges-Lumsden, Joanna Farrow, Emma
Jane Frost, Teresa Goldfinch, Alice Hart, Lucy McKelvie, Kim
Morphew, Katie Rogers, Sarah Tildesley, Jennifer White and Mari
Mererid Williams
Stylists: Penny Markham, Lucy McKelvie, Wei Tang, Helen Trent and
Mari Mererid Williams

## NOTES

★ Both metric and imperial measures are given for the
recipes. Follow either set of measures, not a mixture of
both, as they are not interchangeable.

★ All spoon measures are level.
1 tsp = 5ml spoon; 1 tbsp = 15ml spoon.

★ Ovens and grills must be preheated to the specified
temperature.

★ Medium eggs should be used except where otherwise
specified.

## DIETARY GUIDELINES

★ Note that certain recipes contain raw or lightly cooked
eggs. The young, elderly, pregnant women and anyone
with immune-deficiency disease should avoid these
because of the slight risk of salmonella.

★ Note that some recipes contain alcohol. Check the
ingredients list before serving to children.

# Contents

# Foreword

Chicken has to be queen of the birds – be that for its availability, versatility, price, health properties or mild flavour. Wherever you are in the world, chances are chicken (in some guise) will be on the menu, which I find a pleasing constant. As unhealthy as it might sound, a personal favourite is Southern Fried Chicken. Not that I have deep-fat frying tendencies but when this simple recipe is done well, it's hard to beat – it must be deeply golden, superbly crisp and mouth-wateringly tender all at once. It's a good motto to live by in the kitchen, do things simply and well.

Many factors add to the ultimate flavour and texture of your bird, but age, exercise and diet all contribute. Supermarkets and butchers will sell a variety of chickens, just bear in mind that you get what you pay for. Spend as much as you can on good poultry, the results will be worth it. Also, learn to do your own jointing as it's not only rewarding but will keep pennies in your purse.

Chicken lends itself to all sorts of dining occasions, from speedy family meals to elegant entertaining, summery picnics and sticky barbecues. You'll find this great book packed full of just such recipes, and all have our guarantee to work first time round.

In case you want to spread your wings a little (pun intended!), we've added a chapter on other fluffy friends, from turkey to game.

Enjoy!

*Meike.*

Meike Beck
Chief Home Economist

# Soups

# Chicken and Mushroom Broth

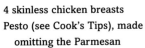

Preparation Time 20 minutes • Cooking Time 20 minutes • Serves 4 • Per Serving 255 calories, 5g fat (of which 1g saturates), 16g carbohydrate, 1.4g salt • Dairy Free • Easy

4 skinless chicken breasts
Pesto (see Cook's Tips), made
    omitting the Parmesan
1.1 litres (2 pints) chicken stock
    (see page 266)
100ml (3½fl oz) medium sherry
150g (5oz) exotic mushrooms,
    cleaned and sliced
1 red chilli, seeded and halved (see
    Cook's Tips)
75g (3oz) conchigliette pasta
2 tbsp soy sauce
a small handful of chopped pak
    choi or spinach leaves
a dash of Tabasco to serve
    (optional)

1 Preheat the oven to 200°C (180°C fan oven) mark 6. Make a few slashes in the chicken breasts, then rub the pesto over the chicken, pushing it into the cuts. Put the chicken into a roasting tin and roast for 20 minutes.

2 Meanwhile, put the stock into a pan with the sherry and bring to the boil. Add the mushrooms, chilli and pasta. Cover the pan and simmer for 3 minutes until the pasta is cooked. Stir in the soy sauce.

3 Slice the chicken into the broth with the pak choi or spinach.

4 Ladle into warmed bowls and serve immediately. Add a dash of Tabasco if you like it hot.

★ COOK'S TIPS
● *Chillies vary enormously in strength, from quite mild to blisteringly hot, depending on the type of chilli and its ripeness. Taste a small piece first to check it's not too hot for you.*
● *Be extremely careful when handling chillies not to touch or rub your eyes with your fingers, as they will sting. Wash knives immediately after handling chillies for the same reason. As a precaution, use rubber gloves when preparing them if you like.*
● ***Pesto***
*Put a 20g pack roughly chopped basil into a food processor. Add 25g (1oz) finely grated Parmesan, 50g (2oz) pinenuts and 4 tbsp extra virgin olive oil and whiz to a rough paste. Alternatively, grind in a pestle and mortar. Season with salt and ground black pepper.*

# Coconut Broth and Chicken Noodles

Preparation Time 5 minutes • Cooking Time 15 minutes • Serves 4 • Per Serving 440 calories, 19g fat (of which 4g saturates), 42g carbohydrate, 1g salt • Easy

1 tbsp vegetable oil
2 tbsp tom yum (or Thai red curry) soup paste
900ml (1½ pints) hot chicken stock (see page 266)
400ml can unsweetened coconut milk
200g (7oz) thread egg noodles
2 × large boneless, skinless chicken breasts, cut into thin strips
350g (12oz) pack stir-fry vegetables
salt and ground black pepper
coriander leaves to garnish
prawn crackers to serve

1 Heat the oil in a large pan. Add the soup paste and fry for about 10 seconds. Add the hot stock and coconut milk and bring to the boil. Reduce the heat and simmer for about 5 minutes.

2 Meanwhile, cook the noodles in plenty of boiling water according to the pack instructions.

3 Add the chicken strips to the simmering soup and cook for 3 minutes. Add the stir-fry vegetables, mix well and season with salt and pepper.

4 Drain the noodles, then divide among four large warmed bowls and pour the soup on top. Garnish with the coriander and serve with prawn crackers.

# Chicken Consommé

Preparation Time 30 minutes • Cooking Time 1¼ hours • Serves 4 • Per Serving 18 calories, 1g fat (of which trace saturates), 1g carbohydrate, 3.1g salt • Dairy Free • A Little Effort

1.7 litres (3 pints) well-flavoured
  fat-free chicken stock (see
  page 266)
350g (12oz) skinless chicken breast,
  minced
2 leeks, trimmed and thinly sliced
2 celery sticks, thinly sliced
2 carrots, thinly sliced
2 shallots, diced
2 medium egg whites, lightly
  whisked
2 medium egg shells, crushed (see
  Cook's Tip)
a dash of sherry or Madeira
  (optional)
salt and ground black pepper

1 Heat the stock in a pan. Combine the chicken and vegetables in another large pan, then mix in the egg whites and shells.

2 Gradually whisk in the hot stock, then bring to the boil, whisking. As soon as it comes to the boil, stop whisking, reduce the heat and simmer very gently for 1 hour. By this time, a crust will have formed on the surface and the stock underneath should be clear.

3 Carefully make a hole in the crust and ladle the clear stock out into a muslin-lined sieve over a large bowl. Allow to drain through slowly, then put back into the cleaned pan and reheat. Check the seasoning and flavour with a little sherry or Madeira, if you like.

★ COOK'S TIP
*Egg shells and whites are used to make soups, such as consommé, clear. When heated slowly, they trap the impurities as they coagulate, forming a scum layer on the top of the soup. Once the layer of scum has formed, the soup is gently strained through kitchen paper or a cloth, leaving behind a clear soup.*

# Chicken and Bean Soup

Preparation Time 10 minutes • Cooking Time 30 minutes • Serves 4 • Per Serving 351 calories, 6g fat
(of which 1g saturates), 48g carbohydrate, 2.7g salt • Dairy Free • Easy

1 tbsp olive oil
1 onion, finely chopped
4 celery sticks, chopped
1 red chilli, seeded and roughly
   chopped (see Cook's Tips,
   page 10)
2 boneless, skinless chicken
   breasts, about 125g (4oz) each,
   cut into strips
1 litre (1¾ pints) hot chicken (see
   page 266) or vegetable stock
100g (3½oz) bulgur wheat
2 × 400g cans cannellini beans,
   drained and rinsed
400g can chopped tomatoes
25g (1oz) flat-leafed parsley,
   roughly chopped
wholegrain bread and Hummus
   (see Cook's Tip) to serve

1 Heat the oil in a large heavy-based pan. Add the onion, celery and chilli and cook over a low heat for 10 minutes or until softened. Add the chicken strips and stir-fry for 3–4 minutes until golden.

2 Add the hot stock to the pan and bring to a simmer. Stir in the bulgur wheat and simmer for 15 minutes.

3 Stir in the cannellini beans and tomatoes and bring to a simmer. Ladle into four warmed bowls and sprinkle with chopped parsley. Serve with bread and hummus.

★ COOK'S TIP
*Hummus*
*Soak 150g (5½oz) dried chickpeas overnight, then drain and rinse. Put into a large pan and cover with 600ml (1 pint) water. Bring to the boil, reduce the heat to a simmer and cook for 2½–3 hours until tender. Drain, reserving the liquid. Keep aside 2–3 tbsp chickpeas for garnishing. Put the remaining chickpeas into a blender with 2 large garlic cloves, the juice of 2 lemons, 75ml (2½fl oz) olive oil and 150ml (¼ pint) of the cooking liquid. Whiz to a purée. Add 150ml (¼ pint) tahini paste (sesame seed paste) and whiz to a soft dropping consistency. Sprinkle with olive oil, freshly chopped flat-leafed parsley and cayenne pepper or paprika to serve.*

# Chicken Noodle Soup

Preparation Time 30 minutes • Cooking Time 15 minutes • Serves 4 • Per Serving 229 calories, 7g fat
(of which 1g saturates), 16g carbohydrate, 1.2g salt • Dairy Free • A Little Effort

1 tbsp olive oil

300g (11oz) boneless, skinless
   chicken thighs, cubed

3 garlic cloves, crushed

2 medium red chillies, seeded and
   finely diced (see Cook's Tips,
   page 10)

1 litre (1¾ pints) chicken stock
   (see page 266)

250g (9oz) each green beans,
   broccoli, sugarsnap peas and
   courgettes, sliced

50g (2oz) vermicelli or spaghetti,
   broken into short lengths

salt

1 Heat the oil in a large pan. Add
the chicken, garlic and chillies and
cook for 5–10 minutes until the
chicken is opaque all over.

2 Add the stock and bring to the
boil, then add the vegetables.
Reduce the heat and simmer for
about 5 minutes or until the chicken
is cooked through.

3 Meanwhile, cook the noodles or
pasta in a separate pan of lightly
salted boiling water for about
5–10 minutes until al dente,
depending on the type of noodles or
pasta.

4 Drain the noodles or pasta, add to
the broth and serve immediately.

# Leftover Roast Chicken Soup

Preparation Time 10 minutes • Cooking Time 45 minutes • Serves 4 • Per Serving 199 calories, 12g fat
(of which 3g saturates), 12g carbohydrate, 0.1g salt • Gluten Free • Easy

3 tbsp olive oil
1 onion, chopped
1 carrot, chopped
2 celery sticks, chopped
2 fresh thyme sprigs, chopped
1 bay leaf
1 stripped roast chicken carcass
150–200g (5–7oz) cooked chicken,
   roughly chopped
200g (7oz) mashed or roast potato
1 tbsp double cream

1 Heat the oil in a large pan. Add
the onion, carrot, celery and thyme
and fry gently for 20–30 minutes
until soft but not brown. Add the
bay leaf, chicken carcass and 900ml
(1½ pints) boiling water to the pan.
Bring to the boil, then reduce the
heat and simmer for 5 minutes.

2 Remove the bay leaf and chicken
carcass and add the chopped
cooked chicken and potato. Simmer
for 5 minutes.

3 Put the soup into a food processor
or blender and whiz until smooth,
then pour back into the pan and
bring to the boil. Stir in the cream
and serve immediately.

# Chicken Soup with Garlic and Parmesan Croûtons

Preparation Time 30 minutes • Cooking Time about 1¼ hours • Serves 6 • Per Serving 340 calories, 16g fat (of which 9g saturates), 26g carbohydrate, 0.3g salt • Easy

1 small chicken, about 1kg (2¼lb),
    cut into pieces
300ml (½ pint) dry white wine
a few black peppercorns
1–2 red chillies, seeded (see Cook's
    Tips, page 10)
2 bay leaves
2 fresh rosemary sprigs
1 celery stick, roughly chopped
4 carrots, 3 roughly chopped and
    1 cut into fine matchsticks
3 onions, 2 quartered and
    1 chopped
75g (3oz) pasta shapes
75g (3oz) butter, plus extra
    to grease
2 garlic cloves, crushed
1 cos lettuce, finely shredded
2 tbsp freshly chopped parsley
4 thick slices white bread
3 tbsp freshly grated Parmesan
salt and ground black pepper

1 Put the chicken pieces into a pan in which they fit snugly. Add the wine, peppercorns, chillies, bay leaves, rosemary and celery. Add the roughly chopped carrots, quartered onions and about 900ml (1½ pints) cold water, which should almost cover the chicken. Bring to the boil, reduce the heat, cover and simmer gently for 1 hour.

2 Leave to cool slightly, then transfer the chicken to a plate and strain the stock. When cool enough to handle, remove the chicken from the bones and tear into bite-size pieces. Put to one side.

3 Preheat the oven to 200°C (180°C fan oven) mark 6. Pour the stock into the pan. Bring back to the boil, then add the pasta and cook for 5 minutes.

4 Heat 25g (1oz) butter in a clean pan. Add the chopped onion and a crushed garlic clove and cook for 5 minutes until softened. Add the carrot matchsticks and cook for 2 minutes. Add the stock and pasta and cook for 5 minutes. Stir in the chicken, lettuce and parsley. Heat gently, stirring, until the lettuce has wilted. Season with salt and pepper.

5 Meanwhile, lightly grease a baking sheet. Mix together 50g (2oz) softened butter and the remaining garlic in a small bowl. Remove the crusts from the bread and spread the slices with the garlic butter, then sprinkle with Parmesan. Cut into squares and put on the prepared baking sheet, spacing them a little apart. Cook in the oven for 8–10 minutes until crisp and golden brown.

6 Serve the chicken soup with the hot garlic and Parmesan croûtons.

# Cream of Chicken Soup

Preparation Time 10 minutes • Cooking Time 30 minutes • Serves 4 • Per Serving 398 calories, 12g fat (of which 6g saturates), 44g carbohydrate, 0.5g salt • Easy

3 tbsp plain flour
150ml (¼ pint) milk
1.1 litres (2 pints) home-made
    chicken stock (see page 266)
125g (4oz) cooked chicken, diced
1 tsp lemon juice
a pinch of freshly grated nutmeg
2 tbsp single cream
salt and ground black pepper
croûtons and fresh parsley sprigs
    to garnish

**1** Put the flour into a large bowl, add a little of the milk and blend until it makes a smooth cream.

**2** Bring the stock to the boil, then stir it into the blended mixture. Put back in the pan and simmer gently for 20 minutes.

**3** Stir in the chicken, lemon juice and nutmeg and season to taste with salt and pepper. Mix the rest of the milk with the cream and stir in, then reheat without boiling.

**4** Taste and adjust the seasoning. Ladle the soup into warmed bowls, sprinkle with croûtons and parsley sprigs and serve.

⭐ COOK'S TIP
*Serve this smooth, rich soup with warmed bridge rolls, before a main course of plain roast or grilled meat.*

# Hearty Chicken Soup with Dumplings

★

Preparation Time 20 minutes • Cooking Time 40 minutes • Serves 4 • Per Serving 335 calories, 15g fat (of which 5g saturates), 31g carbohydrate, 0.3g salt • Easy

2 tbsp olive oil
2 celery sticks, roughly chopped
150g (5oz) carrots, roughly
    chopped
150g (5oz) waxy salad potatoes,
    thinly sliced
275g (10oz) chicken breast,
    thinly sliced
2 litres (3½ pints) hot chicken stock
    (see page 266)
75g (3oz) frozen peas
salt and ground black pepper
a handful of chives, roughly
    chopped, to garnish (optional)

**FOR THE DUMPLINGS**
100g (3½oz) plain flour
½ tsp baking powder
½ tsp salt
1 medium egg, well beaten
25g (1oz) butter, melted
a splash of milk

1 Heat the oil in a large pan. Add the celery, carrots and potatoes and cook for 5 minutes or until the vegetables are beginning to caramelise around the edges. Add the chicken and fry for 3 minutes or until just starting to turn golden. Pour in the hot stock and simmer for 15 minutes, skimming the surface occasionally to remove any scum.

2 To make the dumplings, sift the flour, baking powder and salt into a bowl, then season with pepper. Combine the egg, melted butter and milk in a separate bowl, then stir quickly into the flour to make a stiff batter.

3 Drop half-teaspoonfuls of the dumpling mixture into the soup, then cover and simmer for a further 15 minutes.

4 Stir in the peas and heat through. Check the seasoning, sprinkle with pepper and serve garnished with chives, if you like.

# Thai Chicken and Noodle Soup

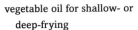

Preparation Time 20 minutes • Cooking Time about 30 minutes • Serves 4 • Per Serving 384 calories, 15g fat (of which 3g saturates), 36g carbohydrate, 2g salt • Dairy Free • Easy

vegetable oil for shallow- or
   deep-frying
225g (8oz) firm tofu, patted dry and
   cut into 1cm (½in) cubes
2.5cm (1in) piece fresh root ginger,
   peeled and finely chopped
2.5cm (1in) piece fresh or dried
   galangal, peeled and thinly sliced
   (optional, see Cook's Tip)
1–2 garlic cloves, crushed
2 lemongrass stalks, halved
   lengthways and bruised
1 tsp chilli powder
½ tsp ground turmeric
275g (10oz) cooked chicken,
   skinned and cut into
   bite-size pieces
175g (6oz) cauliflower, broken into
   small florets and any thick stems
   thinly sliced
1 large carrot, cut into matchsticks
600ml (1 pint) coconut milk
600ml (1 pint) chicken (see page
   266) or vegetable stock
a few green beans, trimmed and
   halved
125g (4oz) fine or medium egg
   noodles
125g (4oz) peeled prawns (optional)
3 spring onions, thinly sliced
75g (3oz) bean sprouts
2 tbsp soy sauce

1 Heat the oil in a wok or deep-fryer to 180°C (test by frying a small cube of bread; it should brown in 40 seconds). Fry the tofu, in batches, for 1 minute or until it is golden brown all over. Drain on kitchen paper.

2 Heat 2 tbsp oil in a large pan. Add the ginger, galangal, if using, garlic, lemongrass, chilli powder, turmeric and chicken pieces and cook, stirring for 2 minutes.

3 Add the cauliflower, carrot, coconut milk and stock or water. Bring to the boil, stirring all the time, then reduce the heat and simmer for 10 minutes. Add the beans and simmer for 5 minutes.

4 Meanwhile, bring a large pan of water to the boil and cook the noodles for about 4 minutes or according to the pack instructions. Drain the noodles and add them to the soup with the prawns, if using, the tofu, spring onions, bean sprouts and soy sauce. Simmer gently for 5 minutes or until heated through. Serve immediately.

★ COOK'S TIP
*Dried galangal, which is similar in flavour to root ginger, needs to be soaked for 30 minutes before using. It is used chopped or grated in many Thai, Indonesian and Malay dishes.*

# Thai Chicken Broth

Preparation Time 5 minutes • Cooking Time 20 minutes • Serves 4 • Per Serving 175 calories, 7g fat
(of which 1g saturates), 7g carbohydrate, 1.2g salt • Gluten Free • Dairy Free • Easy

1 tbsp vegetable oil
1 small onion, sliced
300g (11oz) stir-fry chicken pieces
1–2 tbsp Thai red curry paste
600ml (1 pint) hot chicken stock
   (see page 266)
400g can chopped plum tomatoes
100g (3½oz) sugarsnap peas,
   halved if large
150g (5oz) baby sweetcorn, halved
   if large
4 tbsp freshly chopped coriander
grated zest of ½ lime, plus 4 lime
   wedges to serve

1 Heat the oil in a large frying pan or wok over a medium heat. Add the onion and fry for 5 minutes or until it begins to soften. Add the chicken and cook for a further 5 minutes or until golden brown, then add the curry paste and fry for another minute to warm the spices through and release the flavours.

2 Pour in the hot stock and tomatoes, then simmer for 5 minutes. Add the sugarsnap peas and sweetcorn and cook for a further minute or so until the chicken is cooked through. Divide the soup among four warmed bowls, sprinkle with the coriander and lime zest, and serve with lime wedges to squeeze over the soup.

# Spring Vegetables in Chicken Broth

Preparation Time 15 minutes • Cooking Time 15 minutes • Serves 4 • Per Serving 312 calories, 10g fat (of which 4g saturates), 36g carbohydrate, 1g salt • Easy

1 tbsp olive oil
4 shallots, chopped
1 fennel bulb, chopped
1 leek, trimmed and chopped
5 small carrots, chopped
1.1 litres (2 pints) hot chicken stock
  (see page 266)
2 courgettes, chopped
1 bunch of asparagus, chopped
2 × 400g cans cannellini beans,
  drained and rinsed
50g (2oz) Gruyère or Parmesan
  shavings to serve

1 Heat the oil in a large pan. Add the shallots, fennel, leek and carrots and fry for 5 minutes or until they start to soften.

2 Add the hot stock, cover and bring to the boil. Add the courgettes, asparagus and beans, then reduce the heat and simmer for 5–6 minutes until the vegetables are tender. Ladle into bowls and sprinkle with a little cheese.

# Cock-a-Leekie Soup

Preparation Time 30–40 minutes • Cooking Time 1 hour 20 minutes • Serves 8 • Per Serving 280 calories, 4g fat (of which 1g saturates), 40g carbohydrate, 0.2g salt • Easy

1.4kg (3lb) oven-ready chicken
2 onions, roughly chopped
2 carrots, roughly chopped
2 celery sticks, roughly chopped
1 bay leaf
25g (1oz) butter
900g (2lb) leeks, trimmed and
   sliced
125g (4oz) ready-to-eat dried
   prunes, sliced
salt and ground black pepper
freshly chopped parsley to serve

**FOR THE DUMPLINGS**
125g (4oz) self-raising flour
a pinch of salt
50g (2oz) shredded suet
2 tbsp freshly chopped parsley
2 tbsp freshly chopped thyme

**1** Put the chicken into a pan in which it fits quite snugly, then add the chopped vegetables, bay leaf and chicken giblets (if available). Pour in 1.7 litres (3 pints) water and bring to the boil, then reduce the heat, cover and simmer gently for 1 hour.

**2** Meanwhile, melt the butter in a large pan. Add the leeks and fry gently for 10 minutes or until softened.

**3** Remove the chicken from the pan and leave until cool enough to handle. Strain the stock and put to one side. Strip the chicken from the bones and shred roughly. Add to the stock with the prunes and softened leeks.

**4** To make the dumplings, sift the flour and salt into a bowl. Stir in the suet, herbs and about 5 tbsp water to make a fairly firm dough. Lightly shape the dough into 2.5cm (1in) balls. Bring the soup just to the boil and season well. Reduce the heat, add the dumplings and cover the pan with a lid. Simmer for about 15–20 minutes until the dumplings are light and fluffy. Serve the soup sprinkled with chopped parsley.

 COOK'S TIP
*Make the stock a day ahead, if possible, then cool overnight. The following day, remove any fat from the surface.*

# Hot and Sour Soup

★

Preparation Time 20 minutes • Cooking Time about 35 minutes • Serves 4 • Per Serving 255 calories, 10g fat
(of which 1g saturates), 19g carbohydrate, 0.7g salt • **Dairy Free** • **Easy**

1 tbsp vegetable oil
2 chicken breasts, about 300g
   (11oz), or the same quantity of
   tofu, cut into strips
5cm (2in) piece fresh root ginger,
   peeled and grated
4 spring onions, finely sliced
1–2 tbsp Thai red curry paste
75g (3oz) long-grain wild rice
1.1 litres (2 pints) hot weak chicken
   (see page 266) or vegetable stock
200g (7oz) mangetouts, sliced
juice of 1 lime
4 tbsp freshly chopped coriander
   to garnish

**1** Heat the oil in a deep pan. Add
the chicken or tofu and cook over
a medium heat for 5 minutes or
until browned. Add the ginger and
spring onions and cook for a further
2–3 minutes. Stir in the curry paste
and cook for 1–2 minutes to warm
the spices.

**2** Add the rice and stir to coat in the
curry paste. Pour the hot stock or
boiling water into the pan, stir once
and bring to the boil. Reduce the
heat, cover the pan and simmer
for 20 minutes.

**3** Add the mangetouts and cook
for a further 5 minutes or until the
rice is cooked. Just before serving,
squeeze in the lime juice and stir
to mix.

**4** To serve, ladle into warmed bowls
and sprinkle with the coriander.

# Chicken and Chestnut Soup

Preparation Time 5 minutes • Cooking Time 45 minutes • Serves 4 • Per Serving 330 calories, 10g fat (of which 5g saturates), 52g carbohydrate, 0.2g salt • Gluten Free • Easy

25g (1oz) butter or margarine
1 large onion, chopped
225g (8oz) Brussels sprouts
900ml (1½ pints) chicken stock
   made from leftover carcass and
   any leftover chicken meat (see
   page 266)
400g can whole chestnuts, drained
2 tsp freshly chopped thyme or
   1 tsp dried thyme
salt and ground black pepper
chicken stock or milk to finish
fresh thyme sprigs to garnish

1 Melt the butter in a large heavy-based pan. Add the onion and fry gently for 5 minutes until softened.

2 Trim the sprouts and cut a cross in the base of each one. Add to the onion, then cover the pan with a lid and cook gently for 5 minutes, shaking the pan frequently.

3 Pour in the stock and bring to the boil, then add the remaining ingredients, with salt and pepper to taste. Reduce the heat, cover the pan and simmer for 30 minutes or until the vegetables are tender.

4 Leave the soup to cool a little, then transfer the soup in batches in a blender or food processor and whiz until smooth. Put back into the rinsed-out pan and reheat gently, then thin down with either stock or milk, according to taste.

5 Taste and adjust the seasoning. To serve, ladle into warmed bowls and garnish with thyme sprigs.

 COOK'S TIP
*Serve for an informal family lunch with hot garlic bread, wholemeal toast, cheese on toast or hot sausage rolls.*

 COOK'S TIP
**Grilled Garlic Bread**
*Preheat the grill. Cut 1 large crusty loaf into 2cm (¾in) thick slices. Put 175g (6oz) cubed butter and 3 crushed garlic cloves into a small pan and heat gently until the butter has melted. Season with salt and pepper. Dip a bunch of stiff-stemmed thyme sprigs into the melted butter and brush one side of each slice of bread. Put the slices, buttered side down, on the grill rack. Cook for 1–2 minutes until crisp and golden. Brush the uppermost sides with the remaining butter, turn over and cook the other side. Serve immediately.*

# Chicken, Ham and Spinach Broth

Preparation Time 10 minutes, plus soaking • Cooking Time 16–20 minutes • Serves 4 • Per Serving 244 calories, 6g fat (of which 3g saturates), 32.5g carbohydrate, 1.7g salt • Gluten Free • Easy

125g (4oz) green or yellow split peas, soaked overnight in double their volume of cold water
25g (1oz) butter
225g (8oz) onions, chopped
1 tbsp ground coriander
40g (1½ oz) pearl barley
2 litres (3½ pints) ham or chicken stock (see page 266)
1 bouquet garni (see Cook's Tip)
225g (8oz) potatoes, cut into chunks
400g (14oz) carrots, cut into chunks
150g (5oz) each cooked chicken and ham, cut into chunks
150g (5oz) baby spinach leaves
salt and ground black pepper
fresh coriander sprigs to garnish
50g (2oz) finely grated Parmesan to serve (optional)

1 Drain the split peas, put into a pan and cover with cold water. Bring to the boil, then reduce the heat and simmer for 10 minutes. Drain the peas and discard the liquid.

2 Meanwhile, melt the butter in a pan. Add the onions and cook for 5 minutes or until soft but not coloured. Add the ground coriander and cook for 30 seconds.

3 Add the split peas, pearl barley, stock and bouquet garni to the pan. Bring to the boil, then reduce the heat and simmer for 40 minutes or until the peas and barley are tender. Add the potatoes and cook for 5 minutes, then add the carrots and cook for 5–10 minutes. Season to taste with salt and pepper.

4 Add the chicken, ham and spinach to the pan and bring back to the boil, then reduce the heat and simmer for 2–3 minutes. Ladle into warmed bowls, garnish with coriander sprigs, season with pepper and serve with grated Parmesan, if you like.

★ COOK'S TIP
*To make a bouquet garni, tie together a sprig each of thyme and parsley with 1 bay leaf and 1 celery stick.*

# Salads and
# Light Bites ★

# Chicken, Avocado and Peanut Salad

Preparation Time 15 minutes, plus chilling • Serves 4 • Per Serving 335 calories, 28g fat (of which 4g saturates), 2g carbohydrate, 0.1g salt • Gluten Free • Dairy Free • Easy

2 roast chicken breasts, about
    250g (9oz) total weight, skinned
    and sliced
75g (3oz) watercress
2 tbsp cider vinegar
1 tsp English ready-made mustard
5 tbsp groundnut oil
1 large ripe avocado, halved,
    stoned, peeled and thickly sliced
50g (2oz) roasted salted peanuts,
    roughly chopped
salt and ground black pepper

1 Arrange the sliced chicken on top of the watercress, cover with clingfilm and chill until ready to serve.

2 Put the vinegar, mustard and oil into a bowl, season with salt and pepper and whisk together. Add the avocado and gently toss in the dressing, making sure each slice of avocado is well coated.

3 Just before serving, spoon the avocado and dressing over the chicken and watercress. Sprinkle with the chopped peanuts and serve immediately.

# Quick Chicken and Gruyère Salad

Preparation Time 15 minutes, plus chilling • Serves 8 • Per Serving 507 calories, 40g fat (of which 9g saturates),
7g carbohydrate, 0.7g salt • Gluten Free • Easy

900g–1kg (2–2¼lb) cooked, boned
chicken, skinned and cut into
bite-size pieces
4 celery sticks, thinly sliced
125g (4oz) Gruyère or Emmenthal
cheese, coarsely grated
2 firm red apples, halved, cored
and roughly chopped
125g (4oz) seedless black grapes,
halved
200ml (7fl oz) olive oil
2 tbsp white wine vinegar
4 tbsp soured cream
4 tbsp mayonnaise
4 tbsp freshly chopped parsley
75g (3oz) toasted pecan nuts or
walnuts
salt and ground black pepper
chopped coriander and rocket
to serve

1 Put the chicken, celery, cheese,
apples and grapes into a large bowl.
Add all the other ingredients and
toss well.

2 Adjust the seasoning, cover
and leave to chill in the fridge for at
least 10–15 minutes. Serve with
chopped coriander scattered over
the top and rocket.

★ COOK'S TIPS
● *Any strongly flavoured cheese can
be used for this recipe. You could try
crumbled Danish blue or blue Stilton.*
● *The whole salad can be completed the
day before and kept covered in the fridge
until required. Stir well before serving.*

# Tarragon Chicken and Bean Salad

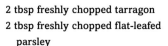

Preparation Time 15–20 minutes • Serves 4 • Per Serving 697 calories, 56g fat (of which 10g saturates), 18g carbohydrate, 1.6g salt • Easy

2 tbsp freshly chopped tarragon

2 tbsp freshly chopped flat-leafed parsley

1 tbsp olive oil

2 tbsp crème fraîche

200ml (7fl oz) mayonnaise

juice of ½ lemon

450g (1lb) cooked chicken, cut into bite-size pieces

400g can cannellini beans, rinsed and drained

50g (2oz) sunblush or sun-dried tomatoes

salt and ground black pepper

finely sliced spring onion to garnish

**FOR THE SHALLOT DRESSING**

2 tbsp sunflower oil

1 tsp walnut oil

2 tsp red wine vinegar

1 small shallot, very finely chopped

a pinch of caster sugar

1 Put the herbs into a food processor and add the olive oil. Whiz until the herbs are chopped. Add the crème fraîche, mayonnaise and lemon juice to the processor and season with salt and pepper. Whiz until well combined. (Alternatively, chop the herbs by hand, mix with the olive oil, then beat in the crème fraîche, mayonnaise, lemon juice and seasoning.) Toss the chicken with the herb dressing in a large bowl and put to one side.

2 To make the shallot dressing, whisk the ingredients together in a small bowl and season.

3 Tip the cannellini beans into a bowl, toss with the shallot dressing and season well. Arrange the cannellini beans in a serving dish. Roughly chop the tomatoes. Top the beans with the dressed chicken and tomatoes and garnish with finely sliced spring onion.

★ TRY SOMETHING DIFFERENT

● *Use 400g can mixed beans, chickpeas or red kidney beans instead of the cannellini beans.*

● *Replace the chicken with cooked turkey, cut into bite-size pieces.*

# Chicken Caesar Salad

Preparation Time 15–20 minutes • Cooking Time 12 minutes • Serves 4 • Per Serving 498 calories, 31g fat (of which 9g saturates), 7g carbohydrate, 1.4g salt • Easy

2 tbsp olive oil

1 garlic clove, crushed

2 thick slices country-style bread, cubed

6 tbsp freshly grated Parmesan

1 cos lettuce, chilled and cut into bite-size pieces

700g (1½lb) cooked chicken breast, sliced

**FOR THE DRESSING**

4 tbsp mayonnaise

2 tbsp lemon juice

1 tsp Dijon mustard

2 anchovy fillets, very finely chopped

salt and ground black pepper

1 Preheat the oven to 180°C (160°C fan oven) mark 4. Put the oil, garlic and bread cubes into a bowl and toss well. Tip on to a baking sheet and cook in the oven for 10 minutes, turning halfway through.

2 Sprinkle the Parmesan over the croûtons and cook for 2 minutes or until the cheese has melted and the bread is golden.

3 Put all the dressing ingredients into a bowl, season with salt and pepper and mix.

4 Put the lettuce and sliced chicken into a bowl, pour the dressing over and toss. Top with the cheese croûtons.

# Cheese Coleslaw with Roast Chicken

Preparation Time 15 minutes • Serves 4 • Per Serving 270 calories, 23g fat (of which 7g saturates), 8g carbohydrate, 0.6g salt • Gluten Free • Easy

1 baby white cabbage, thinly shredded
4 spring onions, finely chopped
1 large carrot, finely shredded
75g (3oz) mature Cheddar, grated
6 tbsp mayonnaise
ground black pepper
cress to garnish
sliced roast chicken to serve

1 Put the white cabbage, spring onions, carrot, cheese and mayonnaise into a large bowl and season with pepper.

2 Divide the coleslaw among four small bowls or plates and snip some cress over them. Serve with slices of roast chicken.

★ TRY SOMETHING DIFFERENT
● *Use either Gruyère or Emmenthal instead of Cheddar.*
● *Add freshly chopped chives or parsley.*
● *Sprinkle with 1 tbsp mixed seeds just before serving.*

# Chargrilled Chicken Waldorf

Preparation Time 10 minutes • Cooking Time 16–20 minutes • Serves 4 • Per Serving 702 calories, 61g fat (of which 14g saturates), 10g carbohydrate, 1.9g salt • Gluten Free • Easy

125g (4oz) walnuts
olive oil to brush
2 skinless chicken breasts, about
    125g (4oz) each
100g (3½oz) salad leaves
125g (4oz) black seedless grapes
2 crisp, red apples, such as
    Braeburn, cored and thinly sliced
4 celery sticks, sliced into
    matchsticks
175g (6oz) Roquefort cheese, thinly
    sliced
150ml (¼ pint) mayonnaise
salt and ground black pepper
freshly chopped chives to garnish
    (optional)

1 Put the walnuts into a dry pan and toast over a medium-high heat, tossing regularly, for 2–3 minutes until golden brown. Set aside. Brush a griddle or frying pan with a little oil and put over a medium heat. Season the chicken with salt and pepper and cook for 8–10 minutes on each side or until cooked through. Put to one side.

2 Toss the salad leaves, grapes, apples, celery, walnuts and about two-thirds of the Roquefort together in a large bowl. Thickly slice the chicken and arrange on four plates with some salad.

3 Crumble the remaining cheese into the mayonnaise and mix well. Spoon 2 tbsp mayonnaise on to each plate, or serve separately, and garnish with chopped chives, if you like.

# Zesty Orange, Chicken and Tarragon Salad

Preparation Time 15 minutes, plus chilling • Serves 4 • Per Serving 252 calories, 8g fat (of which 2g saturates), 20g carbohydrate, 0.5g salt • Gluten Free • Dairy Free • Easy

50g (2oz) pecan nuts or walnuts
350g (12oz) smoked chicken or
    cooked chicken breast, skinned
    and cut into long strips
2 oranges
2 small chicory heads

**FOR THE DRESSING**
grated zest and juice of 2 oranges
2 tbsp white wine vinegar
1 tsp caster sugar
5 tbsp olive oil
3 tbsp freshly chopped tarragon
1 large egg yolk
salt and ground black pepper

**1** Put the nuts into a dry pan and toast over a medium-high heat, tossing regularly, for 2–3 minutes until golden brown. Chop roughly.

**2** Whisk all the dressing ingredients together in a small bowl. Put the chicken strips into another bowl, spoon over the dressing, cover and chill for at least 1 hour.

**3** Use a sharp knife to remove the peel and pith from the oranges, then cut into slices.

**4** Put a layer of chicory into a large flat salad bowl, add the orange slices, then spoon the chicken and dressing over. Sprinkle the toasted nuts over the top and serve.

★ COOK'S TIPS
*Instant flavour ideas for chicken*
● *Snip bacon into a frying pan, cook until crisp and golden, then stir into warm, boiled new potatoes with shredded roast chicken and mustard mayonnaise. Serve with green salad.*
● *Roast a chicken with lots of tarragon, peppers, whole garlic cloves and olive oil. Serve with couscous, into which you've stirred the roasting juices.*
● *Pan-fry chicken breasts that have been marinating in olive oil with rosemary, thyme and crushed garlic. Serve with a fresh tomato sauce made by whizzing together ripe tomatoes, olive oil, basil and seasoning.*
● *Pan-fry chicken breasts in butter and put to one side. Add flaked almonds and pitted fresh cherries to the pan, toss over a high heat for 1–2 minutes and serve with the cooked chicken.*

# Warm Chicken Liver Salad

★

Preparation Time 20 minutes • Cooking Time 8–10 minutes • Serves 4 • Per Serving 236 calories, 15g fat
(of which 3g saturates), 3g carbohydrate, 0.8g salt • Gluten Free • Dairy Free • Easy

450g (1lb) chicken livers
1–2 tbsp balsamic vinegar
1 tsp Dijon mustard
3 tbsp olive oil
50g (2oz) streaky bacon rashers,
 rind removed, cut into small,
 neat pieces (lardons)
50g (2oz) sun-dried tomatoes or
 roasted red peppers, cut into
 thin strips
½ curly endive, about 175g (6oz)
100g (3½oz) rocket
1 bunch of spring onions, sliced
salt and ground black pepper

1 Drain the chicken livers on kitchen paper, then trim and cut into pieces.

2 To make the dressing, put the vinegar, mustard, 2 tbsp oil and salt and pepper into a small bowl. Whisk together and put to one side.

3 Fry the lardons in a non-stick frying pan until beginning to brown, stirring from time to time. Add the tomatoes or red peppers and heat through for 1 minute. Add the remaining oil and the chicken livers and stir-fry over a high heat for about 2–3 minutes until the livers are just pink in the centre.

4 Meanwhile, toss the endive, rocket and spring onions with the dressing in a large bowl. Divide among four plates, arrange the warm livers and bacon on top and serve at once.

# Chicken with Bulgur Wheat Salad

★

Preparation Time 20 minutes, plus marinating • Cooking Time 30 minutes • Serves 4 • Per Serving 429 calories, 12g fat (of which 1g saturates), 45g carbohydrate, 0.2g salt • Dairy Free • Easy

grated zest and juice of 1 lemon
4 skinless chicken breasts,
   about 125g (4oz) each, slashed
   several times
1 tbsp ground coriander
2 tsp olive oil

**FOR THE SALAD**
225g (8oz) bulgur wheat
6 tomatoes, chopped
½ cucumber, chopped
4 spring onions, chopped
50g (2oz) dried dates, chopped
50g (2oz) almonds, chopped
3 tbsp freshly chopped flat-leafed
   parsley
3 tbsp freshly chopped mint
salt and ground black pepper

1 Put half the lemon zest and juice into a bowl, then add the chicken breasts, coriander and 1 tsp oil. Toss well to mix. Leave to marinate while you prepare the salad. Preheat the grill to high.

2 To make the salad, cook the bulgur wheat for 10 minutes or according to the pack instructions. Put into a bowl, add the remaining salad ingredients and season well with salt and pepper. Add the remaining lemon zest, juice and oil and stir well.

3 Grill the chicken for 10 minutes on each side or until cooked through – the juices should run clear when the meat is pierced with a skewer. Slice the chicken and serve with the salad.

# Basil and Lemon Chicken

★

Preparation Time 15 minutes, plus marinating • Serves 4 • Per Serving 331 calories, 25g fat (of which 5g saturates), 2g carbohydrate, 1.3g salt • Gluten Free • Dairy Free • Easy

grated zest of 1 lemon, plus 4 tbsp
    lemon juice
1 tsp caster sugar
1 tsp Dijon mustard
175ml (6fl oz) lemon-infused oil
4 tbsp freshly chopped basil
2 × 210g packs roast chicken
250g (9oz) baby leaf spinach
55g pack crisp bacon, broken into
    small pieces
salt and ground black pepper

1 Put the lemon zest and juice, sugar, mustard and oil into a small bowl and season with salt and pepper. Whisk together until thoroughly combined, then add the basil.

2 Remove any bones from the roast chicken, leave the skin attached and slice into four or eight pieces. Arrange the sliced chicken in a dish and pour the dressing over, then cover and leave to marinate for at least 15 minutes.

3 Just before serving, lift the chicken from the dressing and put to one side.

4 Put the spinach into a large bowl, pour the dressing over and toss together. Arrange the chicken on top of the spinach and sprinkle the bacon over the top. Serve at once.

# Coronation Chicken

Preparation Time 20 minutes • Cooking Time about 50 minutes • Serves 6 • Per Serving 425 calories, 26g fat (of which 4g saturates), 14g carbohydrate, 0.6g salt • **Easy**

1 tbsp vegetable oil
1 onion, chopped
1 tbsp ground coriander
1 tbsp ground cumin
1½ tsp ground turmeric
1½ tsp paprika
150ml (¼ pint) dry white wine
500ml (18fl oz) chicken stock
   (see page 266)
6 boneless, skinless chicken breasts
   or thighs
2 bay leaves
2 fresh thyme sprigs
2 fresh parsley sprigs
salt and ground black pepper
3–4 tbsp freshly chopped flat-leafed
   parsley to garnish
mixed leaf salad and French bread
   to serve

**FOR THE DRESSING**
150ml (¼ pint) mayonnaise
5 tbsp natural yogurt
2 tbsp Mango Chutney
   (see page 282)
125g (4oz) ready-to-eat dried
   apricots, chopped
juice of ½ lemon

**1** Heat the oil in a large heavy-based pan. Add the onion and fry for about 5–10 minutes until softened and golden. Add the spices and cook, stirring, for 1–2 minutes.

**2** Pour in the wine, bring to the boil and let it bubble for 5 minutes to reduce right down. Add the stock and bring to the boil again.

**3** Season the chicken with salt and pepper, then add to the pan with the bay leaves and herb sprigs. Cover and bring to the boil. Reduce the heat to low and poach the chicken for 25 minutes or until cooked through. Cool quickly by plunging the base of the pan into a sink of cold water, replacing the water as it warms up.

**4** Meanwhile, to make the dressing, mix the mayonnaise, yogurt and mango chutney in a bowl. Drain the cooled stock from the chicken and whisk 200ml (7fl oz) into the mayonnaise mixture. Add the apricots and lemon juice and season well.

**5** Slice the chicken into strips, then stir into the curried mayonnaise. Cover and chill until required. Sprinkle chopped parsley over the top and serve with a mixed leaf salad and French bread.

# Easy Chicken Salad

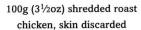

Preparation Time 10 minutes • Serves 1 • Per Serving 323 calories, 18g fat (of which 5g saturates), 17g carbohydrate, 0.9g salt • Gluten Free • Dairy Free • Easy

100g (3½oz) shredded roast
   chicken, skin discarded
1 carrot, chopped
1 celery stick, chopped
¼ cucumber, chopped
a handful of ripe cherry tomatoes,
   chopped
1 tbsp Hummus (see Cook's Tip,
   page 15)
¼ lemon to serve

1 Put the chicken into a shallow bowl. Add the carrot, celery, cucumber and cherry tomatoes.

2 Top with the hummus and serve with lemon for squeezing over the salad.

★ TRY SOMETHING DIFFERENT
● *For an even more nutritious salad, add a few pumpkin seeds or sunflower seeds, or a handful of sprouted seeds such as alfalfa, or chopped watercress.*
● *For extra bite, add a little finely chopped red chilli; for extra sweetness, add some strips of red pepper.*
● *For extra flavour, add some chopped coriander or torn basil leaves.*

# Orange and Chicken Salad

Preparation Time 15 minutes • Cooking Time 10 minutes • Serves 4 • Per Serving 252 calories, 8g fat (of which 2g saturates), 20g carbohydrate, 0.5g salt • Gluten Free • Dairy Free • Easy

50g (2oz) cashew nuts
zest and juice of 2 oranges
2 tbsp marmalade
1 tbsp honey
1 tbsp oyster sauce
400g (14oz) roast chicken, shredded
a handful of chopped raw
    vegetables, such as cucumber,
    carrot, red and yellow pepper
    and Chinese leaves

1 Put the cashew nuts into a dry frying pan over a medium-high heat and cook for 2–3 minutes, tossing regularly, until golden brown. Tip into a large serving bowl.

2 To make the dressing, put the orange zest and juice into the frying pan with the marmalade, honey and oyster sauce. Bring to the boil, stirring, then simmer for about 2–3 minutes until slightly thickened.

3 Add the roast chicken to the serving bowl with the chopped raw vegetables. Pour the dressing over the salad, toss everything together and serve immediately.

★ COOK'S TIP
*Toasting the cashew nuts in a dry frying pan before adding them to the salad brings out their flavour, giving them an intense, nutty taste and a wonderful golden colour.*

# Quick Caribbean Chicken Salad

Preparation Time 10 minutes • Cooking Time 20 minutes • Serves 4 • Per Serving 543 calories, 33g fat (of which 6g saturates), 25g carbohydrate, 0.7g salt • Gluten Free • Dairy Free • Easy

4 chicken breasts, with skin, about 125g (4oz) each
4 tsp jerk seasoning
450g (1lb) Jersey Royal potatoes
100ml (3½fl oz) mayonnaise
2 tbsp wholegrain mustard
2 tbsp vegetable oil
1 red onion, cut into thin wedges
125g (4oz) brown-cap mushrooms, halved
225g (8oz) young spinach leaves
3 tbsp freshly chopped chives
lemon juice to taste
salt and ground black pepper

1 Preheat the grill to high. Season the chicken breasts with salt and pepper and rub with jerk seasoning. Grill the chicken breasts for about 5 minutes on each side or until cooked through. Put to one side.

2 Meanwhile, cook the potatoes in lightly salted boiling water for about 10 minutes or until tender. Drain, cool a little, then cut into chunks. Mix the mayonnaise and mustard together, then add to the potatoes, stir and put to one side.

3 Heat the oil in a large frying pan, add the onion and fry for 5 minutes. Add the mushrooms and cook for a further 2 minutes, then season with salt and pepper.

4 Combine the potato and mushroom mixtures in a bowl and add the spinach. Toss with the chives, add the lemon juice and season with salt and pepper. Cut the chicken into thick slices on the diagonal and serve with the salad.

# Spring Chicken Salad with Sweet Chilli Sauce

Preparation Time 15 minutes, plus soaking • Cooking Time 10 minutes • Serves 4 • Per Serving 307 calories, 15g fat (of which 3g saturates), 8g carbohydrate, 0.2g salt • Gluten Free • Dairy Free • Easy

2 tbsp groundnut oil, plus extra
   to oil
4 boneless, skinless chicken
   breasts, each cut into four strips
1 tbsp Cajun seasoning (see
   Cook's Tip)
salt and ground black pepper

**FOR THE SALAD**
175g (6oz) small young carrots, cut
   into thin matchsticks
125g (4oz) cucumber, halved
   lengthways, seeded and cut into
   matchsticks
6 spring onions, cut into
   matchsticks
10 radishes, sliced
50g (2oz) bean sprouts, rinsed
   and dried
50g (2oz) unsalted peanuts, roughly
   chopped
1 large red chilli, seeded and finely
   chopped (see Cook's Tips,
   page 10)
2 tsp sesame oil
Thai chilli dipping sauce to drizzle

1 Soak eight bamboo skewers in cold water for 20 minutes. Oil a baking sheet.

2 Preheat the grill. Toss the chicken strips in the Cajun seasoning, then season with salt and pepper and brush with the groundnut oil. Thread on to the soaked skewers.

3 Place the skewered chicken strips on the prepared baking sheet and cook under the hot grill for about 3–4 minutes on each side until cooked through.

4 Place all the salad vegetables, peanuts and red chilli in a bowl, toss with the sesame oil and season well with salt and pepper.

5 Divide the vegetables among four serving plates, top with the warm chicken skewers and drizzle with the chilli sauce. Serve immediately.

★ COOK'S TIP
*Cajun seasoning is a spice and herb mixture, which includes chilli, cumin, cayenne and oregano.*

# Warm Chicken Salad with Quick Hollandaise

Preparation Time 15 minutes • Cooking Time about 20 minutes • Serves 4 • Per Serving 411 calories, 34g fat (of which 19g saturates), 2g carbohydrate, 0.8g salt • Gluten Free • Easy

1 tbsp white wine vinegar
1 tbsp lemon juice
1 tbsp olive oil
3 chicken breasts, with skin, about
 125g (4oz) each
150g (5oz) asparagus tips, trimmed
2 large egg yolks
125g (4oz) unsalted butter, melted
200g (7oz) baby salad leaves
 with herbs
salt and ground black pepper
lemon wedges to serve

1 Put the vinegar and lemon juice into a small pan over a medium heat. Bring to the boil, then lower the heat and simmer to reduce by half. Leave to cool slightly.

2 Heat a griddle until hot and brush with the oil. Put the chicken on a board, cover with clingfilm and gently flatten with a rolling pin. Remove the clingfilm, season with salt and pepper and griddle for about 8 minutes on each side or until cooked through. Keep warm.

3 Bring a large pan of lightly salted water to the boil. Cook the asparagus for 2–3 minutes until tender. Drain and keep warm.

4 Meanwhile, put the yolks in a blender and whiz for a few seconds until thickened. With the blender running, pour the reduced vinegar mixture slowly on to the eggs, then gradually add the melted butter – the mixture will start to thicken. If it's too thick, blend in a little hot water to loosen.

5 Cut the chicken into slices and divide among four plates with the asparagus and salad leaves. Serve with the hollandaise for drizzling and lemon wedges to squeeze over.

# Warm Lentil, Chicken and Broccoli Salad

★

**Preparation Time** 20 minutes • **Cooking Time** 25 minutes • **Serves 4** • **Per Serving** 332 calories, 16g fat (of which 3g saturates), 22g carbohydrate, 1.6g salt • **Gluten Free** • **Dairy Free** • **Easy**

125g (4oz) Puy lentils
225g (8oz) broccoli, chopped
1 large garlic clove, crushed
1 tsp English mustard powder
2 tbsp balsamic vinegar
4 tbsp olive oil
1 red pepper, seeded and sliced
   into rings
350g (12oz) smoked chicken breast,
   shredded
salt

**1** Put the lentils into a pan and cover generously with boiling water. Cook for 15 minutes or until tender, or according to the pack instructions. Blanch the broccoli in a pan of boiling water for 2 minutes. Drain, refresh under cold water and put to one side.

**2** Put the garlic into a bowl and use a wooden spoon to combine it with a pinch of salt until creamy, then whisk in the mustard, vinegar and 3 tbsp oil. Put to one side.

**3** Heat the remaining oil in a frying pan, add the red pepper and cook for 5 minutes or until softened.

**4** Add the chicken and broccoli and stir-fry for 1–2 minutes. Stir in the lentils and dressing and serve warm.

★ TRY SOMETHING DIFFERENT
● *Use smoked turkey or duck instead of smoked chicken.*
● *For extra flavour, add 2 fresh rosemary sprigs and 2 bay leaves when cooking the lentils, discarding them when you drain the lentils.*

# Chicken and Salsa Verde Crostini

Preparation Time 20 minutes, plus chilling • Cooking Time 2 minutes • Makes 15 • Per Serving 208 calories, 9g fat (of which 1g saturates), 24g carbohydrate, 1.7g salt • Dairy Free • Easy

50g (2oz) walnuts
1 loaf walnut bread, cut into
    15 × 1cm (½in) slices
2 tbsp olive oil
1 tbsp sea salt flakes
175g (6oz) cooked chicken breast,
    thinly sliced
125g (4oz) sun-dried tomatoes in
    oil, drained and thinly sliced
fresh flat-leafed parsley leaves to
    garnish

**FOR THE SALSA VERDE**
3 tbsp each freshly chopped
    coriander, mint and basil
1 garlic clove, roughly chopped
2 tbsp Dijon mustard
3 anchovy fillets
1 tbsp capers
50ml (2fl oz) olive oil
juice of ½ lemon

1 Put the walnuts into a dry pan and toast over a medium-high heat, tossing regularly, for 2–3 minutes until golden brown. Chop finely and put to one side.

2 Put all the salsa verde ingredients into a food processor or blender and whiz until smooth. (Alternatively, use a pestle and mortar.) Cover and chill.

3 Preheat the grill to high. Put the bread on a baking sheet, brush with the oil and sprinkle with sea salt flakes. Grill for 1 minute on each side or until lightly toasted.

4 To serve, put two or three chicken slices on each crostini base, top with a spoonful of salsa verde and slices of sun-dried tomato, then garnish with a sprinkling of walnuts and flat-leafed parsley.

# Chunky Pâté with Port and Green Peppercorns

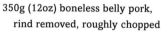

Preparation Time 25 minutes, plus setting • Cooking Time about 1½ hours, plus cooling • Serves 8 •
Per Serving 344 calories, 22g fat (of which 8g saturates), 3g carbohydrate, 0.7g salt • Dairy Free • A Little Effort

350g (12oz) boneless belly pork,
   rind removed, roughly chopped
1 large skinless chicken breast,
   about 150g (5oz)
225g (8oz) chicken livers, trimmed
1 large duck breast, about 200g
   (7oz), skinned and chopped into
   small pieces
125g (4oz) rindless streaky bacon
   rashers, diced
3 tbsp port or brandy
1 tbsp freshly chopped rosemary
2 tbsp green peppercorns
salt and ground black pepper
crusty bread to serve

**TO FINISH**
a few bay leaves
2 tsp powdered gelatine
150ml (¼ pint) white port or sherry

1 Preheat the oven to 170°C (150°C fan oven) mark 3. Coarsely mince the belly pork in a food processor, retaining some small chunks. Mince the chicken breast in the processor, then mince the chicken livers.

2 Mix all the meats together in a large bowl with the port or brandy, 1 tsp salt, some pepper, the chopped rosemary and green peppercorns.

3 Pack the mixture into a 1.1 litre (2 pint) terrine and stand in a roasting tin containing 2.5cm (1in) boiling water. Cover with foil and cook in the oven for 1 hour.

4 Remove the foil and arrange a few bay leaves on top of the pâté. Cook for a further 30 minutes or until the juices run clear when the pâté is pierced in the centre with a sharp knife or skewer.

5 Drain the meat juices into a small bowl and leave to cool. Skim off any fat, then sprinkle over the gelatine and leave until softened. Stand the bowl in a pan of gently simmering water until the gelatine has dissolved. Stir in the port or sherry. Make up to 450ml (¾ pint) with water, if necessary.

6 Pour the jellied liquid over the pâté and chill until set. Store the pâté in the fridge for up to two days. Serve with crusty bread.

# Chorizo Chicken

Preparation Time 10 minutes • Cooking Time 10 minutes • Makes 24 • Per Canapé 19 calories, 1g fat (of which trace saturates), trace carbohydrate, 0.3g salt • Gluten Free • Dairy Free • Easy

200g (7oz) boneless, skinless
    chicken breast, cut into
    24 bite-size pieces
100g (3½oz) thinly sliced chorizo
24 fresh sage leaves
12 cherry tomatoes, halved

1 Preheat the oven to 190°C (170°C fan oven) mark 5. Spread the chicken pieces on a board and top each with a slice of chorizo, a sage leaf and half a cherry tomato. Secure with cocktail sticks.

2 Place on a baking sheet and cook for 10 minutes or until the chicken is cooked through. Transfer the chicken and chorizo skewers to a serving plate and serve warm.

★ TRY SOMETHING DIFFERENT
*Replace the chicken with 24 large raw peeled prawns and cook for 5 minutes until the prawns turn pink.*

# Easy Wrap

⭐

**Preparation Time** 10 minutes • **Serves 4** • **Per Serving** 269 calories, 16g fat (of which 3g saturates), 17g carbohydrate, 1.7g salt • **Easy**

1 tsp salt
1 tsp ground black pepper
2 cooked chicken breasts, about
    125g (4oz) each, cut into
    bite-size pieces
1 carrot, grated
1 avocado, halved, stoned, peeled
    and chopped
a small handful of rocket
juice of ½ lemon
3 tbsp mayonnaise
4 flour tortillas

**1** Mix the salt with the pepper in a large bowl. Add the chicken, carrot, avocado and rocket and mix well.

**2** In a separate bowl, mix the lemon juice with the mayonnaise, then spread over the tortillas. Divide the chicken mixture among the tortillas, then roll up and serve in napkins, if you like.

# Lime and Chilli Chicken Goujons

Preparation Time 15 minutes • Cooking Time 20 minutes • Serves 4 • Per Serving 339 calories, 22g fat (of which 4g saturates), 22g carbohydrate, 1.9g salt • **Easy**

300g (11oz) boneless, skinless
   chicken thighs
50g (2oz) fresh breadcrumbs
50g (2oz) plain flour
2 tsp dried chilli flakes
grated zest of 1 lime
1 medium egg, beaten
2 tbsp sunflower oil
salt and ground black pepper
lime wedges to serve

**FOR THE DIP**
6 tbsp natural yogurt
6 tbsp mayonnaise
¼ cucumber, halved lengthways,
   seeded and finely diced
25g (1oz) freshly chopped coriander
juice of 1 lime

1 Put all the dip ingredients into a bowl. Season to taste with salt and pepper and mix well, then chill.

2 Cut the chicken into strips. Put the breadcrumbs into a bowl with the flour, chilli flakes, lime zest and 1 tsp salt and mix well. Pour the egg on to a plate. Dip the chicken in egg, then coat in the breadcrumbs.

3 Heat the oil in a frying pan over a medium heat. Fry the chicken in batches for 7–10 minutes until golden and cooked through. Keep each batch warm while cooking the remainder. Transfer to a serving plate, sprinkle with a little salt, then serve with the dip and lime wedges.

⭐ COOK'S TIP
*For a lower-fat version, bake the goujons in the oven. Preheat the oven to 200°C (180°C fan oven) mark 6. Put the goujons on a lightly oiled baking sheet, brush each with a little oil and bake for 12–15 minutes until golden and cooked through.*

# Tangy Chicken Bites

Preparation Time 10 minutes • Makes 48 • Per Canapé 43 calories, 2g fat (of which 1g saturates), 4g carbohydrate, 0.1g salt • Easy

2 × 50g packs mini croustades
about 275g (10oz) fruity chutney, such as mango (see page 282)
2 roast chicken breasts, skinned, torn into small pieces
250g carton crème fraîche
a few fresh thyme sprigs

1 Place the croustades on a board. Spoon about ½ tsp chutney into each one. Top with a few shreds of chicken, a small dollop of crème fraîche and a few thyme sprigs. Transfer the croustades to a large serving plate and serve immediately.

★ TRY SOMETHING DIFFERENT
● *Use mini poppadoms instead of croustades.*
● *Replace the fruity chutney with cranberry sauce.*
● *Instead of roast chicken, use turkey.*

# Throw-it-all-together Chicken Salad

Preparation Time 10 minutes • Serves 4 • Per Serving 215 calories, 9g fat (of which 2g saturates), 9g carbohydrate, 0.6g salt • Gluten Free • Dairy Free • Easy

4 chargrilled chicken breasts, about
   125g (4oz) each, torn into strips
2 carrots, cut into strips
½ cucumber, halved lengthways,
   seeded and cut into ribbons
a handful of fresh coriander leaves,
   roughly chopped
½ head of Chinese leaves,
   shredded
4 handfuls of watercress
4 spring onions, shredded

**FOR THE DRESSING**
5 tbsp peanut butter
2 tbsp sweet chilli sauce
juice of 1 lime
salt and ground black pepper

1 Put the chicken strips and all the salad ingredients into a large salad bowl.

2 To make the dressing, put the peanut butter, chilli sauce and lime juice into a small bowl and mix well. Season with salt and pepper. If the dressing is too thick to pour, add 2–3 tbsp cold water, a tablespoon at a time, to thin it – use just enough water to make the dressing the correct consistency.

3 Drizzle the dressing over the salad, toss gently together and serve.

★ COOK'S TIPS
● *Use leftover roast chicken or beef, or cooked ham.*
● *Use washed and prepared salad instead of the Chinese leaves and watercress, if you like.*

# Oven-cooked Dishes

# Glazed Chicken with Roast Lemons

★

Preparation Time 20 minutes • Cooking Time 1 hour 5 minutes • Serves 6 • Per Serving 340 calories, 5g fat
(of which 2g saturates), 44g carbohydrate, 0.2g salt • Gluten Free • Dairy Free • Easy

**250g (9oz) caster sugar**
**3 large lemons**
**6 chicken breast quarters**
  **(breast and wing) about 300g**
  **(11oz) each**
**salt and ground black pepper**
**fresh flat-leafed parsley to garnish**

**1** Put the caster sugar and 600ml (1 pint) water into a large pan and dissolve slowly over a low heat. Bring to the boil and bubble for 2 minutes. Pierce the skin of the lemons with a fork and put them into the sugar syrup, then cover and cook for 20 minutes.

**2** Remove the lemons, bubble the liquid over a medium heat for about 12 minutes or until reduced by half and a golden caramel colour. Cut the lemons in half.

**3** Preheat the oven to 230°C (210°C fan oven) mark 8. Season the chicken quarters with salt and pepper and put, skin side down, into a roasting tin that is just large enough to hold them in a single layer with the lemon halves. Pour the sugar syrup over the chicken and lemons.

**4** Put the roasting tin on the middle shelf of the oven and cook for about 30–35 minutes or until cooked through. Baste the chicken from time to time and turn it over halfway through cooking.

**5** Serve each piece of chicken with a lemon half (eat the flesh only, not the skin) and garnish with parsley.

# Tarragon Chicken with Fennel

Preparation Time 10 minutes • Cooking Time 45–55 minutes • Serves 4 • Per Serving 334 calories, 26g fat (of which 15g saturates), 3g carbohydrate, 0.5g salt • Easy

1 tbsp olive oil
4 chicken thighs
1 onion, finely chopped
1 fennel bulb, finely chopped
juice of ½ lemon
200ml (7fl oz) hot chicken stock
(see page 266)
200ml (7fl oz) crème fraîche
1 small bunch of tarragon,
roughly chopped
salt and ground black pepper
new potatoes and broccoli to serve

1 Preheat the oven to 200°C (180°C fan oven) mark 6. Heat the oil in a large flameproof casserole over a medium-high heat. Add the chicken thighs and fry for 5 minutes or until browned, then remove and put them to one side to keep warm.

2 Add the onion to the casserole and fry for 5 minutes, then add the fennel and cook for 5–10 minutes until softened.

3 Add the lemon juice to the casserole, followed by the hot stock. Bring to a simmer and cook until the sauce is reduced by half.

4 Stir in the crème fraîche and put the chicken back into the casserole. Stir once to mix, then cover and cook in the oven for 25–30 minutes. Stir the tarragon into the sauce, season with salt and pepper and serve with potatoes and broccoli.

# Chicken in Lemon Vinaigrette

Preparation Time 10 minutes • Cooking Time 40 minutes • Serves 6 • Per Serving 353 calories, 21g fat (of which 4g saturates), 10g carbohydrate, 0.3g salt • Gluten Free • Dairy Free • Easy

2 lemons
175g (6oz) shallots or onions, sliced
2 tbsp balsamic vinegar
2 tbsp sherry vinegar
4 tbsp clear honey
150ml (¼ pint) olive oil
6 boneless chicken breasts or
   12 boneless thighs, with skin
salt and ground black pepper
mashed potatoes to serve

1 Preheat the oven to 200°C (180°C fan oven) mark 6. Grate the zest and squeeze the juice of one lemon, then put to one side. Thinly slice the remaining lemon, then scatter the lemon slices and shallots or onions in a small roasting tin – it should be just large enough to hold the chicken comfortably in a single layer.

2 Whisk  the lemon zest and juice, vinegars, honey and oil together in a bowl. Put the chicken into the roasting tin, season with salt and pepper and pour the lemon vinaigrette over it.

3 Roast in the oven, basting regularly, for about 35 minutes or until the chicken is golden and cooked through. Transfer the chicken to a serving dish and keep warm in a low oven. Put the roasting tin, with the juices, over a medium heat on the hob. Bring to the boil and bubble for 2–3 minutes until syrupy. Spoon over the chicken and serve with mashed potatoes.

 GET AHEAD

**To prepare ahead** *Complete the recipe to the end of step 2, then cool, cover and chill for up to one day in a non-metallic dish. Transfer the chicken to a roasting tin before cooking.*
**To use** *Complete the recipe.*

# Chicken with Peperonata Sauce

★

Preparation Time 20 minutes • Cooking Time 40 minutes • Serves 4 • Per Serving 383 calories, 17g fat (of which 4g saturates), 20g carbohydrate. 0.4g salt • Gluten Free • Dairy Free • Easy

2 onions, sliced
4 chicken legs
100ml (3½fl oz) dry white wine
  or chicken stock (see page 266)
1 tbsp vegetable oil
ground black pepper
new potatoes to serve

**FOR THE PEPERONATA
  SAUCE**
2 large red peppers, halved
  and seeded
2 large yellow peppers, halved
  and seeded
1 tbsp extra virgin olive oil
1 fat garlic clove, roughly chopped

1 Preheat the oven to 200°C (180°C fan oven) mark 6. Spread the onions over the base of a large roasting tin. Put the chicken legs on top, then pour 50ml (2fl oz) wine, water or stock over the chicken. Roast the chicken in the oven for 15 minutes, then brush with the vegetable oil to crisp up the skin, and season with pepper. Pour in the remaining wine if the onions are browning too quickly and roast for a further 25 minutes.

2 Meanwhile, make the peperonata sauce. Using a swivel-headed peeler, peel the peppers as thoroughly as you can. Apply as little pressure as possible, so you don't take off too much flesh under the skin. Cut the peppers into thin strips and put them into a frying pan with the olive oil. Cook over a medium heat for 5–7 minutes until they are just soft. Add the garlic for the last 2 minutes of cooking. Stir the peperonata sauce into the onions and cook for a further 5 minutes.

3 To serve, divide the chicken among four warm plates and serve with a spoonful of the peperonata sauce and steamed new potatoes.

# Chicken Rarebit

Preparation Time 5 minutes • Cooking Time 25 minutes • Serves 4 • Per Serving 446 calories, 24g fat (of which 14g saturates), 9g carbohydrate, 1.3g salt • Easy

4 large chicken breasts, with skin, about 150g (5oz) each
15g (½oz) butter
1 tbsp plain flour
75ml (2½fl oz) full-fat milk
175g (6oz) Gruyère cheese, grated
25g (1oz) fresh white breadcrumbs
1 tsp ready-made English mustard
2 fat garlic cloves, crushed
1 medium egg yolk
boiled new potatoes and green beans to serve

1 Preheat the oven to 200°C (180°C fan oven) mark 6. Put the chicken in a single layer into an ovenproof dish and roast in the oven for 20 minutes or until cooked through.

2 Meanwhile, melt the butter in a pan over a low heat, then add the flour and stir for 1 minute. Gradually add the milk and stir to make a smooth sauce.

3 Add the cheese, breadcrumbs, mustard and garlic to the sauce and cook for 1 minute. Cool briefly, then beat in the egg yolk. Preheat the grill to medium-high.

4 Discard the skin from the cooked chicken and beat any juices from the dish into the cheese mixture. Spread the paste evenly over each chicken breast, then grill for 2–3 minutes until golden. Serve with new potatoes and green beans.

# Herb Chicken with Roasted Vegetables

Preparation Time 15 minutes, plus marinating • Cooking Time 40 minutes • Serves 4 • Per Serving 453 calories, 29g fat (of which 7g saturates), 10g carbohydrate, 0.3g salt • Gluten Free • Dairy Free • Easy

2 garlic cloves
25g (1oz) fresh basil
25g (1oz) fresh mint
8 fresh lemon thyme sprigs
4 tbsp olive oil
4 whole chicken legs (drumsticks and thighs)
1 small aubergine, chopped
200g (7oz) baby plum tomatoes
2 red peppers, seeded and chopped
2 courgettes, sliced
juice of 1 lemon
salt and ground black pepper
green salad to serve

1 Whiz the garlic, two-thirds of the basil and mint and the leaves from 4 lemon thyme sprigs in a food processor, adding half the oil gradually until the mixture forms a thick paste. (Alternatively, use a pestle and mortar.)

2 Rub the paste over the chicken legs, then put into a bowl. Cover, then chill and leave to marinate for at least 30 minutes.

3 Preheat the oven to 200°C (180° fan oven) mark 6. Put the aubergine, plum tomatoes, red peppers and courgettes into a large roasting tin with the remaining oil and season with salt and pepper. Toss to coat. Add the chicken and roast in the oven for 30–40 minutes until the vegetables are tender and the chicken is cooked through.

4 Squeeze the lemon juice over the chicken and sprinkle over the remaining herbs. Serve immediately with a crisp green salad.

# Oven-baked Chicken with Garlic Potatoes

Preparation Time 10 minutes • Cooking Time 1½ hours • Serves 6 • Per Serving 376 calories, 16g fat (of which 5g saturates), 32g carbohydrate, 1.2g salt • Easy

2 medium baking potatoes, thinly sliced
a little freshly grated nutmeg
600ml (1 pint) white sauce (use a ready-made sauce or make your own, see Cook's Tip)
½ × 390g can fried onions
250g (9oz) frozen peas
450g (1lb) cooked chicken, shredded
20g pack garlic butter, sliced
a little butter to grease
salt and ground black pepper
Granary bread to serve (optional)

1 Preheat the oven to 180°C (160°C fan oven) mark 4. Layer half the potatoes over the base of a 2.4 litre (4¼ pint) shallow ovenproof dish and season with the nutmeg, salt and pepper. Pour the white sauce over and shake the dish, so that the sauce settles through the gaps in the potatoes.

2 Spread half the onions on top, then scatter on half the peas. Arrange the shredded chicken on top, then add the remaining peas and onions. Finish with the remaining potatoes, arranged in an even layer, and dot with garlic butter. Season with salt and pepper.

3 Cover tightly with buttered foil and cook in the oven for 1 hour. Increase the heat to 200°C (180°C fan oven) mark 6, remove the foil and cook for 20–30 minutes until the potatoes are golden and tender. Serve with Granary bread, if you like, to mop up the juices.

 COOK'S TIP

**White Sauce**
*To make 600ml (1 pint) white sauce, melt 25g (1oz) butter in a pan, then stir in 25g (1oz) plain flour. Cook, stirring constantly, for 1 minute. Remove from the heat and gradually pour in 600ml (1 pint) milk, beating after each addition. Return to the heat and cook, stirring, until the sauce has thickened and is velvety and smooth. Season with salt, pepper and freshly grated nutmeg.*

# Orange and Herb Chicken

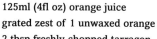

Preparation Time 10 minutes • Cooking Time 20–30 minutes • Serves 4 • Per Serving 180 calories, 4g fat (of which 1g saturates), 5g carbohydrate, 0.2g salt • Gluten Free • Dairy Free • Easy

125ml (4fl oz) orange juice

grated zest of 1 unwaxed orange

2 tbsp freshly chopped tarragon

2 tbsp freshly chopped flat-leafed parsley

1 tbsp olive oil

1 garlic clove, crushed

4 skinless chicken breasts, about 125g (4oz) each

4 small orange wedges

salt and ground black pepper

brown rice and watercress to serve

1 Preheat the oven to 200°C (180°C fan oven) mark 6. Whisk the orange juice, orange zest, herbs, oil and garlic together in a large bowl. Season with salt and pepper.

2 Slash the chicken breasts several times and put into a large ovenproof dish. Pour the marinade over them and top each chicken breast with an orange wedge.

3 Cook in the oven for 20–30 minutes until cooked through. Serve with brown rice and watercress.

# Saffron Risotto with Lemon Chicken

★

Preparation Time 20 minutes • Cooking Time 30 minutes • Serves 4 • Per Serving 830 calories, 44g fat (of which 15g saturates), 50g carbohydrate, 0.9g salt • Gluten Free • Easy

zest and juice of 1 lemon
a small handful of fresh parsley
25g (1oz) blanched almonds
1 tbsp dried thyme
1 garlic clove
75ml (2½fl oz) olive oil
450ml (¾ pint) chicken stock
   (see page 266)
4 boneless chicken breasts
   with skin
50g (2oz) butter
225g (8oz) onions, finely chopped
a small pinch of saffron threads
225g (8oz) risotto (arborio) rice
125ml (4fl oz) white wine
50g (2oz) freshly grated Parmesan
salt and ground black pepper
fresh thyme leaves and lemon
   wedges to garnish

1 Preheat the oven to 200°C (180°C fan oven) mark 6. Whiz the lemon zest, parsley, almonds, thyme and garlic in a food processor for a few seconds, then slowly add the oil and whiz until combined. Season with salt and pepper. Heat the stock in a pan to a steady low simmer.

2 Spread the lemon and herb mixture under the skin of the chicken. Put the chicken into a roasting tin, brush with 25g (1oz) melted butter and pour the lemon juice over it. Cook in the oven for 25 minutes, basting occasionally.

3 Meanwhile, make the risotto. Heat the remaining butter in a pan. Add the onions and fry until soft. Stir in the saffron and rice. Add the wine to the rice. Gradually add the hot stock, a ladleful at a time, stirring with each addition and allowing it to be absorbed before adding more. This will take about 25 minutes. Take the pan off the heat and stir in the Parmesan. Serve with the chicken, pouring any juices from the roasting tin over it. Garnish with thyme leaves and lemon wedges.

# Simple Chicken

Preparation Time 5 minutes • Cooking Time about 25 minutes  • Serves 4 • Per Serving 350 calories, 27g fat
(of which 12g saturates), 0g carbohydrate, 0.3g salt • Gluten Free • Easy

**6 fresh tarragon sprigs**
**4 chicken breasts with skin**
**50g (2oz) butter, diced**
**4 garlic cloves, sliced**
**a little olive oil**
**ground black pepper**
**1 large glass of dry white wine**
**lightly crushed new potatoes and**
    **broad beans to serve**

1 Preheat the oven to 220°C (200°C fan oven) mark 7. Push a sprig of tarragon under the skin of each chicken breast. Place skin side up, into a small roasting tin just large enough to hold the chicken comfortably.

2 Dot half the butter over the top, scatter the garlic over, drizzle with a little oil and season with pepper. Roast in the oven for 20–25 minutes until cooked through. The juices should run clear when the chicken is pierced with a skewer. Baste the chicken with the juices halfway through cooking.

3 Remove the chicken from the roasting tin and keep warm. Put the tin over a high heat and whisk in the wine, scraping up the sticky bits from the base of the tin.

4 While still bubbling, whisk the remaining butter into the sauce. Stir in the remaining tarragon. Divide the chicken among four plates and serve with the warm juices and lightly crushed new potatoes and broad beans.

# Spicy One-pan Chicken

Preparation Time 5 minutes • Cooking Time 1 hour  • Serves 1 • Per Serving 410 calories, 10g fat (of which 2g saturates), 51g carbohydrate, 0.9g salt • Dairy Free • Easy

½ **red or white onion, sliced**
½ **yellow pepper, sliced**
**1 small parsnip, chopped**
**1 potato, cut into chunks**
**227g can chopped tomatoes**
**1 tbsp medium curry paste**
**150ml (¼ pint) hot vegetable stock**
**1 chicken leg**
**a little vegetable oil**
**salt and ground black pepper**

**1** Preheat the oven to 200°C (180°C fan oven) mark 6. Put all the vegetables into a roasting tin or ovenproof dish, together with the tomatoes. Stir the curry paste into the hot stock and pour over the vegetables. Season with pepper and cook in the oven for 30 minutes.

**2** Put the chicken leg on top of the vegetables and drizzle with a little oil, then season with salt and pepper. Put the casserole back into the oven for 30 minutes until the vegetables are tender and the chicken is cooked and the juices run clear when the thickest part of the leg is pierced with a skewer.

# Stuffed Chicken with Potatoes and Tomatoes

Preparation Time 10 minutes • Cooking Time 30–40 minutes • Serves 4 • Per Serving 488 calories, 25g fat (of which 11g saturates), 32g carbohydrate, 0.5g salt • Gluten Free • Easy

3 large potatoes, sliced
3 tbsp olive oil
4 chicken breasts with skin
125g (4oz) cream cheese with herbs
300g (11oz) cherry tomatoes on the vine
salt and ground black pepper

1 Preheat the oven to 220°C (200°C fan oven) mark 7. Line a roasting tin with baking parchment and spread the potatoes in the tin. Drizzle with 2 tbsp oil, toss to coat, then roast for 20–25 minutes.

2 Using a sharp knife, ease the skin away from each chicken breast, leaving it attached along one side. Spread the cream cheese across each breast, then smooth the skin back over it. Brush the skin with the remaining oil and season with salt and pepper.

3 Heat a non-stick frying pan over a medium heat until hot, add the chicken, skin side down, and fry for 5 minutes until browned. Carefully turn over and fry for 5 minutes on the other side.

4 Reduce the temperature to 190°C (170°C fan oven) mark 5. Put the chicken on top of the potatoes, add the tomatoes and roast for a further 10–12 minutes or until the chicken is cooked through. Serve with the potatoes and tomatoes.

# Sticky Chicken Thighs

⭐

Preparation Time 5 minutes • Cooking Time 20 minutes • Serves 4 • Per Serving 218 calories, 12g fat (of which 3g saturates), 5g carbohydrate, 0.4g salt • **Gluten Free** • **Dairy Free** • **Easy**

1 garlic clove, crushed
1 tbsp clear honey
1 tbsp Thai sweet chilli sauce
4 chicken thighs
rice (optional) and green salad
  to serve

1 Preheat the oven to 200°C (180°C fan oven) mark 6. Put the garlic into a bowl with the honey and chilli sauce and stir to mix. Add the chicken thighs and toss to coat.

2 Put the chicken into a roasting tin and roast in the oven for 15–20 minutes until golden and cooked through and the juices run clear when the thighs are pierced with a skewer. Serve with rice, if you like, and a crisp green salad.

⭐ TRY SOMETHING DIFFERENT
● *Try this with sausages instead of the chicken, if you like.*
● *Italian Marinade*
*Mix 1 crushed garlic clove with 4 tbsp olive oil, the juice of 1 lemon and 1 tsp dried oregano. If you like, leave to marinate for 1–2 hours before cooking.*
● *Oriental Marinade*
*Mix together 2 tbsp soy sauce, 1 tsp demerara sugar, 2 tbsp dry sherry or apple juice, 1 tsp finely chopped fresh root ginger and 1 crushed garlic clove.*
● *Honey and Mustard Marinade*
*Mix together 2 tbsp grain mustard, 3 tbsp clear honey and the grated zest and juice of 1 lemon.*

# Stuffed Chicken Breasts

Preparation Time 5 minutes • Cooking Time 20 minutes • Serves 4 • Per Serving 297 calories, 13g fat (of which 7g saturates), trace carbohydrate, 1.4g salt • Gluten Free • Easy

vegetable oil to oil
150g (5oz) ball mozzarella
4 skinless chicken breasts, about
    125g (4oz) each
4 sage leaves
8 slices Parma ham
ground black pepper
new potatoes and spinach to serve

1 Preheat the oven to 200°C (180°C fan oven) mark 6. Lightly oil a baking sheet. Slice the mozzarella into eight, then put two slices on each chicken piece. Top each with a sage leaf.

2 Wrap each piece of chicken in two slices of Parma ham, covering the mozzarella. Season with pepper.

3 Put on the prepared baking sheet and cook in the oven for 20 minutes or until the chicken is cooked through. Serve with new potatoes and spinach.

★ COOK'S TIP
*Sage has a strong, pungent taste, so you need only a little to flavour the chicken. Don't be tempted to add more than just one leaf to each chicken breast or it will overpower the finished dish.*

# Peppered Chicken with Orange

Preparation Time 5 minutes • Cooking Time 25 minutes • Serves 6 • Per Serving 464 calories, 28g fat (of which 14g saturates), 2g carbohydrate, 0.7g salt • Easy

6 chicken breast fillets with skin
1 tbsp olive oil
125g (4oz) butter, chilled
125g (4oz) onions, finely chopped
2 tsp peppercorns in brine
200ml (7fl oz) brandy
450ml (¾ pint) chicken stock
   (see page 266)
pared zest and juice of 1 large
   orange
salt and ground black pepper
fresh flat-leafed parsley sprigs to
   garnish
freshly cooked potatoes of your
   choice to serve

1 Preheat the oven to 180°C (160°C fan oven) mark 4. Season the chicken with plenty of pepper.

2 Heat the oil in a non-stick frying pan. Add the chicken breasts and cook for about 5 minutes until golden. Put the chicken into an ovenproof dish and cook in the oven for about 20 minutes until done.

3 Meanwhile, heat 25g (1oz) butter in the pan. Add the onions and peppercorns and cook, stirring, for 10 minutes until golden and soft. Add the brandy and bubble to reduce by half. Add the stock, pared orange zest and juice and bubble again for about 7 minutes to reduce by half.

4 Dice the remaining butter and add a little at a time, whisking after each addition. Season with salt and pepper and keep warm.

5 Pour the sauce over the cooked chicken, garnish with parsley and serve with potatoes.

# Chicken and Mushroom Pies

Preparation Time 20 minutes, plus chilling • Cooking Time 55 minutes–1 hour 5 minutes • Serves 4
Per Serving 805 calories, 58g fat (of which 14g saturates), 49g carbohydrate, 1.2g salt • Easy

2 tbsp olive oil
1 leek, about 200g (7oz), trimmed
   and finely sliced
2–3 garlic cloves, crushed
350g (12oz) boneless, skinless
   chicken thighs, cut into 2.5cm
   (1in) cubes
200g (7oz) chestnut mushrooms,
   sliced
150ml (¼ pint) double cream
2 tbsp freshly chopped thyme
500g pack puff pastry, thawed if
   frozen
plain flour to dust
1 medium egg, beaten
salt and ground black pepper

1 Heat the oil in a pan. Add the leek and fry over a medium heat for 5 minutes. Add the garlic and cook for 1 minute. Add the chicken and continue to cook for 8–10 minutes. Add the mushrooms and cook for 5 minutes or until all the juices have disappeared.

2 Pour the cream into the pan and bring to the boil. Cook for 5 minutes to make a thick sauce. Add the thyme, then season well with salt and pepper. Tip into a bowl and leave to cool.

3 Roll out the pastry on a lightly floured surface until it measures 33 × 33cm (13 × 13in). Cut into four squares. Brush the edges with water and spoon the chicken mixture into the middle of each square. Bring each corner of the square up to the middle to make a parcel. Crimp the edges to seal, leaving a small hole in the middle. Brush the pies with beaten egg, put on a baking sheet and chill for 20 minutes.

4 Preheat the oven to 200°C (180°C fan oven) mark 6. Cook the pies for 30–40 minutes until golden.

⭐ TRY SOMETHING DIFFERENT
*For a vegetarian alternative, replace the chicken with 200g (7oz) cooked, peeled (or vacuum-packed) chestnuts, roughly chopped. Add another finely sliced leek and increase the quantity of mushrooms to 300g (11oz).*

# Chicken Kiev

★

Preparation Time 15 minutes, plus chilling • Cooking Time 45 minutes • Serves 6 • Per Serving 594 calories, 41g fat (of which 19g saturates), 20g carbohydrate, 1.2g salt • A Little Effort

175g (6oz) butter, softened
grated zest of ½ lemon
1 tbsp lemon juice
1 tbsp freshly chopped parsley
1 garlic clove, crushed
6 large boneless, skinless chicken
   breasts
25g (1oz) seasoned flour
1 medium egg, beaten
125g (4oz) fresh breadcrumbs
vegetable oil for deep-frying
salt and ground black pepper
potato wedges and peas to serve

1 Put the butter, lemon zest and juice, parsley, garlic and salt and pepper to taste into a bowl and beat well to combine. Alternatively, whiz in a food processor. Form into a roll, cover and chill for at least 1 hour.

2 Place the chicken breasts on a flat surface and, using a meat mallet or rolling pin, pound them to an even thickness. Cut the butter into six pieces and place one piece on the centre of each chicken breast. Roll up, folding the ends in to enclose the butter completely. Secure the rolls with wooden cocktail sticks.

3 Place the seasoned flour, beaten egg and breadcrumbs in three separate flat dishes. Coat each chicken roll with the flour, then turn them in the beaten egg and coat them with breadcrumbs, patting the crumbs firmly on to the chicken.

4 Place the rolls on a baking sheet, cover lightly with non-stick or greaseproof paper and chill in the fridge for 2 hours or until required, to allow the coating to dry.

5 Heat the oil in a deep-fryer to 160°C (test by frying a small cube of bread; it should brown in 60 seconds). Put two chicken rolls into a frying basket and lower into the oil. Fry for 15 minutes – the chicken is cooked when it is browned and firm when pressed with a fork. Do not pierce.

6 Remove the rolls from the fryer, drain on kitchen paper and keep them warm while you cook the remaining chicken. Remove the cocktail sticks before serving.

7 Serve with potato wedges and peas.

★ TRY SOMETHING DIFFERENT
**Spicy Chicken Kiev**
*To make the butter filling, sauté 1 finely chopped shallot with 2 tsp cayenne pepper in 1 tbsp butter until soft but not brown. Stir in 1 tbsp freshly chopped parsley. Combine with 175g (6oz) softened butter and season. Complete the recipe from step 2 as above.*

# Mediterranean Chicken

**Preparation Time** 5 minutes • **Cooking Time** 20 minutes • **Serves 4** • **Per Serving** 223 calories, 7g fat (of which 1g saturates), 3g carbohydrate, 0.2g salt  • **Gluten Free** • **Dairy Free** • **Easy**

1 red pepper, seeded and chopped
2 tbsp capers
2 tbsp freshly chopped rosemary
2 tbsp olive oil
4 skinless chicken breasts, about
   125g (4oz) each
salt and ground black pepper
rice or new potatoes to serve

**1** Preheat the oven to 200°C (180°C fan oven) mark 6. Put the red pepper into a bowl with the capers, rosemary and oil. Season with salt and pepper and mix well.

**2** Put the chicken breasts into an ovenproof dish and spoon the pepper mixture over the top. Cook in the oven for 15–20 minutes until the chicken is cooked through and the topping is hot. Serve with rice or new potatoes.

★ TRY SOMETHING DIFFERENT
*Use chopped black olives instead of the capers.*

# Chicken and Leek Filo Pie

★

Preparation Time 15 minutes • Cooking Time about 50 minutes • Serves 6 • Per Serving 331 calories, 18g fat
(of which 10g saturates), 27g carbohydrate, 0.4g salt • Easy

75g (3oz) unsalted butter
2 large leeks, trimmed and
   finely sliced
2 large carrots, finely chopped
1 tbsp plain flour
400ml (14fl oz) hot chicken stock
   (see page 266)
2 tsp Dijon mustard
3 tbsp double cream
350g (12oz) cooked chicken
   (leftovers are fine), cut into
   chunks
2 tbsp freshly chopped parsley
12 sheets filo pastry, thawed if
   frozen
salt and ground black pepper
green salad to serve

3 Melt the remaining butter in a
small pan. Unroll the filo pastry and
cover with a clean, damp teatowel.
Put a single sheet on a board and
brush with a little of the melted
butter. Roughly scrunch up the
pastry and put on top of the
chicken mixture. Continue with
the remaining filo until the top of
the pie is covered.

4 Cook the pie in the oven for
20–25 minutes until the filo is
golden and the chicken mixture is
bubbling. Serve with a green salad.

★ GET AHEAD
**To prepare ahead** *Complete the recipe*
*to the end of step 2, but allow the sauce*
*to cool completely before adding the*
*chicken. Chill for up to two days or freeze*
*for up to one month.*
**To use** *If frozen, thaw overnight at*
*cool room temperature, then complete*
*the recipe.*

1 Preheat the oven to 200°C (180°C
fan oven) mark 6. Melt 25g (1oz)
butter in a pan over a low heat. Add
the leeks and carrots and cook for
15 minutes or until softened but not
coloured. Stir in the flour and cook
for 1 minute. Gradually add the hot
stock, stirring constantly, until the
sauce is smooth, then simmer for
10 minutes.

2 Stir in the mustard and cream and
season with salt and pepper. Add
the cooked chicken and chopped
parsley and tip into a 1.7 litre
(3 pint) ovenproof dish.

# Easy Chicken and Ham Pie

Preparation Time 15 minutes • Cooking Time 30–35 minutes • Serves 6 • Per Serving 364 calories, 22g fat (of which 6g saturates), 17g carbohydrate, 1.1g salt • Easy

4 ready-roasted chicken breasts, shredded
100g (3½oz) cooked smoked ham, cubed
150ml (¼ pint) double cream
75ml (2½fl oz) chicken gravy
2 tbsp freshly chopped tarragon
1 tsp cornflour
½ tsp English mustard
250g (9oz) ready-rolled puff pastry
1 medium egg, beaten
ground black pepper

1 Preheat the oven to 200°C (180°C fan oven) mark 6. Put the chicken into a large bowl with the ham, then add the cream, gravy, tarragon, cornflour and mustard. Season with pepper and mix well.

2 Spoon into a shallow 1 litre (1¾ pint) baking dish. Unroll the puff pastry and position over the top of the dish to cover. Trim to fit the dish, then press the edges down lightly around the rim. Brush the egg over the pastry. Cook in the oven for 30–35 minutes until the pastry is golden and puffed up. Serve hot.

# Chicken and Artichoke Pie

⭐

Preparation Time 20 minutes • Cooking Time 45 minutes • Serves 4 • Per Serving 241 calories, 9g fat (of which 5g saturates), 7g carbohydrate, 0.2g salt • Easy

3 boneless, skinless chicken
   breasts, about 350g (12oz)
150ml (¼ pint) dry white wine
225g (8oz) reduced-fat cream
   cheese with garlic and herbs
400g can artichoke hearts, drained
   and quartered
4 sheets filo pastry, thawed
   if frozen
olive oil to brush
1 tsp sesame seeds
salt and ground black pepper

1 Preheat the oven to 200°C (180°C fan oven) mark 6. Put the chicken and wine into a pan and bring to the boil, then cover, reduce the heat and simmer for 10 minutes. Remove the chicken with a slotted spoon and put to one side. Add the cheese to the wine and mix until smooth. Bring to the boil, then reduce the heat and simmer until thickened.

2 Cut the chicken into bite-size pieces, then add to the sauce with the artichokes. Season and mix well.

3 Put the mixture into an ovenproof dish. Brush the pastry lightly with oil, scrunch slightly and put on top of the chicken. Sprinkle with sesame seeds, then cook in the oven for 30–35 minutes until crisp. Serve hot.

⭐ TRY SOMETHING DIFFERENT
*Replace the artichoke hearts with 225g (8oz) brown-cap mushrooms, cooked in a little water with some sea salt and pepper and lemon juice.*

# Chicken and Leek Pie

★

Preparation Time 15 minutes • Cooking Time 40–45 minutes • Serves 4 • Per Serving 591 calories, 23g fat (of which 15g saturates), 54g carbohydrate, 0.3g salt • Gluten Free • Easy

5 large potatoes, chopped into
   chunks
200g (7oz) crème fraîche
3 boneless chicken breasts, with
   skin, about 125g (4oz) each
3 large leeks, trimmed and chopped
   into chunks
about 10 fresh tarragon leaves,
   finely chopped
salt and ground black pepper

1 Preheat the oven to 200°C (180°C fan oven) mark 6. Put the potatoes into a pan of lightly salted cold water. Cover the pan and bring to the boil, then reduce the heat and simmer for 10–12 minutes until soft. Drain and put back into the pan. Add 1 tbsp crème fraîche, season with salt and pepper and mash well.

2 Meanwhile, heat a frying pan, add the chicken, skin side down, and fry gently for 5 minutes or until the skin is golden. Turn the chicken over and fry for 6–8 minutes. Remove the chicken from the pan and put on to a board. Tip the leeks into the pan and cook in the juices over a low heat for 5 minutes to soften.

3 Discard the chicken skin and cut the flesh into bite-size pieces (don't worry if it is not quite cooked through). Put the chicken back into the pan, stir in the remaining crème fraîche and heat for 2–3 minutes until bubbling. Stir in the tarragon and season with salt and pepper, then spoon into a 1.7 litre (3 pint) ovenproof dish and spread the mash on top.

4 Cook the pie in the oven for 20–25 minutes until golden and heated through. Serve hot.

★ TRY SOMETHING DIFFERENT

● *To use leftover chicken or turkey, don't fry the meat at step 2. Add it to the pan with the crème fraîche at step 3. Cook the leeks in 2 tsp olive oil.*

● *For a different flavour, make the mash with 2 large potatoes and a small celeriac, that has been peeled, cut into chunks and cooked with the potato.*

# Chicken Pot Pies

★

Preparation Time 45 minutes • Cooking Time about 1 hour • Serves 4 • Per Serving 610 calories, 34g fat
(of which 14g saturates), 47g carbohydrate, 1.2g salt • Easy

25g (1oz) butter
25g (1oz) plain flour, plus extra
   to dust
400ml (14fl oz) chicken stock
   (see page 266)
2 tbsp double cream
450g cooked chicken, shredded
100g (3½oz) each frozen peas and
   sweetcorn
2 tbsp freshly chopped parsley
275g (10oz) ready-made shortcrust
   pastry
plain flour to dust
1 medium egg, beaten

1 Melt the butter in a pan over a medium heat. Stir in the flour and cook for 1 minute, then remove from the heat and gradually blend in the stock. Cook over a gentle heat, stirring, until thickened. Simmer for 5 minutes, then add the cream and cook for 5 minutes.

2 Stir the chicken meat into the sauce with the peas, sweetcorn and parsley. Leave to cool a little.

3 Preheat the oven to 200°C (180°C fan oven) mark 6. Roll out the pastry on a lightly floured surface to 3mm (⅛in) thick. Use the top of a 300ml (½ pint) ovenproof basin as a guide and cut out four circles of pastry 2cm (¾in) larger than the diameter. Put to one side.

4 Divide the chicken mixture among four 300ml (½ pint) ovenproof basins. Dampen the edges of the pastry with water and use to top the basins, folding it over the edges. Cut a slit in the pastry to let out the steam and use the trimmings to decorate the pies, if you like. Brush with the beaten egg and bake in the oven for 30 minutes until golden on top and the filling is piping hot.

# Roasts

# Roast Chicken with Stuffing and Gravy

Preparation Time 30 minutes • Cooking Time about 1 hour 20 minutes, plus resting • Serves 5 • Per Serving 682 calories, 49g fat (of which 21g saturates), 17g carbohydrate, 1g salt • Easy

1.4kg (3lb) chicken
2 garlic cloves
1 onion, cut into wedges
2 tsp sea salt
2 tsp ground black pepper
4 fresh parsley sprigs
4 fresh tarragon sprigs
2 bay leaves
50g (2oz) butter, cut into cubes
salt and ground black pepper

**FOR THE STUFFING**
40g (1½oz) butter
1 small onion, chopped
1 garlic clove, crushed
75g (3oz) fresh white breadcrumbs
finely grated zest and juice of
   1 small lemon, halves reserved
   for the chicken
2 tbsp each freshly chopped
   flat-leafed parsley and tarragon
1 medium egg yolk

**FOR THE GRAVY**
200ml (7fl oz) white wine
1 tbsp Dijon mustard
450ml (¾ pint) hot chicken stock
   (see page 266)
25g (1oz) butter, mixed with 25g
   (1oz) plain flour (beurre manié,
   see Cook's Tip)

**1** Preheat the oven to 190°C (170°C fan oven) mark 5. To make the stuffing, melt the butter in a pan, add the onion and garlic and fry for 5–10 minutes until soft. Cool, then add the remaining ingredients, stirring in the egg yolk last. Season well with salt and pepper.

**2** Put the chicken on a board, breast upwards, then put the garlic, onion, reserved lemon halves and half the salt, pepper and herb sprigs into the body cavity.

**3** Lift the loose skin at the neck and fill the cavity with stuffing. Turn the bird on to its breast and pull the neck flap over the opening to cover the stuffing. Rest the wing tips across it and truss the chicken. Weigh the stuffed bird to calculate the cooking time, and allow 20 minutes per 450g (1lb), plus an extra 20 minutes.

**4** Put the chicken on a rack in a roasting tin. Season with the remaining salt and pepper, then top with the remaining herbs and the bay leaves. Dot with the butter and roast, basting halfway through, until cooked and the juices run clear when the thickest part of the thigh is pierced with a skewer.

**5** Put the chicken on a serving dish and cover with foil. Leave to rest while you make the gravy. Pour off all but about 3 tbsp fat from the tin, put the tin over a high heat, add the wine and boil for 2 minutes. Add the mustard and hot stock and bring back to the boil. Gradually whisk in knobs of the butter mixture until smooth, then season with salt and pepper. Carve the chicken and serve with the stuffing and gravy.

★ COOK'S TIP
*Beurre Manié*
*Beurre manié is a mixture of equal parts of softened butter and flour that has been kneaded together to form a paste. It is used to thicken sauces and stews and is whisked in towards the end of cooking, then boiled briefly to allow it to thicken.*

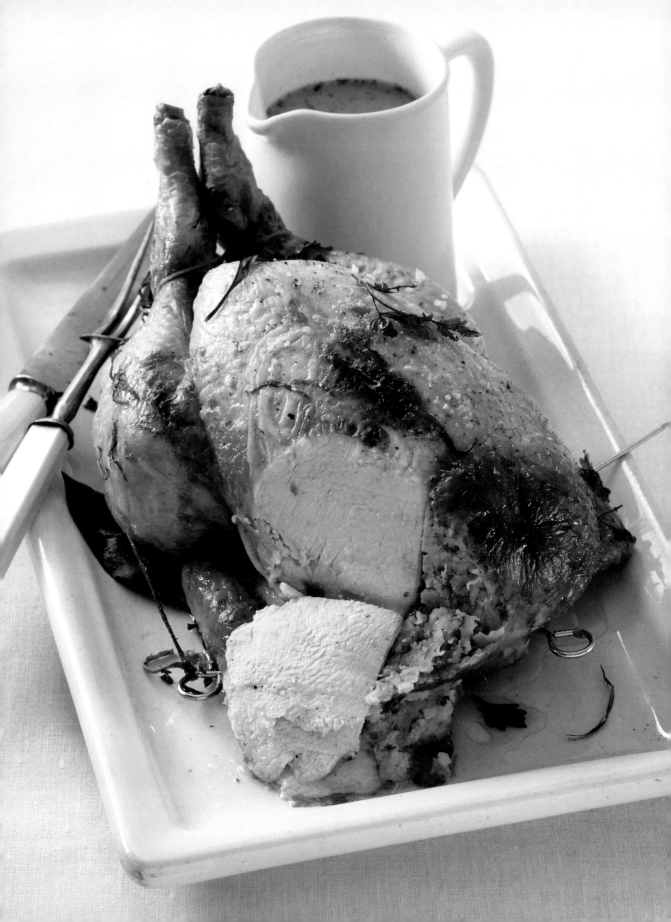

# Garlic and Rosemary Roast Chicken

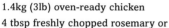

**Preparation Time** 10 minutes • **Cooking Time** about 1 hour 20 minutes, plus resting • **Serves 4–6** •
**Per Serving** 700–470 calories, 47–31g fat (of which 13–9g saturates), 18–12g carbohydrate, 2.3g salt • **Easy**

1.4kg (3lb) oven-ready chicken
4 tbsp freshly chopped rosemary or
  1 tbsp dried rosemary
450g (1lb) each red and yellow
  peppers, quartered and seeded
450g (1lb) courgettes, cut into
  wedges or halved lengthways
  if small
125g (4oz) pitted black olives
2 tbsp capers
2 garlic cloves
50ml (2fl oz) olive oil
125g (4oz) streaky bacon or
  pancetta
2 tsp cornflour
300ml (½ pint) white wine

300ml (½ pint) chicken stock
  (see page 266)
salt and ground black pepper
fresh flat-leafed parsley to garnish

**1** Preheat the oven to 200°C (180°C fan oven) mark 6. Fill the chicken cavity with half the rosemary.

**2** Put the peppers, courgettes, black olives, capers, garlic, oil and seasoning into a roasting tin. Cover the chicken with the remaining rosemary, streaky bacon or pancetta

and sit it on the vegetables. Season and cover the chicken with foil.

**3** Cook in the oven for 1¼ hours, removing the foil halfway through the cooking time until the chicken is cooked and the juices run clear when the thickest part of the thigh is pierced with a skewer.

**4** Put the chicken and vegetables on a warmed serving plate and cover with foil to keep warm. Leave the garlic in the roasting tin with the cooking juices.

**5** Mix the cornflour to a paste with 2 tbsp white wine. Add to the roasting tin with the remaining wine, the stock and seasoning, mashing the garlic into the liquid with a fork. Bring to the boil, stirring, then bubble for 5 minutes or until lightly thickened. Adjust the seasoning and serve with the chicken. Garnish with parsley.

★ TRY SOMETHING
DIFFERENT
*Make with chicken breasts: prepare peppers and courgettes as step 2; put with the olives, capers, garlic and oil into a roasting tin. Preheat the oven to 200°C (180°C fan oven) mark 6 and cook for 30–35 minutes. Add six chicken pieces. Snip the bacon and sprinkle it over the portions with the rosemary. Roast in the oven for 25–30 minutes. Remove the chicken and vegetables. Complete the gravy as steps 4 and 5.*

# Pesto Roast Chicken

★

Preparation Time 10 minutes • Cooking Time about 1 hour 25 minutes, plus resting • Serves 4 • Per Serving 715 calories, 58g fat (of which 14g saturates), 1g carbohydrate, 0.6g salt • Gluten Free • Easy

20g (¾oz) fresh basil, roughly
   chopped
25g (1oz) freshly grated Parmesan
50g (2oz) pinenuts
4 tbsp extra virgin olive oil
1.4kg (3lb) chicken
salt and ground black pepper
new or roast potatoes and green
   vegetables to serve

1 Preheat the oven to 200°C (180°C fan oven) mark 6. To make the pesto, put the basil, Parmesan, pinenuts and oil into a food processor and mix to a rough paste. (Alternatively, grind the ingredients using a pestle and mortar.) Season with salt and pepper.

2 Put the chicken into a roasting tin. Ease your fingers under the skin of the neck end to separate the breast skin from the flesh, then push about three-quarters of the pesto under the skin, using your hands to spread it evenly. Smear the remainder over the chicken legs. Season with pepper and roast in the oven for 1 hour 25 minutes or until the chicken is cooked and the juices run clear when the thickest part of the thigh is pierced with a skewer.

3 Put the chicken on a board, cover with foil and leave to rest for 15 minutes. Carve and serve with potatoes and green vegetables.

# Mediterranean Roast Chicken

Preparation Time 40 minutes • Cooking Time about 1½ hours • Serves 4 • Per Serving 843 calories, 58g fat (of which 26g saturates), 42g carbohydrate, 0.9g salt • Gluten Free • Easy

900g (2lb) floury potatoes, such as Maris Piper, peeled and cut into chunks
125g (4oz) butter, softened
4 tbsp freshly chopped sage leaves, stalks reserved, plus extra leaves
4 tbsp freshly chopped thyme, stalks reserved, plus extra sprigs
1.4kg (3lb) chicken
juice of 1 lemon, halves reserved
2 fennel bulbs, cut into wedges
1 red onion, cut into wedges
salt and ground black pepper

1 Preheat the oven to 190°C (170°C fan oven) mark 5. Put the potatoes into a large pan of lightly salted cold water and bring to the boil. Cook for 5 minutes.

2 Meanwhile, put the butter into a bowl and mix in the chopped sage and thyme. Season well.

3 Put the chicken on a board and push the lemon halves and herb stalks into the cavity. Ease your fingers under the skin of the neck end to separate the breast skin from the flesh, then push the herby butter up under the skin, reserving a little. Season well.

4 Put the chicken into a large roasting tin, pour the lemon juice over it, then top with the extra sage and thyme and reserved butter. Drain the potatoes and shake in a colander to roughen their edges. Put around the chicken with the fennel and red onion. Roast in the oven for 1 hour 20 minutes or until the juices run clear when the thickest part of the thigh is pierced with a skewer. Carve and serve with the vegetables.

# Spicy Roast Chicken with Red Peppers

Preparation Time 30 minutes • Cooking Time about 1½ hours • Serves 4 • Per Serving 787 calories, 49g fat (of which 11g saturates), 45g carbohydrate, 0.5g salt • Gluten Free • Dairy Free • Easy

900g (2lb) floury potatoes, such as Maris Piper, peeled and cut into chunks
2 tbsp sweet paprika
1 tbsp ground coriander
a large pinch of saffron threads, crushed
1 tsp each ground ginger and ground cinnamon
1 head of garlic, plus 2 crushed cloves
juice of ½ orange, plus 1 orange, cut into wedges
2 tbsp olive oil
1.4kg (3lb) chicken
1 small onion, halved
2 red peppers, seeded and cut into eighths
75g (3oz) pinenuts
salt and ground black pepper

1 Preheat the oven to 190°C (170°C fan oven) mark 5. Put the potatoes into a large pan of lightly salted cold water and bring to the boil. Cook for 5 minutes.

2 Meanwhile, put the paprika, coriander, saffron, ginger, cinnamon, 2 crushed garlic cloves, orange juice and oil into a bowl. Add ½ tsp each of salt and pepper and mix well. Put the chicken into a roasting tin and push the orange wedges and onion into the cavity. Season well, then rub the spice mix all over the chicken.

3 Drain the potatoes and shake in a colander to roughen their edges. Put around the chicken. Add the head of garlic and peppers and roast in the oven for 1 hour 20 minutes or until cooked.

4 About 10 minutes before the end of cooking, sprinkle the pinenuts over the chicken. Continue to cook until the juices run clear when the thickest part of the thigh is pierced with a skewer. Carve and serve with the vegetables.

# Devilled Roast Chicken

Preparation Time 10 minutes • Cooking Time 1¼ hours, plus resting • Serves 4 • Per Serving 580 calories, 33g fat (of which 19g saturates), 31g carbohydrate, 1.3g salt • A Little Effort

2 tbsp olive oil
125g (4oz) onions, roughly chopped
2 red peppers, deseeded and
    roughly chopped
2 garlic cloves, crushed
1 tbsp Worcestershire sauce
1 tbsp cider vinegar
1 tsp dried marjoram
1 tsp dried thyme
2 tbsp dark muscovado sugar
300ml (½ pint) lager
700g (1½lb) corn on the cob
400g can chickpeas, drained
    and rinsed

50g (2oz) butter, softened
2 tsp ground paprika
1.4kg (3lb) oven-ready chicken
salt

1 Preheat the oven to 200°C (180°C fan oven) mark 6. Heat the oil in a large roasting tin. Add the onions, peppers and garlic and fry, stirring, for 4–5 minutes until golden. Add the Worcestershire sauce, cider vinegar, marjoram, thyme, sugar and lager. Bring to the boil, reduce the heat and simmer for 5 minutes.

2 Cook the corn on the cob in a pan of lightly salted boiling water for 5–7 minutes, then strain, putting the cooking liquid to one side. Slice the corn on the cob thickly to remove the kernels. Add the corn and chickpeas to the roasting tin.

3 Mix together the butter, paprika and seasoning. Spread all over the chicken. Put the chicken into a large roasting tin, lying on one breast, and spoon over the corn mixture.

4 Cook for 1¼ hours until the juices run clear when the thickest part of the thigh is pierced with a skewer. After 20 minutes cooking, turn the chicken on to the other breast for 20 minutes, then on to its back for the remaining cooking time.

5 Put the chicken on a warmed plate and cover with foil. Pour off the excess fat and add 300ml (½ pint) reserved cooking liquid to the roasting tin. Bring the juices to the boil on the hob and bubble for 4–5 minutes. Adjust the seasoning and serve with the chicken.

★ TRY SOMETHING DIFFERENT
*Make with chicken breasts: complete steps 1 and 2. Spread six chicken pieces with flavoured butter and put into a roasting tin on top of the sauce and corn mixture. Preheat the oven to 200°C (180°C fan oven) mark 6 and bake for 20–25 minutes until tender. Complete the sauce as in step 5.*

# Roast Chicken with Lemon and Garlic

Preparation Time 5 minutes • Cooking Time 1 hour–1¼ hours, plus resting • Serves 4 • Per Serving 639 calories, 46g fat (of which 13g saturates), 0g carbohydrate, 0.6g salt • Easy

1 chicken, about 1.8kg (4lb)
25g (1oz) butter, softened
2 tbsp olive oil
1½ lemons, cut in half
1 small head of garlic, cut in half horizontally
salt and ground black pepper
potatoes and seasonal vegetables to serve

1 Preheat the oven to 220°C (200°C fan oven) mark 7. Put the chicken into a roasting tin just large enough to hold it comfortably. Spread the butter all over the chicken, then drizzle with the oil and season with salt and pepper.

2 Squeeze lemon juice over the chicken, then put one lemon half inside the chicken. Put the other halves and the garlic into the roasting tin.

3 Roast the chicken in the oven for 15 minutes, then turn the heat down to 190°C (170°C fan oven) mark 5 and roast for a further 45 minutes–1 hour until the juices run clear when the thickest part of the thigh is pierced with a skewer. While the bird is cooking, baste from time to time with the pan juices. Add a splash of water to the tin if the juices dry out.

4 Put the chicken on a warmed plate, cover with foil and leave for 15 minutes, so that the juices that have risen to the surface can soak back into the meat. This will make it more moist and easier to slice. Mash some of the garlic into the pan juices and serve the gravy with the chicken. Serve with potatoes and seasonal vegetables.

# Poussins with Pancetta, Artichoke and Potato Salad

Preparation Time 20 minutes, plus marinating • Cooking Time 1 hour 40 minutes, plus resting • Serves 6 •
Per Serving 442 calories, 27g fat (of which 8g saturates), 13g carbohydrate, 1.5g salt • Gluten Free • Dairy Free • Easy

grated zest of 1 lemon
5 large fresh rosemary sprigs,
   leaves stripped
4 tbsp white wine vinegar
150ml (¼ pint) fruity white wine
4 garlic cloves, crushed
3 tbsp freshly chopped oregano or
   a pinch of dried oregano
290g jar marinated artichokes,
   drained, oil reserved
3 poussins, about 450g (1lb) each
½ tsp cayenne pepper
450g (1lb) new potatoes, quartered
225g (8oz) pancetta, prosciutto or
   streaky bacon, roughly chopped
350g (12oz) peppery salad leaves,
   such as watercress, mustard leaf
   and rocket
salt and ground black pepper

1 Put the lemon zest and rosemary leaves into a large bowl with the vinegar, wine, garlic, oregano and 4 tbsp oil from the artichokes. Stir well. Using a fork, pierce the skin of the poussins in five or six places, then season well with black pepper and the cayenne pepper. Put the birds, breast side down, in the bowl and spoon the marinade over them. Cover and chill overnight.

2 Cook the potatoes in lightly salted boiling water for 2 minutes. Drain. Preheat the oven to 200°C (180°C fan oven) mark 6.

3 Lift the poussins from the marinade and place, breast side up, in a large roasting tin. Scatter the potatoes, pancetta and artichokes around them and pour the marinade over. Cook for 1½ hours, basting occasionally, or until golden and cooked through.

4 Cut each poussin in half lengthways and keep warm. Toss the salad leaves with about 5 tbsp warm cooking juices. Arrange the leaves on warmed plates, then top with the potatoes, pancetta, artichokes and poussins.

⭐ COOK'S TIP
*Use the oil drained from the artichokes to make a salad dressing.*

# Grills, Pan-fries, Stir-fries and Pasta

# Garlic and Thyme Chicken

Preparation Time 10 minutes • Cooking Time 10–15 minutes • Serves 4 • Per Serving 135 calories, 6g fat (of which 1g saturates), trace carbohydrate, 0.2g salt • Gluten Free • Dairy Free • Easy

2 garlic cloves, crushed
2 tbsp freshly chopped thyme
   leaves, plus extra sprigs to
   garnish
2 tbsp olive oil
4 chicken thighs
salt and ground black pepper

1 Preheat the barbecue or grill. Mix the garlic with the chopped thyme and oil in a large bowl. Season with salt and pepper.

2 Using a sharp knife, make two or three slits in each chicken thigh. Put the chicken into the bowl and toss to coat thoroughly. Barbecue or grill for 5–7 minutes on each side until golden and cooked through. Garnish with thyme sprigs.

# Chicken with Black-eye Beans and Greens

Preparation Time 5 minutes • Cooking Time 15 minutes • Serves 4 • Per Serving 491 calories, 26g fat (of which 4g saturates), 31g carbohydrate, 1.5g salt • Dairy Free • Gluten Free • Easy

2 tsp Jamaican jerk seasoning
4 skinless chicken breasts, about 125g (4oz) each
1kg (2¼lb) spring greens or cabbage, core removed and shredded
2 × 300g cans black-eye beans, drained and rinsed
8 tbsp olive oil
juice of 1¼ lemons
salt and ground black pepper

1 Preheat the grill. Rub the jerk seasoning into the chicken breasts and sprinkle with salt. Cook under the grill for 15 minutes or until cooked through, turning from time to time.

2 Cook the spring greens or cabbage in lightly salted boiling water until just tender – bringing the water back to the boil after adding the greens is usually enough to cook them. Drain and put back into the pan.

3 Add the beans and oil to the greens and season well with salt and pepper. Heat through and add the juice of 1 lemon.

4 To serve, slice the chicken and put on the bean mixture, then drizzle over the remaining lemon juice and serve immediately.

# Grilled Chicken Breasts with a Cheese and Herb Crust

Preparation Time 15 minutes • Cooking Time 15 minutes • Serves 4 • Per Serving 600 calories, 53g fat (of which 11g saturates), trace carbohydrate, 1.4g salt • Easy

125g (4oz) olive oil bread, such as ciabatta, roughly chopped
75g (3oz) Gruyère cheese, grated
4 skinless chicken breast fillets, about 450g (1lb)
4 tbsp garlic mayonnaise or hollandaise sauce, plus extra to serve
4 tsp olive oil
salt and ground black pepper
fresh flat-leafed parsley to garnish
tomato salad to serve

1 Preheat the grill. Whiz the bread in a food processor until fine crumbs form. Transfer to a bowl, stir in the grated cheese and season well with salt and pepper.

2 Coat each chicken breast with 1 tbsp garlic mayonnaise or hollandaise, then dip in the crumbs until coated. Put on a baking sheet and drizzle each chicken breast with 1 tsp oil.

3 Cook the chicken under the hot grill, as far away from the heat as possible, for about 5–6 minutes on each side or until cooked through.

4 Slice the chicken, or leave whole, garnish with parsley and serve with a tomato salad and garlic mayonnaise or hollandaise.

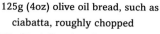 COOK'S TIP
*The crisp cheesy crumbs used for the crust keep the chicken breasts tender and moist as they cook under the grill.*

# Grilled Chicken with Pesto Butter

★

**Preparation Time** 10 minutes • **Cooking Time** 20–30 minutes • **Serves** 4 • **Per Serving** 340 calories, 23g fat (of which 12g saturates), trace carbohydrate, 0.6g salt • **Gluten Free** • **Easy**

**4 skinless chicken breast fillets**
**75g (3oz) butter, softened**
**3 tbsp Pesto (see Cook's Tips,**
    **page 10)**
**lemon juice to sprinkle**
**salt and ground black pepper**
**freshly chopped parlsey, to garnish**
**tomato salad, new potatoes and**
    **lemon wedges to serve**

**1** Make three or four deep cuts on each side of the chicken breasts. Season well with salt and pepper.

**2** Put the butter into a bowl and gradually work in the pesto. Spread half of the pesto butter over the chicken and sprinkle with a little lemon juice.

**3** Preheat the grill. Lay the chicken breasts on the grill rack and grill for about 10 minutes. Turn the chicken over, spread with the remaining pesto butter and sprinkle with a little more lemon juice. Grill for about 10 minutes or until cooked and the juices run clear when pierced with a skewer.

**4** Serve the chicken on warmed plates, with any pan juices poured over, with tomato salad, potatoes and lemon wedges and garnished with chopped parsley.

# Sticky Chicken Wings

Preparation Time 10 minutes, plus marinating (optional) • Cooking Time 20–45 minutes • Serves 4 •
Per Serving 257 calories, 14g fat (of which 4g saturates), 13g carbohydrate, 0.5g salt • Gluten Free • Dairy Free • Easy

4 tbsp clear honey
4 tbsp wholegrain mustard
12 large chicken wings
salt and ground black pepper
grilled corn on the cob and green
    salad to serve

1 Put the honey and mustard into a large glass dish and mix together. Add the chicken wings and toss to coat. Season well with salt and pepper. Cook immediately or, if you've time, cover, chill and leave to marinate for about 2 hours.

2 Preheat the barbecue or grill. Lift the chicken from the marinade and cook for about 8–10 minutes on each side or until cooked through. Alternatively, roast in a preheated oven 200°C (180°C fan oven) mark 6 for 40–45 minutes. Serve hot, with grilled corn on the cob and a green salad.

★ TRY SOMETHING DIFFERENT

● *Hoisin, Sesame and Orange Marinade*
*Mix together 6 tbsp hoisin sauce, 1 tbsp sesame seeds and the juice of ½ orange. Add the chicken wings and toss to coat.*

● *Middle Eastern Marinade*
*Mix together 3 tbsp harissa paste (see page 283), 1 tbsp tomato purée and 3 tbsp olive oil. Stir in a small handful each of freshly chopped mint and parsley, add the chicken wings and toss to coat.*

# Chicken Tarragon Burgers

Preparation Time 30 minutes, plus chilling • Cooking Time 12 minutes • Serves 2 • Per Serving 205 calories, 4g fat (of which 1g saturates), 12g carbohydrate, 0.4g salt • Dairy Free • Easy

225g (8oz) minced chicken
2 shallots, finely chopped
1 tbsp freshly chopped tarragon
25g (1oz) fresh breadcrumbs
1 large egg yolk
vegetable oil to oil
salt and ground black pepper
toasted burger buns, mayonnaise or
    Greek yogurt, salad leaves and
    tomato salad to serve

1 Put the chicken into a bowl with the shallots, tarragon, breadcrumbs and egg yolk. Mix well, then beat in about 75ml (2½fl oz) cold water and season with salt and pepper.

2 Lightly oil a foil-lined baking sheet. Divide the chicken mixture into two or four portions (depending on how large you want the burgers) and put on the foil. Using the back of a wet spoon, flatten each portion to a thickness of 2.5cm (1in). Cover and chill for 30 minutes.

3 Preheat the barbecue or grill. If cooking on the barbecue, lift the burgers straight on to the grill rack; if cooking under the grill, slide the baking sheet under the grill. Cook the burgers for 5–6 minutes on each side until cooked through, then serve in a toasted burger bun with a dollop of mayonnaise or Greek yogurt, a few salad leaves and tomato salad.

★ TRY SOMETHING DIFFERENT
**Pork and Apricot Burgers**
*Replace the chicken with minced pork, use freshly chopped sage instead of tarragon, and add 100g (3½oz) chopped ready-to-eat dried apricots to the mixture before shaping.*

# Chicken with Peanut Sauce

★

Preparation Time 10 minutes, plus marinating • Cooking Time about 10 minutes • Serves 4 • Per Serving 408 calories, 20g fat (of which 3g saturates), 19g carbohydrate, 0.5g salt • Gluten Free • Dairy Free • Easy

**4 boneless, skinless chicken breasts, cut into strips**
**1 tbsp ground coriander**
**2 garlic cloves, finely chopped**
**4 tbsp vegetable oil**
**2 tbsp clear honey**
**fresh coriander sprigs to garnish**
**Thai rice to serve (see page 281)**

**FOR THE PEANUT SAUCE**
**1 tbsp vegetable oil**
**2 tbsp curry paste**
**2 tbsp brown sugar**
**2 tbsp peanut butter**
**200ml (7fl oz) coconut milk**

**1** Mix the chicken with the ground coriander, garlic, oil and honey. Cover, chill and leave to marinate for 15 minutes.

**2** To make the peanut sauce, heat the oil in a pan. Add the curry paste, sugar and peanut butter and fry for 1 minute. Add the coconut milk and bring to the boil, stirring all the time, then reduce the heat and simmer for 5 minutes.

**3** Meanwhile, heat a wok or large frying pan and, when hot, stir-fry the chicken and its marinade in batches for 3–4 minutes or until cooked, adding more oil if needed.

**4** Serve the chicken on a bed of Thai rice, with the peanut sauce poured over. Garnish with coriander sprigs.

★ TRY SOMETHING DIFFERENT
*Replace the chicken with pork escalopes or rump steak, cut into thin strips.*

# Pancetta and Orange-wrapped Chicken

Preparation Time 30 minutes • Cooking Time 20–25 minutes • Serves 6 • Per Serving 374 calories, 21g fat (of which 7g saturates), 1g carbohydrate, 2.5g salt • Gluten Free • Dairy Free • Easy

2 garlic cloves

1 tsp sea salt

1 tsp freshly ground black pepper

2 tsp ground coriander

½ tsp ground cumin

finely grated zest of 2 oranges plus juice of ½ orange

12 boneless, skinless chicken thighs

12 thin slices pancetta

12 fresh bay leaves

olive oil

Barbecued Red Peppers to serve (see Cook's Tip)

1 Preheat the barbecue. Put the garlic, salt, pepper and spices into a small bowl and pound to a paste with the end of a rolling pin. (Alternatively, use a pestle and mortar.) Add the orange zest and juice and mix thoroughly.

2 Rub the paste over the chicken thighs. Carefully stretch the pancetta with the back of a knife. Put a bay leaf in the middle of each slice and put a thigh on top, smooth side down, then fold the ends of the pancetta over so they overlap in the middle. Make sure the bay leaf is well tucked in or it will burn during cooking.

3 Push a cocktail stick through each parcel to secure. Brush generously with oil. Barbecue for about 20–25 minutes, turning every 5 minutes until golden and cooked through. Serve drizzled with a little extra olive oil and barbecued red peppers.

## ★ COOK'S TIP

**Barbecued Red Peppers**

*Halve 3 red peppers, remove the seeds, then cut into thick strips. Brush with 1 tbsp olive oil and season with salt and pepper. Cook on the barbecue or on a preheated griddle for 15–20 minutes until the peppers are tender.*

# Chicken Maryland

Preparation Time 30 minutes • Cooking Time about 20 minutes • Serves 4 • Per Serving 1307 calories, 72g fat (of which 20g saturates), 100g carbohydrate, 4.1g salt • **Easy**

3 tbsp seasoned flour
1 medium egg, beaten
125g (4oz) fresh breadcrumbs
1.4kg (3lb) chicken, jointed into fairly small pieces (see page 267)
25g (1oz) butter
3–4 tbsp vegetable oil

**TO SERVE (see Cook's Tips)**
Corn Fritters
4 Fried Bananas
4 Bacon Rolls

1 Place the seasoned flour, beaten egg and breadcrumbs in three separate flat dishes. Coat each chicken piece with flour, then turn them in the beaten egg and coat them with breadcrumbs, patting the crumbs firmly on to the chicken.

2 Heat the butter and oil in a large frying pan. Add the chicken and fry until lightly browned. Continue frying gently, turning the pieces once, for about 20 minutes or until tender. (Alternatively, heat vegetable oil in a deep-fryer to 190°C, test by frying a small cube of bread; it should brown in 20 seconds and deep-fry them for 5–10 minutes.)

3 Drain on kitchen paper, then serve with the corn fritters, fried bananas and bacon rolls.

 COOK'S TIPS
● *Corn Fritters*
*Make up a batter from 125g (4oz) plain flour, a pinch of salt, 1 medium egg and 150ml (¼ pint) milk. Fold in 300g (11oz) drained or thawed sweetcorn kernels. Fry spoonfuls in a little hot fat until crisp and golden, turning them once. Drain well on kitchen paper.*
● *Fried Bananas*
*Peel and slice 4 bananas lengthways and fry gently for about 3 minutes in a little hot butter until lightly browned.*
● *Bacon Rolls*
*Roll up rashers of streaky bacon, rind removed, then thread on to a metal skewer and grill for about 3–5 minutes until crisp.*

# Quick Chicken Stir-fry

Preparation Time 10 minutes • Cooking Time 12 minutes • Serves 4 • Per Serving 316 calories, 3g fat (of which 1g saturates), 46g carbohydrate, 0.5g salt • Gluten Free • Dairy Free • Easy

1 tsp groundnut oil
300g (11oz) boneless, skinless
    chicken breasts, sliced
4 spring onions, chopped
200g (7oz) medium rice noodles
100g (3½oz) mangetouts
200g (7oz) purple sprouting
    broccoli, chopped
2–3 tbsp sweet chilli sauce
coriander leaves to garnish
lime wedges (optional) to serve

1 Heat the oil in a wok or large frying pan. Add the chicken and spring onions and stir-fry over a high heat for 5–6 minutes until the chicken is golden.

2 Meanwhile, soak the rice noodles in boiling water for 4 minutes or according to the pack instructions.

3 Add the mangetouts, broccoli and chilli sauce to the chicken. Continue to stir-fry for 4 minutes.

4 Drain the noodles, then add to the pan and toss everything together. Scatter the coriander leaves over the top and serve with lime wedges to squeeze over the stir-fry, if you like.

★ TRY SOMETHING DIFFERENT
*Other vegetables are just as good in this dish: try pak choi, button mushrooms, carrots cut into matchsticks, or baby sweetcorn.*

# Fried Chicken

Preparation Time 5 minutes • Cooking Time 35–45 minutes • Serves 4 • Per Serving 565 calories, 41.7g fat (of which 9.9g saturates), 8.8g carbohydrate, 0.5g salt • **Easy**

**4 chicken joints or pieces**
**3 tbsp plain flour**
**50g (2oz) butter or 3 tbsp**
**    vegetable oil**
**salt and ground black pepper**
**green salad to serve**

**1** Wipe the chicken joints and pat dry with kitchen paper. Season with salt and pepper.

**2** Toss the chicken in the flour until completely coated.

**3** Heat the butter or oil in a large frying pan or flameproof casserole over a high heat. Add the chicken and cook until golden brown on both sides. Reduce the heat and cook for 30–40 minutes until tender. Drain on kitchen paper. Serve with a green salad.

★ COOK'S TIP
*To ensure that the chicken pieces remain moist, the surface should be browned at a high temperature to seal in all the juices and give a good colour; the heat should then be reduced for the remaining cooking time.*

# Chicken with Wine and Capers

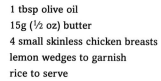

Preparation Time 5 minutes • Cooking Time 25 minutes • Serves 4 • Per Serving 234 calories, 10g fat (of which 5g saturates), trace carbohydrate, 0.3g salt • Gluten Free • Easy

1 tbsp olive oil
15g (½ oz) butter
4 small skinless chicken breasts
lemon wedges to garnish
rice to serve

**FOR THE WINE AND CAPER SAUCE**
125ml (4fl oz) white wine
3 tbsp capers, rinsed and drained
juice of 1 lemon
15g (½oz) butter
1 tbsp freshly chopped flat-leafed parsley

1 Heat the oil and butter in a large frying pan over a medium heat. Add the chicken breasts and fry for about 10–12 minutes on each side until cooked through. Transfer to a warmed plate, then cover and keep warm.

2 To make the sauce, add the wine and capers to the same pan. Bring to the boil, then reduce the heat and simmer for 2–3 minutes until the wine is reduced by half. Add the lemon juice and butter and stir in the parsley.

3 Divide the chicken among four warmed plates, pour the sauce over the chicken, garnish each serving with a lemon wedge and serve immediately with boiled rice.

# Grilled Spicy Chicken

Preparation Time 10 minutes, plus marinating • Cooking Time about 20 minutes • Serves 4 • Per Serving 157 calories, 2g fat (of which 1g saturates), 3g carbohydrate, 0.2g salt • Gluten Free • Easy

4 boneless, skinless chicken breasts
1 tbsp coriander seeds, crushed
1 tsp ground cumin
2 tsp mild curry paste
1 garlic clove, crushed
450g (1lb) natural yogurt
3 tbsp freshly chopped coriander
salt and ground black pepper
fresh coriander sprigs to garnish
mixed salad and rice to serve

1 Prick the chicken breasts all over with a fork, cover with clingfilm and lightly beat with a rolling pin to flatten them slightly.

2 Mix the coriander seeds with the cumin, curry paste, garlic and yogurt in a large shallow dish. Season with salt and pepper and stir in the chopped coriander.

3 Add the chicken and turn to coat with the spiced yogurt. Cover and leave to marinate in the fridge for at least 30 minutes or overnight.

4 Preheat the barbecue or griddle. Lift the chicken out of the marinade and cook over a medium-high heat, turning occasionally, for about 20 minutes or until cooked through. Serve immediately, with a mixed salad and rice, garnished with coriander sprigs.

# One-pan Chicken with Tomatoes

Preparation Time 5 minutes • Cooking Time 20–25 minutes • Serves 4 • Per Serving 238 calories, 4g fat (of which 1g saturates), 20g carbohydrate, 1g salt • Gluten Free • Dairy Free

4 chicken thighs
1 red onion, sliced
400g can chopped tomatoes
   with herbs
400g can mixed beans, drained
   and rinsed
2 tsp balsamic vinegar
freshly chopped flat-leafed parsley
   to garnish

1 Heat a non-stick pan and fry the chicken thighs, skin side down, for about 5 minutes or until golden. Turn over and fry the other side for 5 minutes.

2 Add the onion and fry for about 5 minutes. Add the tomatoes, mixed beans and vinegar, then cover and simmer for 10–12 minutes or until piping hot. Garnish with parsley and serve immediately.

 TRY SOMETHING DIFFERENT
*Use flageolet beans or other canned beans instead of mixed beans, and garnish with fresh basil or oregano.*

# Mild Spiced Chicken and Quinoa

★

Preparation Time 15 minutes • Cooking Time 20 minutes • Serves 4 • Per Serving 268 calories, 3g fat
(of which trace saturates), 37g carbohydrate, 0.4g salt • Gluten Free • Dairy Free • Easy

2 tbsp Mango Chutney
   (see page 282)
juice of ½ lemon
1 tbsp olive oil
2 tsp mild curry powder
1 tsp paprika
350g (12oz) skinless chicken breast,
   cut into thick strips
200g (7oz) quinoa (see Cook's Tip)
1 cucumber, roughly chopped
½ bunch of spring onions, sliced
75g (3oz) ready-to-eat dried
   apricots, sliced
2 tbsp freshly chopped mint, basil
   or tarragon
salt and ground black pepper
fresh mint sprigs to garnish

1 Put the chutney, lemon juice, ½ tbsp oil, the curry powder, paprika and salt and pepper into a bowl and mix together. Add the chicken strips and toss to coat.

2 Cook the quinoa in boiling water for 10–12 minutes until tender or according to the pack instructions. Drain thoroughly. Put into a bowl, then stir in the cucumber, spring onions, apricots, herbs and remaining oil.

3 Put the chicken and marinade into a pan and fry over a high heat for 2–3 minutes, then add 150ml (¼ pint) water. Bring to the boil, then reduce the heat and simmer for 5 minutes or until the chicken is cooked through. Serve with the quinoa garnished with mint.

★ COOK'S TIP
*Quinoa is a tiny, bead-shaped grain with a slightly nutty flavour. It's easy to prepare and nearly quadruples in size and looks translucent when cooked. It can be substituted for rice or couscous.*

# Spiced Chicken with Garlic Butter Beans

Preparation Time 10 minutes • Cooking Time 15 minutes • Serves 4 • Per Serving 443 calories, 16g fat (of which 3g saturates), 42g carbohydrate, 2g salt • Dairy Free • Easy

4 boneless, skinless chicken
   breasts, about 100g (3½oz) each
1 tbsp olive oil
1 tsp ground coriander
1 tsp ground cumin
100g (3½oz) couscous
3 tbsp extra virgin olive oil
1 garlic clove, sliced
2 × 400g cans butter beans, drained
   and rinsed
juice of 1 lemon
1 small red onion, thinly sliced
50g (2oz) marinated roasted
   peppers, drained
2 medium tomatoes, seeded and
   chopped
1 tbsp freshly chopped coriander
1 tbsp freshly chopped flat-leafed
   parsley
salt and ground black pepper
green salad and lemon wedges
   to serve

1 Put the chicken on a board, cover with clingfilm and flatten lightly with a rolling pin. Put the olive oil into a large bowl with the ground coriander and cumin. Mix together, then add the chicken and turn to coat.

2 Heat a large frying pan and cook the chicken for 5–7 minutes on each side until golden and the juices run clear when pierced with a skewer.

3 While the chicken is cooking, put the couscous into a bowl and add 100ml (3½fl oz) boiling water. Cover with clingfilm and set aside.

4 Put the extra virgin olive oil into a small pan with the garlic and butter beans and warm through for about 3–4 minutes over a low heat. Stir in the lemon juice and season with salt and pepper.

5 Fluff up the couscous with a fork and tip in the warm butter beans. Add the onion, peppers, tomatoes and herbs and stir together. Slice each chicken breast into four pieces and arrange alongside the bean salad. Serve with a green salad and lemon wedges to squeeze over.

# Peas and Bacon with Pan-fried Chicken

Preparation Time 5 minutes • Cooking Time 20 minutes • Serves 4 • Per Serving 314 calories, 21g fat (of which 5g saturates), 7g carbohydrate, 0.9g salt • Gluten Free • Easy

4 skinless chicken breasts, about
   125g (4oz) each
2 tbsp olive oil
2 shallots, finely sliced
3 unsmoked, rindless streaky bacon
   rashers, chopped
200g (7oz) frozen peas, thawed
2 tbsp sunblush tomato pesto
salt and ground black pepper
buttered new potatoes to serve

1 Preheat a griddle. Season the chicken generously with salt and pepper, then brush with 1 tbsp oil and cook on the griddle, skin side down, for 8–10 minutes. Turn over and continue to cook on the other side for 8–10 minutes until cooked through and the juices run clear when the chicken is pierced with a skewer.

2 Meanwhile, heat the remaining oil in a frying pan. Add the shallots and bacon and fry until the shallots are softened and the bacon is golden. Add the peas and cook for 2 minutes, then stir in the pesto.

3 Serve the peas and bacon with the chicken breasts and new potatoes.

# Lemon Chicken

Preparation Time 2 minutes • Cooking Time 6–8 minutes • Serves 4 • Per Serving 231 calories, 7g fat (of which 1g saturates), 13g carbohydrate, 0.2g salt • Gluten Free • Dairy Free • Easy

**4 small skinless chicken breasts, about 125g (4oz) each**
**juice of 2 lemons**
**2 tbsp olive oil**
**4–6 tbsp demerara sugar**
**salt**
**green salad and lemon wedges to serve**

**1** Put the chicken into a large bowl and season with salt. Add the lemon juice and oil and stir to mix.

**2** Preheat the grill to medium. Spread the chicken out on a large baking sheet and sprinkle over 2–3 tbsp demerara sugar. Grill for about 3–4 minutes or until caramelised, then turn the chicken over, sprinkle with the remaining sugar and grill until the chicken is golden and cooked through.

**3** Divide the chicken among four plates and serve with a green salad and lemon wedges.

# Chicken Stir-fry with Noodles

Preparation Time 20 minutes • Cooking Time 20 minutes • Serves 4 • Per Serving 355 calories, 10g fat (of which 2g saturates), 29g carbohydrate, 0.5g salt • Dairy Free • Easy

250g pack thick egg noodles

2 tbsp vegetable oil

2 garlic cloves, crushed

4 boneless, skinless chicken breasts, each sliced into 10 pieces

3 medium carrots, about 450g (1lb), cut into thin strips, about 5cm (2in) long

1 bunch of spring onions, sliced

200g (7oz) mangetouts

155g jar sweet chilli and lemongrass sauce

1 Cook the noodles in boiling water according to the pack instructions.

2 Meanwhile, heat the oil in a wok or frying pan. Add the garlic and stir-fry for 1–2 minutes. Add the chicken and stir-fry for 5 minutes, then add the carrot strips and stir-fry for a further 5 minutes.

3 Add the spring onions, mangetouts and sauce to the wok and stir-fry for 5 minutes.

4 Drain the cooked noodles well and add to the wok. Toss everything together and serve.

★ TRY SOMETHING DIFFERENT

*Use turkey or pork escalopes instead of the chicken: you will need 450g (1lb), cut into thin strips.*

# Marinated Poussins

★

Preparation Time 30 minutes, plus marinating and soaking • Cooking Time 30 minutes • Serves 4 •
Per Serving 508 calories, 30g fat (of which 8g saturates), 10g carbohydrate, 1.6g salt • Gluten Free • Dairy Free • Easy

150ml (¼ pint) bourbon
15g (½oz) soft brown sugar
50ml (2fl oz) clear honey
50ml (2fl oz) tomato ketchup
2 tbsp wholegrain mustard
1 tbsp white wine vinegar
3 garlic cloves, crushed
1 tsp each salt and ground black
   pepper
4 poussins
chargrilled peppers, tomatoes and
   onions, garnished with flat-leafed
   parsley, to serve

1 Mix the bourbon, sugar, honey, tomato ketchup and mustard together. Stir in the vinegar, garlic, salt and pepper.

2 Put the poussins, breast side down, on a chopping board, then cut through either side of the backbone with poultry shears or a pair of strong sharp scissors and remove it. Open out the poussins, cover them with clingfilm and flatten them slightly by tapping them with the base of a pan. Put the poussins in a shallow glass dish and pour the bourbon marinade over the top, then cover, chill and leave to marinate overnight.

3 Preheat the barbecue or grill. Soak eight wooden skewers in water for 20 minutes. Thread the skewers through the legs and breasts of the poussins, keeping the marinade to one side. Cook the poussins for 30 minutes or until cooked through, basting from time to time with the reserved marinade. Serve with the peppers, tomatoes and onions garnished with the parsley.

★ TRY SOMETHING DIFFERENT
*Use chicken joints instead of the poussins, if you like.*

# Chicken with Oyster Sauce

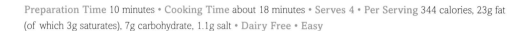

Preparation Time 10 minutes • Cooking Time about 18 minutes • Serves 4 • Per Serving 344 calories, 23g fat (of which 3g saturates), 7g carbohydrate, 1.1g salt • Dairy Free • Easy

6 tbsp vegetable oil

450g (1lb) boneless, skinless chicken breasts, cut into bite-size pieces

3 tbsp oyster sauce

1 tbsp dark soy sauce

100ml (3½fl oz) chicken stock (see page 266)

2 tsp lemon juice

1 garlic clove, thinly sliced

6–8 large flat mushrooms, about 250g (9oz) total weight, sliced

125g (4oz) mangetouts

1 tsp cornflour mixed with 1 tbsp water

1 tbsp toasted sesame oil

salt and ground black pepper

rice to serve

1 Heat 3 tbsp vegetable oil in a wok or large frying pan. Add the chicken and cook over a high heat, stirring continuously for 2–3 minutes until lightly browned. Remove the chicken with a slotted spoon and drain on kitchen paper.

2 Mix the oyster sauce with the soy sauce, stock and lemon juice. Add the chicken and mix thoroughly.

3 Heat the remaining vegetable oil in the pan over a high heat and stir-fry the garlic for about 30 seconds. Add the mushrooms and cook for 1 minute. Add the chicken mixture, cover and simmer for 8 minutes.

4 Stir in the mangetouts and cook for a further 2–3 minutes. Remove the pan from the heat and stir in the cornflour mixture. Put the pan back on the heat, add the sesame oil and stir until the sauce has thickened. Season with salt and pepper and serve immediately with rice.

# Chicken and Basil Pasta

★

Preparation Time 5 minutes • Cooking Time 15 minutes • Serves 4 • Per Serving 415 calories, 9g fat
(of which 2g saturates), 62g carbohydrate, 0.9g salt • Dairy Free • Easy

300g (11oz) pasta
1 tbsp olive oil
1 garlic clove, crushed
2 × 400g cans cherry tomatoes
300g (11oz) cooked chicken,
   shredded
50g (2oz) pitted black olives
a handful of torn basil leaves
salt and ground black pepper
green salad to serve (optional)

1 Cook the pasta in a large pan of
lightly salted boiling water or
according to the pack instructions.

2 Meanwhile, heat the oil in a pan.
Add the garlic and cook for about
1–2 minutes, then add the tomatoes
and cook for a further 5–7 minutes.

3 Add the shredded chicken and
black olives to the pan and cook for
2–3 minutes. Stir in the basil and
season with salt and pepper.

4 Drain the pasta, toss in the sauce
and serve immediately with a green
salad, if you like.

# Chicken with Vegetables and Noodles

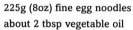

Preparation Time 10 minutes • Cooking Time about 12 minutes • Serves 2 • Per Serving 584 calories, 19g fat (of which 3g saturates), 67g carbohydrate, 4.1g salt • Dairy Free • Easy

225g (8oz) fine egg noodles

about 2 tbsp vegetable oil

1 large boneless, skinless chicken breast, about 150g (5oz), cut into very thin strips

2.5cm (1in) piece fresh root ginger, peeled and finely chopped

1 garlic clove, finely chopped

1 red pepper, seeded and thinly sliced

4 spring onions, thinly sliced

2 carrots, thinly sliced

125g (4oz) shiitake or button mushrooms, halved

a handful of bean sprouts (optional)

3 tbsp hoisin sauce

2 tbsp light soy sauce

1 tbsp chilli sauce

shredded spring onion and sesame seeds to garnish

**1** Bring a large pan of water to the boil and cook the noodles for about 3 minutes or according to the pack instructions. Drain thoroughly and toss with a little of the oil to prevent them sticking together. Set aside.

**2** Heat the remaining oil in a wok or large frying pan. Add the chicken, ginger and garlic and stir-fry over a very high heat for about 5 minutes or until the chicken is browned on the outside and cooked right through.

**3** Add all the vegetables to the pan and stir-fry over a high heat for about 2 minutes or until they are just cooked, but still crunchy.

**4** Stir in the hoisin, soy and chilli sauces and mix well. Add the noodles, toss well to mix and cook for a couple of minutes until heated through. Serve immediately sprinkled with shredded spring onion and sesame seeds.

★ TRY SOMETHING DIFFERENT

● *Replace the chicken with thinly sliced turkey escalopes.*

● *Increase the heat of the dish by frying a chopped chilli with the garlic and ginger.*

# Pasta with Chicken, Cream and Basil

★

Preparation Time 10 minutes • Cooking Time 25 minutes • Serves 4 • Per Serving 612 calories, 27g fat (of which 12g saturates), 67g carbohydrate, 0.4g salt • Easy

1 tbsp olive oil
2 shallots, chopped
400g (14oz) boneless chicken, cubed
125g (4oz) chestnut mushrooms, sliced
50g (2oz) sultanas
a pinch of ground cinnamon
50ml (2fl oz) dry white wine
125ml (4fl oz) hot chicken stock (see page 266)
300g (11oz) farfalle pasta
142ml carton double cream
2 tsp Dijon mustard
2 tsp freshly chopped basil
salt

**1** Heat the oil in a pan. Add the shallots and fry for 4–5 minutes. Add the chicken and cook until browned. Add the mushrooms and cook for 2 minutes. Stir in the sultanas and cinnamon.

**2** Pour in the wine and hot stock and simmer for 12–15 minutes until the chicken is cooked.

**3** Meanwhile, cook the pasta in a large pan of lightly salted boiling water according to the pack instructions.

**4** Stir the cream, mustard and basil into the chicken and season with salt. Drain the pasta and return to the pan, then add the sauce, toss and serve.

# Chicken, Bacon and Leek Pasta Bake

★

**Preparation Time** 10 minutes • **Cooking Time** about 20 minutes • **Serves 4** • **Per Serving** 650 calories, 24g fat (of which 6g saturates), 68g carbohydrate, 2.2g salt • **Easy**

1 tbsp olive oil

100g (3½oz) bacon lardons

450g (1lb) boneless, skinless chicken thighs, chopped

3 medium leeks, trimmed and chopped

300g (11oz) macaroni or other pasta shapes

350g carton ready-made cheese sauce

2 tsp Dijon mustard

25g (1oz) freshly grated Parmesan

salt

2 tbsp freshly chopped flat-leafed parsley to garnish

**1** Heat the oil in a large frying pan. Add the bacon and chicken and cook for 7–8 minutes. Add the leeks and continue cooking for 4–5 minutes.

**2** Meanwhile, cook the pasta in a large pan of lightly salted boiling water according to the pack instructions. Drain well.

**3** Preheat the grill. Add the cheese sauce to the pasta with the mustard and chicken mixture. Mix well, then tip into a 2.1 litre (3¾ pint) ovenproof dish and sprinkle with Parmesan. Grill for 4–5 minutes until golden, then garnish with chopped parsley.

# Grilled Chicken with Mango Salsa

Preparation Time 10 minutes • Cooking Time 20 minutes • Serves 4 • Per Serving 288 calories, 14g fat (of which 4g saturates), 7g carbohydrate, 0.2g salt • Gluten Free • Dairy Free • Easy

4 chicken breasts
juice of ½ lime
oil-water spray (see Cook's Tip)
salt and ground black pepper
rocket to serve

**FOR THE SALSA**
1 mango, peeled, stoned and diced
1 small fennel bulb, trimmed and diced
1 fresh chilli, seeded and finely diced (see Cook's Tips, page 10)
1 tbsp balsamic vinegar
juice of ½ lime
2 tbsp freshly chopped flat-leafed parsley
2 tbsp freshly chopped mint

1 Preheat the grill. Put the chicken on a grill pan and season generously with salt and pepper. Sprinkle with the lime juice and spray with the oil-water blend. Grill for 8–10 minutes on each side until cooked through and the juices run clear when pierced with a skewer. Put to one side.

2 Combine all the salsa ingredients in a bowl and season generously with salt and pepper. Spoon alongside the chicken and serve with rocket.

★ COOK'S TIP
*Oil-water spray is far lower in calories than oil alone and, as it sprays on thinly and evenly, you'll use less. Fill one-eighth of a travel-sized spray bottle with oil such as sunflower, light olive or vegetable (rapeseed), then top up with water. To use, shake well before spraying. Store in the fridge.*

# Casseroles, Stews and Braises ★

# Classic Coq au Vin

Preparation Time 15 minutes • Cooking Time 2 hours • Serves 6 • Per Serving 740 calories, 44g fat
(of which 17g saturates), 26g carbohydrate, 1.8g salt • A Little Effort

1 large chicken jointed (see page
    267) or 6–8 chicken joints
2 tbsp well-seasoned flour
100g (3½oz) butter
125g (4oz) lean bacon, diced
1 medium onion, quartered
1 medium carrot, quartered
4 tbsp brandy
600ml (1 pint) red wine
1 garlic clove, crushed
1 bouquet garni (see Cook's Tip,
    page 31)
1 sugar lump
2 tbsp vegetable oil
450g (1lb) button onions
a pinch of sugar
1 tsp wine vinegar
225g (8oz) button mushrooms
6 slices white bread, crusts
    removed
salt and ground black pepper

1 Coat the chicken pieces with
1 tbsp seasoned flour. Melt 25g
(1oz) butter in a flameproof
casserole. Add the chicken and fry
gently until golden brown on all
sides. Add the bacon, onion and
carrot and fry until softened.

2 Heat the brandy in a small pan,
pour over the chicken and ignite,
shaking the pan so that all the
chicken pieces are covered in
flames. Pour in the wine and stir to
dislodge any sediment from the
base of the casserole. Add the
garlic, bouquet garni and sugar
lump and bring to the boil. Reduce
the heat, cover and simmer for
1–1½ hours or until the chicken is
cooked through.

3 Meanwhile, melt 25g (1oz) butter
with 1 tsp oil in a frying pan. Add
the button onions and fry until they
begin to brown. Add the pinch of
sugar and vinegar together with
1 tbsp water. Cover and simmer for
10–15 minutes until just tender.
Keep warm.

4 Melt 25g (1oz) butter with 2 tsp
oil in a pan. Add the mushrooms
and cook for a few minutes, then
turn off the heat and keep warm.

5 Remove the chicken from the
casserole and place in a dish.
Surround with the onions and
mushrooms and keep hot.

6 Discard the bouquet garni. Skim
the excess fat from the cooking
liquid, then boil the liquid in the
casserole briskly for 3–5 minutes to
reduce it.

7 Add the remaining oil to the fat in
the frying pan and fry the pieces of
bread until golden brown on both
sides. Cut each slice into triangles.

8 Work the remaining butter and
flour to make a beurre manié (see
page 106). Remove the casserole
from the heat and add small pieces
of the beurre manié to the cooking
liquid. Stir until smooth, then put
back on to the heat and bring just to
the boil. The sauce should be thick
and shiny. Take off the heat and
adjust the seasoning. Return the
chicken, onions and mushrooms
to the casserole and stir to combine.
Garnish with the fried bread
and serve.

# Chicken with Chorizo and Beans

Preparation Time 10 minutes • Cooking Time 1 hour 5 minutes–1 hour 10 minutes • Serves 6 • Per Serving 690 calories, 41g fat (of which 12g saturates), 33g carbohydrate, 2.6g salt • **Dairy Free** • **Easy**

1 tbsp olive oil

12 chicken pieces (6 drumsticks and 6 thighs)

175g (6oz) chorizo sausage, cubed

1 onion, finely chopped

2 large garlic cloves, crushed

1 tsp mild chilli powder

3 red peppers, seeded and roughly chopped

400g (14oz) passata

2 tbsp tomato purée

300ml (½ pint) hot chicken stock (see page 266)

2 × 400g cans butter beans, drained and rinsed

200g (7oz) new potatoes, halved

1 small bunch of thyme

1 bay leaf

200g (7oz) baby leaf spinach

**1** Preheat the oven to 190°C (170°C fan oven) mark 5. Heat the oil in a large flameproof casserole and brown the chicken all over. Remove from the pan and set aside. Add the chorizo to the casserole and fry for 2–3 minutes until its oil starts to run. Add the onion, garlic and chilli powder and fry over a low heat for 5 minutes or until soft.

**2** Add the peppers and cook for 2–3 minutes until soft. Stir in the passata, tomato purée, hot stock, butter beans, potatoes, thyme sprigs and bay leaf. Cover and simmer for 10 minutes.

**3** Return the chicken and any juices to the casserole. Bring to a simmer, then cover and cook in the oven for 30–35 minutes. If the sauce looks thin, return the casserole to the hob over a medium heat and simmer to reduce until nicely thick.

**4** Remove the thyme and bay leaf, then stir in the spinach until it wilts. Serve immediately.

★ TRY SOMETHING DIFFERENT
*Use mixed beans instead of the butter beans.*

# One-pot Chicken

Preparation Time 20 minutes • Cooking Time 1 hour 40 minutes • Serves 6 • Per Serving 474 calories, 33g fat (of which 9g saturates), 6g carbohydrate, 0.6g salt • Dairy Free • Easy

2 tbsp olive oil
1 large onion, cut into wedges
2 rindless streaky bacon rashers, chopped
1 chicken, about 1.6kg (3½lb)
6 carrots
2 small turnips, cut into wedges
1 garlic clove, crushed
bouquet garni (1 bay leaf, a few fresh parsley and thyme sprigs)
600ml (1 pint) hot chicken stock (see page 266)
100ml (3½fl oz) dry white wine
12 button mushrooms
3 tbsp freshly chopped flat-leafed parsley
salt and ground black pepper
mashed potatoes to serve (optional)

1 Heat the oil in a non-stick flameproof casserole. Add the onion and bacon and fry for 5 minutes or until golden. Remove and put to one side.

2 Add the whole chicken to the casserole and fry for 10 minutes, turning carefully to brown all over. Remove and put to one side.

3 Preheat the oven to 200°C (180°C fan oven) mark 6. Add the carrots, turnips and garlic to the casserole and fry for 5 minutes, then add the onion and bacon. Put the chicken back into the casserole, add the bouquet garni, hot stock and wine and season with salt and pepper. Bring to a simmer, then cover the pan and cook in the oven for 30 minutes.

4 Remove the casserole from the oven and add the mushrooms. Baste the chicken, then re-cover and cook for a further 50 minutes.

5 Lift out the chicken, then stir the parsley into the cooking liquid. Carve the chicken and serve with the vegetables and cooking liquid, and mashed potatoes, if you like.

★ TRY SOMETHING DIFFERENT
*Use chicken pieces such as drumsticks or thighs, reducing the cooking time in step 4 to 20 minutes.*

# Chicken in Red Wine

Preparation Time 15 minutes • Cooking Time 1 hour 10 minutes • Serves 4 • Per Serving 358 calories, 14g fat (of which 4g saturates), 8g carbohydrate, 1.1g salt • Dairy Free • Easy

8 slices prosciutto

8 large boneless, skinless chicken thighs

1 tbsp olive oil

1 fat garlic clove, crushed

about 12 shallots or button onions

225g (8oz) fresh shiitake mushrooms

1 tbsp plain flour

300ml (½ pint) red wine

300ml (½ pint) hot chicken stock (see page 266)

1 tbsp Worcestershire sauce

1 bay leaf

salt and ground black pepper

crusty bread to serve

1 Wrap a slice of prosciutto around each chicken thigh. Heat the oil in a large non-stick frying pan and fry the chicken thighs in batches for 8–10 minutes until golden brown all over. Transfer to a plate and put to one side.

2 Add the garlic and shallots or button onions and fry over a low heat for 5 minutes or until the shallots are beginning to soften and turn golden. Stir in the mushrooms and flour and cook over a low heat for 1–2 minutes.

3 Put the chicken back in the pan and add the wine, hot stock, Worcestershire sauce and bay leaf. Season lightly with salt and pepper, bring to the boil for 5 minutes, then reduce the heat to low, cover and simmer for 45 minutes or until the chicken is cooked through and the juices run clear when the thickest part of the thigh is pierced with a skewer. Serve with crusty bread.

★ COOK'S TIPS

● *If you can't buy prosciutto, thinly cut smoked streaky bacon will work just as well.*

● *Use button mushrooms if you can't find shiitake.*

★ FREEZING TIP

**To freeze** *This dish is ideal for freezing for an easy meal another day. Double the quantities and make another meal for four or make two meals for two people and freeze. Complete the recipe, cool quickly, then put into a freezerproof container and freeze for up to three months.*

**To use** *Thaw overnight at cool room temperature, then put back into a large pan. Bring slowly to the boil, then reduce the heat and simmer gently for about 10–15 minutes until piping hot.*

# Chicken in White Wine Sauce

Preparation Time 45 minutes • Cooking Time about 1 hour • Serves 4 • Per Serving 787 calories, 51g fat (of which 22g saturates), 24g carbohydrate, 1.5g salt • A Little Effort

750ml bottle full-bodied white wine, such as Chardonnay
4 tbsp brandy
2 bouquet garni (see Cook's Tip, page 31)
1 garlic clove, bruised
plain flour to coat
1 chicken, about 1.4kg (3lb), jointed (see page 267), or 2 boneless breasts, halved, plus 2 drumsticks and 2 thighs
125g (4oz) butter
125g (4oz) rindless unsmoked bacon rashers, cut into strips
225g (8oz) baby onions, peeled with root ends intact
225g (8oz) brown-cap mushrooms, halved, or quartered if large
25g (1oz) butter mixed with 25g (1oz) plain flour (beurre manié, see Cook's Tip, page 106)
salt and ground black pepper
buttered noodles or rice to serve

1 Preheat the oven to 180°C (160°C fan oven) mark 4. Pour the wine and brandy into a pan. Add 1 bouquet garni and the garlic. Bring to the boil, then reduce the heat and simmer until reduced by half. Cool.

2 Season the flour with salt and pepper and use to coat the chicken joints lightly. Melt half the butter in a large frying pan. When foaming, add the chicken joints and brown all over (in batches if necessary). Transfer to a flameproof casserole. Add the bacon to the frying pan and fry until golden. Remove with a slotted spoon and add to the chicken.

3 Strain the cooled reduced wine mixture over the chicken and add the other bouquet garni. Bring to the boil, cover and cook in the oven for 30 minutes.

4 Meanwhile, melt the remaining butter in a frying pan and fry the onions until tender and lightly browned. Add the mushrooms and fry until softened.

5 Add the mushrooms and onions to the casserole, cover and cook for a further 10 minutes or until the chicken is tender. Lift out the chicken and vegetables with a slotted spoon and put into a warmed serving dish. Cover and keep warm.

6 Bring the cooking liquid in the casserole to the boil. Whisk in the beurre manié, a piece at a time, until the sauce is shiny and syrupy. Check the seasoning.

7 Pour the sauce over the chicken. Serve with buttered noodles or rice.

# Chicken and Vegetable Hotpot

Preparation Time 5 minutes • Cooking Time 30 minutes • Serves 4 • Per Serving 338 calories, 14g fat (of which 3g saturates), 14g carbohydrate, 1.2g salt • Dairy Free • Easy

**4 chicken breasts, with skin, about 125g (4oz) each**
**2 large parsnips, chopped**
**2 large carrots, chopped**
**300ml (½ pint) ready-made gravy**
**125g (4oz) cabbage, shredded**
**ground black pepper**

**1** Heat a non-stick frying pan or flameproof casserole until hot. Add the chicken breasts, skin side down, and cook for 5–6 minutes. Turn them over, add the parsnips and carrots and cook for a further 7–8 minutes.

**2** Pour the gravy over the chicken and vegetables, then cover the pan and cook gently for 10 minutes.

**3** Season with pepper and stir in the cabbage, then cover and continue to cook for 4–5 minutes until the chicken is cooked through, the cabbage has wilted and the vegetables are tender. Serve hot.

# Slow-braised Garlic Chicken

Preparation Time 30 minutes • Cooking Time about 2 hours • Serves 6 • Per Serving 506 calories, 28g fat (of which 9g saturates), 10g carbohydrate, 1g salt • A Little Effort

2 tbsp olive oil
1 tbsp freshly chopped thyme
125g (4oz) chestnut mushrooms, finely chopped
6 whole chicken legs (drumsticks and thighs)
18 thin slices pancetta
2 tbsp plain flour
25g (1oz) butter
18 small shallots
12 garlic cloves, unpeeled but split
750ml bottle full-bodied white wine, such as Chardonnay
2 bay leaves
salt and ground black pepper

**1** Preheat the oven to 180°C (160°C fan oven) mark 4. Heat 1 tbsp oil in a frying pan. Add the thyme and mushrooms and fry until the moisture has evaporated. Season with salt and pepper and cool.

**2** Loosen the skin away from one chicken leg and spoon a little of the mushroom paste underneath. Season the leg all over with salt and pepper, then wrap three pancetta slices around the thigh end. Repeat with the remaining chicken legs, then dust using 1 tbsp flour.

**3** Melt the butter in a frying pan with the remaining oil over a high heat. Fry the chicken legs, in batches, seam side down, until golden. Turn the legs, brown the other side, then transfer to a casserole. The browning should take 8–10 minutes per batch.

**4** Put the shallots and garlic into the frying pan and cook for 10 minutes or until browned. Sprinkle over the remaining flour and cook for 1 minute. Pour in the wine and bring to the boil, stirring. Pour into the casserole with the chicken and add the bay leaves. Cover and cook in the oven for 1½ hours. Serve hot.

★ FREEZING TIP

*To freeze* Complete the recipe to the end of step 4. Cool quickly, then freeze in an airtight container for up to one month.
*To use* Thaw overnight at cool room temperature. Preheat the oven to 220°C (200°C fan oven) mark 7. Put the chicken back into the casserole and reheat in the oven for 15 minutes. Reduce the oven temperature to 180°C (160°C fan oven) mark 4 and cook for a further 25 minutes.

# Easy Chicken Casserole

Preparation Time 15 minutes • Cooking Time 50 minutes • Serves 6 • Per Serving 323 calories, 18g fat (of which 5g saturates), 17g carbohydrate, 0.9g salt • Gluten Free • Dairy Free • Easy

1 fresh rosemary sprig
2 bay leaves
1.4kg (3lb) chicken
1 red onion, cut into wedges
2 carrots, cut into chunks
2 leeks, trimmed and cut into chunks
2 celery sticks, cut into chunks
12 baby new potatoes
900ml (1½ pints) hot chicken stock (see page 266)
200g (7oz) green beans, trimmed
salt and ground black pepper

1 Preheat the oven to 180°C (160°C fan oven) mark 4. Put the herbs and chicken into a large, flameproof casserole. Add the onion, carrots, leeks, celery, potatoes, stock and seasoning. Bring to the boil, then cook in the oven for 45 minutes or until the chicken is cooked through. To test the chicken, pierce the thickest part of the leg with a knife; the juices should run clear.

2 Add the beans and cook for 5 minutes. Remove the chicken and spoon the vegetables into six bowls. Carve the chicken and divide among the bowls, then ladle the cooking liquid over.

★ TRY SOMETHING DIFFERENT
*Omit the baby new potatoes and serve with mashed potatoes.*

# Dishes From Around the World ★

# Alsace Chicken

★

**Preparation Time** 20 minutes • **Cooking Time** 1 hour 20 minutes • **Serves 4** • **Per Serving** 484 calories, 24g fat (of which 8g saturates), 11g carbohydrate, 1.4g salt • **Easy**

2 tbsp vegetable oil

8 chicken pieces (such as breasts, thighs and drumsticks)

125g (4oz) rindless smoked streaky bacon rashers, cut into strips

12 shallots, peeled but left whole

3 fresh tarragon sprigs

1 tbsp plain flour

150ml (¼ pint) Alsace Riesling white wine

500ml (18fl oz) hot chicken stock (see page 266)

3 tbsp crème fraîche

salt and ground black pepper

new potatoes (optional) and green beans to serve

**1** Heat half the oil in a frying pan over a medium heat. Fry the chicken, in batches, until golden, adding more oil to the pan as necessary. Set aside.

**2** Put the bacon into the same pan and fry gently to release its fat. Add the shallots and cook for 5 minutes, stirring occasionally, or until both the shallots and bacon are lightly coloured.

**3** Strip the leaves from the tarragon and put both the leaves and stalks to one side. Sprinkle the flour over the shallots and bacon and stir to absorb the juices. Cook for 1 minute, then gradually add the wine, hot stock and tarragon stalks. Put the chicken back into the pan, cover and simmer over a gentle heat for 45 minutes–1 hour until the chicken is cooked through.

**4** Remove the chicken, bacon and shallots with a slotted spoon and keep warm. Discard the tarragon stalks. Bubble the sauce until reduced by half. Stir in the crème fraîche and tarragon leaves. Season with salt and pepper.

**5** Turn off the heat, put the chicken, bacon and shallots back into the pan and stir to combine. Serve with new potatoes and green beans.

# Chicken and Mushroom Stroganoff

Preparation Time 20 minutes • Cooking Time 30 minutes • Serves 4 • Per Serving 494 calories, 43g fat (of which 17g saturates), 4g carbohydrate, 0.3g salt • Easy

2 tbsp olive oil
1 onion, roughly chopped
2 garlic cloves, crushed
4 × 125g (4oz) chicken thighs,
   including skin and bones
250g (9oz) closed-cup mushrooms,
   roughly chopped
200g (7oz) brown rice, rinsed
175ml (6fl oz) hot chicken stock
   (see page 266)
150ml (¼ pint) double cream
leaves from 2 thyme sprigs, plus
   extra to garnish (optional)
50g (2oz) baby leaf spinach
salt and ground black pepper

1 Heat 1 tbsp oil in a pan. Add the onion and garlic, cover and cook gently for 10–15 minutes until soft. Remove from the pan and put to one side. Increase the heat to medium and add the remaining oil. Fry the chicken until golden. Add the mushrooms and cook for 5 minutes or until most of the liquid has evaporated.

2 Put the rice into a separate pan, then pour in 450ml (¾ pint) hot water. Cover and bring to the boil, then reduce the heat and cook according to the pack instructions.

3 Return the onion mixture to the chicken pan and gradually stir in the hot stock. Use a wooden spoon to scrape all the goodness from the base of the pan, then stir in the cream and thyme leaves. Simmer for 5 minutes.

4 Remove the chicken, discard the skin and bones and pull the meat into pieces. Return it to the pan. Add the spinach and stir to wilt. Taste for seasoning.

5 To serve, divide the rice among four warmed plates and ladle the stroganoff over the top. Garnish with thyme leaves, if you like.

# Chicken Tabbouleh with Tomato Dressing

Preparation Time 50 minutes, plus marinating and soaking • Cooking Time 45 minutes • Serves 4 •
Per Serving 777 calories, 33g fat (of which 6g saturates), 50g carbohydrate, 0.6g salt • Dairy Free • Easy

1 large red chilli, seeded and finely
    chopped (see Cook's Tips,
    page 10)
3 garlic cloves, crushed
juice of 4 limes: about 8 tbsp juice
½ tsp ground turmeric
4 chicken breast quarters (breast
    and wing), about 300g (11oz)
    each, lightly scored
450g (1lb) tomatoes, preferably
    plum, chopped
2 tbsp capers
1 tbsp sugar
225g (8oz) bulgur wheat
125g (4oz) cucumber, chopped
50g (2oz) pinenuts, toasted
3 tbsp freshly chopped parsley
3 tbsp freshly chopped chives
50g (2oz) raisins
5 tbsp olive oil
225g (8oz) onions, thinly sliced
salt and ground black pepper
lime slices and fresh flat-leafed
    parsley to garnish (optional)

1 Put the chilli into a non-metallic
bowl with the garlic, 3 tbsp lime
juice and the turmeric. Add the
chicken and stir well to coat. Cover
the bowl, chill and leave to marinate
for at least 3 hours.

2 Mix the tomatoes with the capers,
2 tbsp lime juice, the sugar and
seasoning.

3 Put the bulgur wheat into a bowl,
cover with 600ml (1 pint) boiling
water and leave to soak for
30 minutes. Drain, then stir in the
cucumber, pinenuts, herbs, raisins,
remaining lime juice and 3 tbsp oil.
Season with salt and pepper.

4 Preheat the oven to 240°C (220°C
fan oven) mark 9. Drain the chicken,
putting the marinade to one side.
Put, skin side up, in a roasting tin
with the remaining oil and onions.
Cook in the oven for 30–35 minutes
until done. Put to one side. Add the
tomato mixture and remaining
marinade to the roasting tin and put
back in the oven for 5 minutes.

5 Spoon the dressing over the
chicken. Garnish with lime slices
and parsley, if you like, and serve
at room temperature with the
tabbouleh.

 COOK'S TIP
*Bulgur wheat is grains of wheat that
have been boiled until they crack, and
then dried. It is reconstituted in water.*

# Chicken Cacciatore

Preparation Time 5 minutes • Cooking Time 40 minutes • Serves 4 • Per Serving 327 calories, 17g fat
(of which 4g saturates), 3g carbohydrate, 1.3g salt • Gluten Free • Dairy Free • Easy

2 tbsp olive oil
8 boneless, skinless chicken thighs
2 garlic cloves, crushed
1 tsp dried thyme
1 tsp dried tarragon
150ml (¼ pint) white wine
400g can chopped tomatoes
12 pitted black olives
12 capers, rinsed and drained
ground black pepper
brown rice and broad beans or peas
   to serve

1 Heat the oil in a flameproof casserole over a high heat. Add the chicken and brown all over. Reduce the heat and add the garlic, thyme, tarragon and wine to the casserole. Stir for 1 minute, then add the tomatoes and season with pepper.

2 Bring to the boil, then reduce the heat, cover the casserole and simmer for 20 minutes or until the chicken is tender.

3 Lift the chicken out of the casserole and put to one side. Bubble the sauce for 5 minutes or until thickened, add the olives and capers, stir well and cook for a further 2–3 minutes.

4 Put the chicken into the sauce. Serve with brown rice and broad beans or peas.

# Spanish Chicken Parcels

Preparation Time 15 minutes • Cooking Time about 30 minutes • Serves 6 • Per Serving 444 calories, 29g fat
(of which 9g saturates), 4g carbohydrate, 3.1g salt • Gluten Free • Dairy Free • Easy

12 boneless, skinless chicken
   thighs, about 900g (2lb)
180g jar pimientos or roasted red
   peppers, drained
12 thin slices chorizo sausage
2 tbsp olive oil
1 onion, finely chopped
4 garlic cloves, crushed
225g can chopped tomatoes
4 tbsp dry sherry
18 queen green olives (see
   Cook's Tip)
salt and ground black pepper
rice or crusty bread to serve

1 Put the chicken thighs on a board,
season well with salt and pepper
and put a piece of pimiento or
roasted pepper inside each one.
Wrap a slice of chorizo around the
outside and secure with two cocktail
sticks. Put to one side.

2 Heat the oil in a pan over a
medium heat. Add the onion and fry
for 10 minutes. Add the garlic and
cook for 1 minute. Put the chicken
parcels, chorizo side down, into the
pan and brown them all over for
10–15 minutes.

3 Add the tomatoes and sherry
to the pan and bring to the boil.
Reduce the heat and simmer for
5 minutes or until the juices run
clear when the chicken is pierced
with a skewer. Add the olives and
warm through. Remove the
cocktail sticks and serve with
rice or crusty bread.

⭐ COOK'S TIP
*Queen green olives are large meaty olives
with a mild flavour. Remember to tell
people the olives still have stones.*

# Saffron Paella

Preparation Time 35 minutes • Cooking Time 50 minutes • Serves 6 • Per Serving 609 calories, 22g fat (of which 6g saturates), 59g carbohydrate, 1.5g salt • **Dairy Free** • **Easy**

½ tsp saffron threads

900ml–1.1 litres (1½–2 pints) hot chicken stock (see page 266)

5 tbsp olive oil

2 × 70g packs sliced chorizo sausage

6 boneless, skinless chicken thighs, each cut into three pieces

1 large onion, chopped

4 large garlic cloves, crushed

1 tsp paprika

2 red peppers, seeded and sliced

400g can chopped tomatoes in tomato juice

350g (12oz) long-grain rice

200ml (7fl oz) dry sherry

500g pack ready-cooked mussels

200g (7oz) cooked tiger prawns, drained

juice of ½ lemon

salt and ground black pepper

fresh flat-leafed parsley sprigs to garnish (optional)

lemon wedges to serve

1 Add the saffron to the hot stock and leave to infuse for 30 minutes. Meanwhile, heat half the oil in a large heavy-based frying pan. Add half the chorizo and fry for about 3–4 minutes or until crisp. Remove with a slotted spoon and drain on kitchen paper. Repeat with the remaining chorizo, then put the chorizo to one side.

2 Heat 1 tbsp oil in the pan. Add half the chicken and cook for 3–5 minutes until pale golden brown. Remove from the pan and put to one side. Cook the remaining chicken and put to one side.

3 Reduce the heat slightly, heat the remaining oil and add the onion. Cook for 5 minutes or until soft. Add the garlic and paprika and cook for 1 minute. Put the chicken back into the pan, then add the peppers and the tomatoes.

4 Stir the rice into the pan, then add one-third of the stock and bring to the boil. Season with salt and pepper, reduce the heat and simmer, uncovered, stirring continuously until most of the liquid has been absorbed.

5 Add the remaining stock, a little at a time, allowing the liquid to become absorbed after each addition (this should take about 25 minutes). Add the sherry and cook for a further 2 minutes.

6 Add the mussels and their juices to the pan with the prawns, lemon juice and reserved chorizo. Cook for 5 minutes to heat through. Adjust the seasoning and garnish with the parsley, if you like, and serve with lemon wedges.

# Moroccan Chicken with Chickpeas

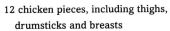

Preparation Time 10 minutes • Cooking Time 50 minutes • Serves 6 • Per Serving 440 calories, 18g fat
(of which 6g saturates), 33g carbohydrate, 1g salt • Easy

12 chicken pieces, including thighs,
   drumsticks and breasts
25g (1oz) butter
1 large onion, sliced
2 garlic cloves, crushed
2 tbsp harissa paste (see page 283)
a generous pinch of saffron threads
1 tsp salt
1 cinnamon stick
600ml (1 pint) chicken stock
   (see page 266)
75g (3oz) raisins
2 × 400g cans chickpeas, drained
   and rinsed
ground black pepper
plain naan or pitta bread to serve

1 Heat a large wide non-stick pan.
Add the chicken pieces and fry until
well browned all over. Add the
butter and, when melted, add the
onion and garlic. Cook, stirring, for
5 minutes.

2 Add the harissa, saffron, salt and
cinnamon stick, then season well
with pepper. Pour in the stock and
bring to the boil. Reduce the heat,
cover the pan and simmer gently for
25–30 minutes.

3 Add the raisins and chickpeas and
bring to the boil, then reduce the
heat and simmer, uncovered, for
5–10 minutes.

4 Serve with warm flatbread such as
plain naan or pitta.

⭐ FREEZING TIP
**To freeze** *Freeze leftover portions
separately. Complete the recipe, then cool
quickly. Put into a sealable container and
freeze for up to three months.*
**To use** *Thaw overnight in the fridge.
Put into a pan, cover and bring to the
boil. Reduce the heat to low, then reheat
for 40 minutes or until the chicken is hot
right through.*

# Moroccan Spiced Chicken Kebabs

Preparation Time 10 minutes, plus marinating and soaking • Cooking Time 10–12 minutes • Serves 4 •
Per Serving 190 calories, 7g fat (of which 1g saturates), 1g carbohydrate, 0.2g salt • Gluten Free • Dairy Free • Easy

2 tbsp olive oil

15g (½oz) fresh flat-leafed parsley

1 garlic clove

½ tsp paprika

1 tsp ground cumin

zest and juice of 1 lemon

4 skinless chicken breasts, cut into
  bite-size chunks

salt

shredded lettuce, sliced cucumber
  and tomatoes, and lime wedges
  to serve

1 Put the oil into a blender and add the parsley, garlic, paprika, cumin, lemon zest and juice and a pinch of salt. Whiz to make a paste.

2 Put the chicken into a medium-sized shallow dish and rub in the spice paste. Leave to marinate for at least 20 minutes. Meanwhile, soak some wooden skewers in water and preheat the grill to high.

3 Thread the marinated chicken on to the skewers and grill for 10–12 minutes, turning every now and then, until the meat is cooked through. Serve with shredded lettuce, sliced cucumber and tomatoes, and lime wedges.

⭐ TRY SOMETHING
DIFFERENT
*Instead of chicken, use 700g (1½lb) lean lamb fillet or leg of lamb, cut into chunks.*

# Jambalaya

★

Preparation Time 15 minutes • Cooking Time about 50 minutes, plus standing • Serves 4 • Per Serving 558 calories, 25g fat (of which 6g saturates), 49g carbohydrate, 0g salt • Gluten Free • Dairy Free • Easy

2 tbsp olive oil

300g (11oz) boneless, skinless chicken thighs, cut into chunks

75g (3oz) French sausage, such as saucisse sèche, chopped

2 celery sticks, chopped

1 large onion, finely chopped

225g (8oz) long-grain rice

1 tbsp tomato purée

2 tsp Cajun spice mix

500ml (18fl oz) hot chicken stock (see page 266)

1 bay leaf

4 large tomatoes, roughly chopped

200g (7oz) raw tiger prawns, peeled and deveined (see Cook's Tip)

1 Heat 1 tbsp oil in a large pan. Add the chicken and sausage and fry over a medium heat until browned. Remove with a slotted spoon and put to one side.

2 Add the remaining oil to the pan with the celery and onion. Fry gently for 15 minutes or until the vegetables are softened but not coloured. Tip in the rice and stir for 1 minute to coat in the oil. Add the tomato purée and spice mix and cook for a further 2 minutes.

3 Pour in the hot stock and return the browned chicken and sausage to the pan with the bay leaf and chopped tomatoes. Simmer for 20–25 minutes until the stock has been fully absorbed and the rice is cooked.

4 Stir in the prawns and cover the pan. Leave to stand for 10 minutes or until the prawns have turned pink. Serve immediately.

★ COOK'S TIP

*To devein prawns, using a small sharp knife, make a shallow cut along the back of the prawn. Using the point of the knife, remove and discard the black vein (intestinal tract) that runs along the back of the prawn.*

# Caribbean Chicken

Preparation Time 40 minutes, plus marinating • Cooking Time 45–50 minutes • Serves 5 • Per Serving 617 calories, 39g fat (of which 12g saturates), 25g carbohydrate, 2.1g salt • Easy

10 chicken pieces (such as thighs, drumsticks, wings or breasts), skinned
1 tsp salt
1 tbsp ground coriander
2 tsp ground cumin
1 tbsp paprika
a pinch of ground nutmeg
1 fresh Scotch bonnet or other hot red chilli, seeded and chopped (see Cook's Tips, page 10)
1 onion, chopped
5 fresh thyme sprigs
4 garlic cloves, crushed
2 tbsp dark soy sauce
juice of 1 lemon
2 tbsp vegetable oil
2 tbsp light muscovado sugar
350g (12oz) American easy-cook rice
3 tbsp dark rum (optional)
25g (1oz) butter
2 × 300g cans black-eye beans, drained
ground black pepper
a few freshly chopped thyme sprigs to garnish

1 Pierce the chicken pieces with a knife, put into a container and sprinkle with ½ tsp salt, some pepper, the coriander, cumin, paprika and nutmeg. Add the chilli, onion, thyme leaves and garlic. Pour the soy sauce and lemon juice over and stir to combine. Cover, chill and leave to marinate for at least 4 hours.

2 Heat a 3.4 litre (6 pint) heavy-based pan over a medium heat for 2 minutes. Add the oil and sugar and cook for 3 minutes or until it turns a golden caramel colour. (Don't overcook it as the mixture will blacken and taste burnt – watch it closely.) Remove the chicken from the marinade. Add to the caramel mixture. Cover and cook over a medium heat for 5 minutes. Turn the chicken and cook, covered, for another 5 minutes or until evenly browned. Add the onion mixture and any marinade juices. Turn again, then re-cover and cook for 10 minutes.

3 Add the rice and stir to combine with the chicken, then pour in 900ml (1½ pints) cold water. Add the rum, if using, the butter and the remaining ½ tsp salt. Cover and simmer over a gentle heat, without lifting the lid, for 20 minutes or until the rice is tender and most of the liquid has been absorbed.

4 Add the black-eye beans to the pan and mix well. Cover the pan and cook for 3–5 minutes until the beans are warmed through and all the liquid has been absorbed, taking care that the rice doesn't stick to the base of the pan. Garnish with the chopped thyme and serve hot.

# Chicken Fajitas

Preparation Time 10 minutes • Cooking Time 20 minutes • Serves 4 • Per Serving 651 calories, 23g fat
(of which 8g saturates), 63g carbohydrate, 1.6g salt • Easy

700g (1½lb) boneless, skinless
    chicken breasts, cut into
    chunky strips
2 tbsp fajita seasoning
1 tbsp sunflower oil
1 red pepper, seeded and sliced
360g jar fajita sauce
1 bunch of spring onions, halved
8 large flour tortillas
150g (5oz) tomato salsa
125g (4oz) guacamole dip
150ml (¼ pint) soured cream

1 Put the chicken breasts into a shallow dish and toss together with the fajita seasoning. Heat the oil in a large non-stick frying pan. Add the chicken and cook for 5 minutes or until golden brown and tender.

2 Add the red pepper and cook for 2 minutes. Pour in the fajita sauce and bring to the boil, then reduce the heat and simmer for 5 minutes or until thoroughly heated. Add a splash of boiling water if the sauce becomes too thick. Stir in the spring onions and cook for 2 minutes.

3 Meanwhile, warm the tortillas in a microwave on full power for 45 seconds, or wrap in foil and warm in a preheated oven at 180°C (160°C fan oven) mark 4 for 10 minutes.

4 Transfer the chicken to a serving dish and take to the table, along with the tortillas, salsa, guacamole and soured cream. Let everyone help themselves.

# Chicken Falafels

**Preparation Time** 20 minutes, plus soaking • **Cooking Time** 20 minutes • **Serves 4** • **Per Serving** 287 calories, 14g fat (of which 3g saturates), 10g carbohydrate, 1.1g salt • **Dairy Free** • **Easy**

450g (1lb) minced chicken
3 shallots, finely chopped
125g (4oz) canned chickpeas (about ½ can), drained and rinsed
2.5cm (1in) piece fresh root ginger, peeled and grated
½ tsp salt
20g (¾oz) freshly chopped coriander
1 medium egg
3 tbsp olive oil
400g can chopped tomatoes
1 tsp caster sugar

**FOR THE COUSCOUS SALAD**
200g (7oz) couscous
350ml (12fl oz) hot chicken stock (see page 266)
grated zest and juice of ½ lemon
25g (1oz) pinenuts
seeds from ½ pomegranate
3 tbsp extra virgin olive oil
2–3 tbsp freshly chopped parsley

**1** First, make the couscous salad. Put the couscous into a bowl and add the hot stock and lemon zest. Leave to soak for 20 minutes. Meanwhile, toast the pinenuts in a dry pan, tossing regularly, until golden. Use a fork to fluff up the couscous, then stir in the pinenuts, pomegranate seeds, lemon juice, extra virgin olive oil and parsley.

**2** Put the minced chicken into a food processor. Add 1 chopped shallot, the chickpeas, grated ginger and salt and whiz to combine.

**3** Add the coriander and egg and whiz again briefly. With damp hands, shape into 12 balls, each measuring 6.5cm (2½in).

**4** Heat 2 tbsp olive oil in a frying pan. Fry the patties for 2–3 minutes on each side until golden brown.

**5** Meanwhile, fry the remaining shallots in a pan with the remaining olive oil. Stir in the tomatoes and sugar and simmer for 10 minutes or until slightly thickened. Serve the patties with the couscous salad, and with the sauce on the side.

# Chicken Kebabs with Tabbouleh

★

Preparation Time 35 minutes, plus marinating and soaking • Cooking Time 10–12 minutes • Serves 4 •
Per Serving 330 calories, 8g fat (of which 1g saturates), 19g carbohydrate, 0.3g salt • Dairy Free • Easy

1 tbsp balsamic vinegar

6 tbsp olive oil

grated zest of 1 lime and juice
   of 2 limes

2 garlic cloves, crushed

4 large skinless chicken breasts,
   about 700g (1½lb), cut into
   2.5cm (1in) cubes

75g (3oz) bulgur wheat

½ cucumber, halved lengthways,
   seeded and diced

4 plum tomatoes, seeded and diced

1 small red onion, finely chopped

4 tbsp freshly chopped mint

4 tbsp freshly chopped flat-leafed
   parsley

ground black pepper

lime wedges and mint sprigs to
   garnish

1 Whisk the balsamic vinegar,
3 tbsp oil, the zest and juice of
1 lime and 1 garlic clove together in
a large bowl. Add the chicken, mix
well, then cover, chill and leave to
marinate for at least 2 hours,
preferably overnight.

2 To make the tabbouleh, put the
bulgur wheat into a bowl, cover
with double its volume of boiling
water and leave to soak for 15
minutes. Drain the bulgur wheat,
squeeze out the liquid and put back
into the bowl. Stir in the cucumber,
tomatoes, onion and herbs and
season with pepper.

3 Whisk the remaining oil, lime juice
and garlic together in a small bowl.
Add to the bulgur wheat and mix
gently but thoroughly until the
bulgur is well coated. Cover and
chill in the fridge.

4 Preheat the barbecue, grill or
griddle. Soak eight wooden skewers
in water for 20 minutes. Remove the
chicken from the marinade, thread
on to the skewers and cook for
10–12 minutes, turning every now
and then, or until cooked through.
Serve with the tabbouleh, garnished
with lime wedges and mint sprigs.

# Chicken Satay Skewers

Preparation Time 30 minutes, plus chilling and soaking • Cooking Time 8–10 minutes • Serves 4 •
Per Serving 687 calories, 51g fat (of which 21g saturates), 11g carbohydrate, 2.1g salt • Gluten Free • Dairy Free • Easy

1 tbsp each coriander and
  cumin seeds
2 tsp ground turmeric
4 garlic cloves, roughly chopped
grated zest and juice of 1 lemon
2 bird's eye chillies, finely chopped
  (see Cook's Tips, page 10)
3 tbsp vegetable oil
4 boneless, skinless chicken
  breasts, about 550g (1¼lb), cut
  into finger-length strips
salt and ground black pepper
½ cucumber, cut into sticks
  to serve

**FOR THE SATAY SAUCE**
200g (7oz) salted peanuts
1 tbsp molasses sugar
½ lemongrass stalk, chopped
2 tbsp dark soy sauce
juice of ½ lime
200ml (7fl oz) coconut cream

1 Put the coriander and cumin seeds and the turmeric into a dry frying pan and heat for 30 seconds. Tip into a blender and add the garlic, lemon zest and juice, chillies, 1 tbsp oil and 1 tsp salt. Whiz for 1–2 minutes.

2 Put the paste into a large shallow dish, add the chicken and toss everything together. Cover and chill in the fridge for at least 20 minutes or up to 12 hours.

3 To make the satay sauce, put the peanuts, sugar, lemongrass, soy sauce, lime juice and coconut cream into a food processor and add 2 tbsp water. Whiz to make a thick chunky sauce, then spoon into a dish. Cover and chill.

4 Preheat the barbecue or grill until hot. Soak 24 bamboo skewers in water for 20 minutes. Thread the chicken on to the skewers, drizzle with the remaining oil and cook for 4–5 minutes on each side or until cooked through. Serve with the satay sauce and the cucumber.

★ TRY SOMETHING DIFFERENT
*Replace the chicken with strips of pork tenderloin or beef rump.*

# Chicken Chow Mein

Preparation Time 10 minutes • Cooking Time 10 minutes • Serves 4 • Per Serving 451 calories, 11g fat (of which 2g saturates), 59g carbohydrate, 1.3g salt • Dairy Free • Easy

250g (9oz) medium egg noodles
1 tbsp toasted sesame oil
2 boneless, skinless chicken breasts, about 125g (4oz) each, cut into thin strips
1 bunch of spring onions, thinly sliced diagonally
150g (5oz) mangetouts, thickly sliced diagonally
125g (4oz) bean sprouts
100g (3½oz) cooked ham, finely shredded
120g sachet chow mein sauce
salt and ground black pepper
light soy sauce to serve

1 Cook the noodles in boiling water for 4 minutes or according to the pack instructions. Drain, rinse thoroughly in cold water, drain again and put to one side.

2 Meanwhile, heat a wok or large frying pan until hot, then add the oil. Add the chicken and stir-fry over a high heat for 3–4 minutes until browned all over. Add the spring onions and mangetouts and stir-fry for 2 minutes. Stir in the bean sprouts and ham and cook for a further 2 minutes.

3 Add the drained noodles, then pour the chow mein sauce into the pan and toss together to coat evenly. Stir-fry for 2 minutes or until piping hot. Season with salt and pepper and serve immediately with light soy sauce to drizzle over the chow mein.

# Exotic Chicken

Preparation Time 20 minutes • Cooking Time 1¾ hours • Serves 6 • Per Serving 370 calories, 17g fat
(of which 6g saturates), 22g carbohydrate, 0.5g salt • Easy

1 large red chilli, seeded and finely
   chopped (see Cook's Tips,
   page 10)
2.5cm (1in) piece fresh root ginger,
   peeled and thinly sliced
10cm (4in) piece lemongrass, cut
   into thin matchsticks
2 kaffir lime leaves (or a little extra
   grated lime zest), cut into thin
   matchsticks
grated zest of 1 lime
2 garlic bulbs, halved
2 tbsp freshly chopped coriander
1.8kg (4lb) oven-ready chicken
1 tbsp chilli sauce
3 tbsp rapeseed oil
1 tsp ground turmeric
800g (1¾lb) baby new potatoes
3 tbsp desiccated coconut
juice of 2 limes
salt and ground black pepper
fresh coriander to garnish

1 Preheat the oven to 200°C (180°C fan oven) mark 6. Cut two pieces of non-stick baking parchment, each measuring about 75 × 40cm (30 × 16in). Sprinkle each with water to dampen slightly, then put one on top of the other.

2 Combine the chilli, ginger, lemongrass, kaffir lime leaves, some grated lime zest and the garlic with the coriander. Pile in the centre of the baking parchment. Season inside the chicken generously with salt and pepper, then scatter the rest of the grated lime zest over and put the chicken on top of the spices.

3 Mix the chilli sauce with 1 tbsp oil and brush all over the chicken. Bring the edges of the baking parchment together and tie at the top with kitchen string to encase the chicken completely. Put into a large roasting tin just big enough to hold the parcel and cook in the oven for 1 hour 40 minutes.

4 Mix the remaining oil with the turmeric and potatoes in a roasting tin and toss well to coat evenly. Put on a tray above the chicken for the last 40 minutes of the cooking time. Roast until golden and tender. Remove the potatoes from the oven, add the desiccated coconut and stir to coat evenly. Put back in the oven and cook for a further 5 minutes or until the coconut has turned golden. Keep warm.

5 Untie the parcel and allow any juices inside the chicken to run into a pan. Lift the chicken out and add as much of the flavouring ingredients as possible to the pan. Cover the chicken with foil and keep warm in a low oven. Add the lime juice to the pan and bring to the boil. Bubble furiously for 1 minute. Keep hot.

6 Carve the chicken and serve with the roast potatoes and cooking juices. Garnish with fresh coriander.

# Hot and Spicy ★

# Chicken Enchiladas

★

Preparation Time 30 minutes • Cooking Time 45 minutes • Serves 6 • Per Serving 433 calories, 17g fat (of which 10g saturates), 37g carbohydrate, 1.3g salt • Easy

450g (1lb) skinless chicken breasts, cut into strips
1 tsp dried oregano
1 tsp cumin seeds
5 tbsp olive oil, plus extra to oil
2 onions, finely chopped
125g (4oz) celery, cut into strips
2 garlic cloves, crushed
50g (2oz) sun-dried tomatoes in oil, drained and roughly chopped

225g (8oz) brown-cap mushrooms, chopped
250g (9oz) Cheddar, grated
2 tbsp freshly chopped coriander
2 tbsp lemon juice
6 flour tortillas
salt and ground black pepper
Salsa Verde to serve (see page 59)

**1** Preheat the oven to 180°C (160°C fan oven) mark 4. Put the chicken into a bowl, add the oregano, cumin seeds and salt and pepper and toss to coat the chicken.

**2** Heat half the oil in a large frying pan. Add the onions, celery and garlic and cook gently for 5–7 minutes. Add the tomatoes and mushrooms and cook for a further 2–3 minutes. Remove from the pan and put to one side.

**3** Add the remaining oil to the pan and stir-fry the chicken in batches for 2–3 minutes. Add the chicken to the mushroom mixture, with 175g (6oz) cheese, the chopped coriander and lemon juice. Mix well and season with salt and pepper.

**4** Divide the chicken mixture among the tortillas and roll up to enclose the filling. Put, seam side down, into an oiled ovenproof dish, then sprinkle with the remaining cheese. Cook in the oven for 25–30 minutes until golden and bubbling. Spoon the salsa verde over the enchiladas to serve.

# Chicken Chilli

Preparation Time 20 minutes • Cooking Time 55 minutes • Serves 4 • Per Serving 350 calories, 12g fat (of which 3g saturates), 32g carbohydrate, 0.6g salt • **Easy**

2 × 20g packs fresh coriander
2 tbsp olive oil
1 large Spanish onion, finely chopped
1 red chilli, seeded and finely chopped (see Cook's Tips, page 10)
450g (1lb) chicken fillet, diced
1 tbsp plain flour
410g can mixed pulses or mixed beans, drained and rinsed
2 × 400g cans chopped tomatoes with garlic
1–2 tbsp light muscovado sugar
juice of 1 small lime
warm tortillas, grated Cheddar, chopped green chillies and soured cream to serve

**1** Preheat the oven to 170°C (150°C fan oven) mark 3. Chop the leaves from the coriander stalks and cut the stalks finely. Rewrap the leaves and pop them in the fridge.

**2** Heat 1 tbsp oil in a large casserole. Add the onion, coriander stalks and chilli and fry for 5–7 minutes or until the onion is soft and golden. Spoon on to a plate and put to one side.

**3** Add the remaining oil to the casserole. Add the chicken and fry for 5 minutes or until golden.

**4** Return the onion mixture to the casserole and stir in the flour. Add the pulses or beans, tomatoes and sugar, then bring to the boil. Cover with a tight-fitting lid and cook in the oven for 40 minutes.

**5** To serve, finely chop the coriander leaves and stir most of them into the casserole with the lime juice. Serve with warm tortillas, grated Cheddar, chopped green chillies, the remaining coriander and soured cream.

# Chicken with Devilled Sauce

★

Preparation Time 20 minutes • Cooking Time 1 hour 50 minutes, plus resting • Serves 6 • Per Serving 652 calories, 48g fat (of which 17g saturates), 13g carbohydrate, 0.7g salt • Gluten Free • Easy

3 garlic cloves, chopped
1 large onion, chopped
2.3kg (5lb) chicken
450g (1lb) tomatoes, peeled, seeded
    and chopped
salt and ground black pepper
fresh basil sprigs to garnish
90ml (3fl oz) crème fraîche,
    warmed, to serve

**FOR THE DEVILLED SAUCE**
25g (1oz) butter
2 tbsp mango or sweet chutney,
    any large pieces chopped
    (see page 282)
2 tbsp Worcestershire sauce
2 tbsp wholegrain mustard
1 tsp paprika
3 tbsp freshly squeezed orange
    juice

1 Preheat the oven to 190°C (170°C fan oven) mark 5. To make the devilled sauce, melt the butter in a pan. Add the mango or sweet chutney, Worcestershire sauce, mustard, paprika, orange juice and salt and pepper and mix together.

2 Put the garlic and onion into the cavity of the chicken. Put the chicken into a large roasting tin and spoon over some of the devilled sauce. Roast the chicken in the oven, basting frequently with the sauce, for 1¾ hours or until the juices run clear when the thickest part of the thigh is pierced with a skewer. The skin should be slightly charred; if it's becoming too brown, cover it with foil towards the end of the cooking time.

3 Put the chicken on a warmed serving plate and keep warm. Skim off the fat from the juices in the roasting tin and discard, then stir the tomatoes into the juices with any remaining devilled sauce. Heat through and season with salt and pepper. Carve the chicken and serve with the devilled sauce and warmed crème fraîche. Garnish with basil.

★ TRY SOMETHING DIFFERENT
*For a more fiery sauce, add a finely chopped chilli (see Cook's Tips, page 10) to the devilled mixture before basting.*

# Chicken with Spicy Couscous

Preparation Time 15 minutes, plus soaking • Serves 4 • Per Serving 223 calories, 6g fat (of which 2g saturates), 30g carbohydrate, 0.2g salt • Easy

125g (4oz) couscous
1 ripe mango, peeled, stoned and
    cut into 2.5cm (1in) chunks
1 tbsp lemon or lime juice
125g tub fresh tomato salsa
3 tbsp Mango Chutney
    (see page 282)
3 tbsp orange juice
2 tbsp freshly chopped coriander
200g (7oz) chargrilled chicken
    fillets
4 tbsp fromage frais (optional)
salt and ground black pepper
freshly chopped coriander and lime
    wedges to garnish

1 Put the couscous into a large bowl and pour 300ml (½ pint) boiling water over. Season well with salt and pepper, then leave to soak for 15 minutes.

2 Put the mango chunks on a large plate and sprinkle with the lemon or lime juice.

3 Mix the tomato salsa with the mango chutney, orange juice and coriander in a small bowl.

4 Drain the couscous if necessary, fluff the grains with a fork, then stir in the salsa mixture and check the seasoning. Turn out on to a large serving dish and arrange the chicken and mango on top.

5 Just before serving, spoon the fromage frais over the chicken, if you like, then garnish with chopped coriander and lime wedges.

# Fiery Mango Chicken

★

Preparation Time 15 minutes, plus marinating • Cooking Time 10 minutes • Serves 4 • Per Serving 220 calories, 8g fat
(of which 2g saturates), 7g carbohydrate, 0.3g salt • Gluten Free • Easy

4 tbsp hot mango chutney or
   ordinary Mango Chutney (see
   page 282), plus ½ tsp Tabasco
grated zest and juice of 1 lime
4 tbsp natural yogurt
2 tbsp freshly chopped coriander
1 small green chilli (optional),
   seeded and finely chopped (see
   Cook's Tips, page 10)
4 chicken breasts, with skin
1 large ripe mango, peeled and
   stoned
oil to brush
salt and ground black pepper
fresh coriander sprigs and lime
   wedges to garnish

1 Mix together the chutney, lime zest and juice, yogurt, chopped coriander and, if you like it spicy, the finely chopped chilli.

2 Put the chicken breasts, skin side down, on the worksurface, cover with clingfilm and lightly beat with a rolling pin. Slice each into three pieces and put into the yogurt mixture and stir to coat. Cover the bowl, chill and leave to marinate for at least 30 minutes or overnight.

3 Preheat the barbecue or grill. Slice the mango into four thick pieces. Brush lightly with oil and season well with salt and pepper. Cook for about 2 minutes on each side – the fruit should be lightly charred but still firm. Put to one side.

4 Cook the chicken for 3–5 minutes on each side until golden brown. Serve with the cooked mango, garnished with coriander sprigs and lime wedges.

# Tandoori Chicken with Cucumber Raita

Preparation Time 45 minutes, plus marinating • Cooking Time 20 minutes • Serves 4 • Per Serving 399 calories, 20g fat (of which 4g saturates), 15g carbohydrate, 2g salt • Gluten Free • Easy

4 tbsp groundnut oil, plus extra
  to oil
3 × 150g cartons natural yogurt
juice of ½ lemon
4 boneless, skinless chicken
  breasts, about 600g (1lb 5oz), cut
  into finger-width pieces
½ cucumber
salt and ground black pepper
fresh mint leaves to garnish

**FOR THE TANDOORI PASTE**
24 garlic cloves, about 125g (4oz),
  crushed
5cm (2in) piece fresh root ginger,
  peeled and chopped
3 tbsp each coriander seeds, cumin
  seeds, ground fenugreek and
  paprika
3 red chillies, seeded and chopped
  (see Cook's Tips, page 10)
3 tsp English mustard
2 tbsp tomato purée
1 tsp salt

1 Put all the ingredients for the tandoori paste into a food processor with 8 tbsp water and blend to a paste. Divide the paste into three equal portions, freeze two (see Freezing Tip) and put the other in a large bowl.

2 To make the tandoori chicken, add 2 tbsp oil, 2 cartons of yogurt and the lemon juice to the paste. Add the chicken and stir well to coat. Cover the bowl, chill and leave to marinate for at least 4 hours.

3 Preheat the oven to 220°C (200°C fan oven) mark 7. Oil a roasting tin. Put the chicken in it, drizzle the remaining oil over the chicken and roast in the oven for 20 minutes or until cooked through.

4 Meanwhile, prepare the raita. Whisk the remaining carton of yogurt. Using a vegetable peeler, scrape the cucumber into very thin strips. Put the strips in a bowl and pour the whisked yogurt over them. Season, then chill until ready to serve. Garnish the cucumber raita with mint. Sprinkle the chicken with mint and serve with the raita.

⭐ FREEZING TIP
**To freeze the paste** *At the end of step 1, put two of the portions of tandoori paste into separate freezer bags and freeze. They will keep for up to three months.*
**To use the frozen paste** *Put the paste in a microwave and cook on Defrost for 1 minute 20 seconds (based on 900W oven), or thaw at a cool room temperature for 1 hour.*

# Spiced Tikka Kebabs

Preparation Time 10 minutes • Cooking Time 20 minutes • Serves 4 • Per Serving 150 calories, 5g fat (of which 1g saturates), 4g carbohydrate, 0.3g salt • Gluten Free • Easy

2 tbsp tikka paste
150g (5oz) natural yogurt
juice of ½ lime
4 spring onions, chopped
350g (12oz) skinless chicken, cut into bite-size pieces
lime wedges and Mixed Salad (see Cook's Tip) to serve

1 Preheat the grill. Put the tikka paste, yogurt, lime juice and spring onions into a large bowl. Add the chicken and toss well. Thread the chicken on to metal skewers.

2 Grill the chicken for 8–10 minutes on each side, turning and basting with the paste, until cooked through. Serve with lime wedges to squeeze over the kebabs, and mixed salad.

⭐ COOK'S TIP

*Mixed Salad*

*Put 75g (3oz) green salad leaves into a large bowl. Add ¼ chopped avocado, a handful of halved cherry tomatoes, ½ chopped cucumber and the juice of 1 lime. Season to taste with salt and pepper and mix together.*

# Creamy Curried Chicken

Preparation Time 15 minutes • Cooking Time 30–35 minutes • Serves 4 • Per Serving 380 calories, 21g fat (of which 7g saturates), 9g carbohydrate, 0.9g salt • Easy

25g (1oz) butter
700g (1½lb) skinless chicken breast
  fillets, cut into bite-size pieces
1 small onion, chopped
4 celery sticks, chopped
2 tbsp each mild curry paste and
  Mango Chutney (see page 282)
2 tbsp lemon juice
2 tbsp each Greek-style natural
  yogurt and mayonnaise
3 tbsp milk
fresh flat-leafed parsley to garnish
rice to serve

1 Heat the butter in a pan. Add the chicken and fry for 15–20 minutes until cooked, then put to one side. Add the onion and celery to the pan and fry for 5 minutes until soft.

2 Stir in the curry paste, chutney and lemon juice and cook, stirring, for 2 minutes.

3 Take the pan off the heat, add the yogurt, mayonnaise and milk and stir well.

4 Put the chicken back into the pan and bring to simmering point. Cook until piping hot. Divide among four plates, garnish with parsley and serve with rice.

# Thai Red Chicken Curry

Preparation Time 20 minutes • Cooking Time 18–25 minutes • Serves 6 • Per Serving 247 calories, 8g fat (of which 1g saturates), 15g carbohydrate, 1.2g salt • Gluten Free • Dairy Free • Easy

3 tbsp vegetable oil
450g (1lb) onions, finely chopped
200g (7oz) green beans, trimmed
125g (4oz) baby sweetcorn, cut on the diagonal
2 red peppers, seeded and cut into thick strips
1 tbsp Thai red curry paste, or to taste
1 red chilli, seeded and finely chopped (see Cook's Tips, page 10)
1 lemongrass stalk, very finely chopped
4 kaffir lime leaves, bruised
2 tbsp fresh root ginger, peeled and finely chopped
1 garlic clove, crushed
400ml can coconut milk
600ml (1 pint) chicken stock
450g (1lb) cooked chicken, cut into strips
150g (5oz) bean sprouts
fresh basil leaves to garnish

1 Heat the oil in a wok or large frying pan. Add the onions and cook for 4–5 minutes until soft.

2 Add the beans, baby sweetcorn and peppers to the pan and stir-fry for 3–4 minutes. Add the curry paste, chilli, lemongrass, kaffir lime leaves, ginger and garlic and cook for a further 2 minutes, stirring. Remove from the pan and put to one side.

3 Add the coconut milk and stock to the pan, bring to the boil and bubble vigorously for 5–10 minutes until reduced by one-quarter. Return the vegetables to the pan with the chicken and bean sprouts. Bring to the boil, then reduce the heat and simmer for 1–2 minutes until heated through. Serve immediately, garnished with basil leaves.

★ COOK'S TIP
*This is a great way to use leftover chicken.*

# Chicken Curry with Rice

Preparation Time 20 minutes • Cooking Time 30 minutes, plus standing • Serves 4 • Per Serving 453 calories, 12g fat (of which 2g saturates), 49g carbohydrate, 2.4g salt • Gluten Free • Dairy Free • Easy

2 tbsp vegetable oil
1 onion, finely sliced
2 garlic cloves, crushed
6 boneless, skinless chicken thighs,
    cut into strips
2 tbsp tikka masala curry paste
200g can chopped tomatoes
450ml (¾ pint) hot vegetable stock
200g (7oz) basmati rice
1 tsp salt
225g (8oz) baby leaf spinach
poppadums and Mango Chutney
    (see page 282) to serve

1 Heat the oil in a large pan. Add the onion and fry over a medium heat for about 5 minutes or until golden. Add the garlic and chicken and stir-fry for about 5 minutes or until golden.

2 Add the curry paste, tomatoes and hot stock. Stir and bring to the boil, then reduce the heat, cover the pan and simmer over a low heat for 15 minutes or until the chicken is cooked (cut a piece in half to check that it's white all the way through).

3 Meanwhile, cook the rice. Put 600ml (1 pint) water into a medium pan, cover and bring to the boil. Add the rice and salt and stir. Replace the lid and reduce the heat to its lowest setting. Cook according to the pack instructions. Once cooked, cover with a teatowel and the lid. Leave for 5 minutes to absorb the steam.

4 Add the spinach to the curry and cook until it has just wilted.

5 Spoon the rice into bowls, add the curry and serve with poppadums and mango chutney.

# Hot Jungle Curry

Preparation Time 10 minutes • Cooking Time 18–20 minutes • Serves 4 • Per Serving 160 calories, 5g fat (of which 1g saturates), 5g carbohydrate, 1.1g salt • Gluten Free • Dairy Free • Easy

1 tbsp vegetable oil

350g (12oz) boneless, skinless chicken breasts, cut into 5cm (2in) strips

2 tbsp Thai red curry paste

2.5cm (1in) piece fresh root ginger, peeled and thinly sliced

125g (4oz) aubergine, cut into bite-size pieces

125g (4oz) baby sweetcorn, halved lengthways

75g (3oz) green beans, trimmed

75g (3oz) button or brown-cap mushrooms, halved if large

2–3 kaffir lime leaves (optional)

450ml (¾ pint) chicken stock (see page 266)

2 tbsp Thai fish sauce

grated zest of ½ lime, plus extra to garnish

1 tsp tomato purée

1 tbsp soft brown sugar

rice to serve

**1** Heat the oil in a wok or large frying pan. Add the chicken and cook, stirring, for 5 minutes or until the chicken turns golden brown.

**2** Add the curry paste and cook for a further 1 minute. Add the ginger, aubergine, sweetcorn, beans, mushrooms and lime leaves, if using, and stir until coated in the curry paste. Add the remaining ingredients and bring to the boil. Reduce the heat and simmer for 10–12 minutes or until the chicken and vegetables are tender. Sprinkle with lime zest and serve with rice.

★ TRY SOMETHING DIFFERENT
*Add a drained 225g can of bamboo shoots with the other vegetables in step 2, if you like.*

# Chicken, Bean and Spinach Curry

★

Preparation Time 10 minutes • Cooking Time about 20 minutes • Serves 4 • Per Serving 364 calories, 9g fat (of which 1g saturates), 41g carbohydrate, 2.9g salt • Gluten Free • Easy

1 tbsp sunflower oil

350g (12oz) boneless, skinless chicken breasts, cut into strips

1 garlic clove, crushed

300–350g tub or jar curry sauce

400g can aduki beans, drained and rinsed

175g (6oz) ready-to-eat dried apricots

150g (5oz) natural yogurt, plus extra to serve

125g (4oz) baby spinach leaves

naan bread to serve (optional)

1 Heat the oil in a large pan over a medium heat. Add the chicken strips and garlic and fry until golden. Add the curry sauce, aduki beans and apricots, then cover and simmer gently for 15 minutes or until the chicken is tender.

2 Over a low heat, stir in the yogurt, keeping the curry hot without boiling it, then stir in the spinach until it just begins to wilt. Add a spoonful of yogurt and serve with naan bread, if you like.

★ TRY SOMETHING DIFFERENT
*Use pork escalopes, cut into thin strips, instead of chicken.*

# Chicken Tikka Masala

**Preparation Time** 15 minutes • **Cooking Time** 30 minutes • **Serves 4** • **Per Serving** 297 calories, 17g fat (of which 4g saturates), 4g carbohydrate, 0.6g salt • **Dairy Free** • **Easy**

2 tbsp vegetable oil
1 onion, finely sliced
2 garlic cloves, crushed
6 boneless, skinless chicken thighs, cut into strips
2 tbsp tikka masala curry paste
200g can chopped tomatoes
450ml (¾ pint) hot vegetable stock
225g (8oz) baby spinach leaves
fresh coriander leaves to garnish
basmati rice, Mango Chutney (see page 282) and poppadoms to serve

**1** Heat the oil in a large pan. Add the onion and fry over a medium heat for 5–7 minutes until golden. Add the garlic and chicken strips and stir-fry for about 5 minutes or until golden.

**2** Stir in the curry paste, then add the tomatoes and hot stock. Bring to the boil, then reduce the heat, cover the pan and simmer over a low heat for 15 minutes or until the chicken is cooked through.

**3** Add the spinach to the curry, stir and cook until the leaves have just wilted. Garnish with coriander and serve with rice, mango chutney and poppadoms.

# Chicken Tikka with Coconut Dressing

★

Preparation Time 10 minutes • Serves 4 • Per Serving 493 calories, 17g fat (of which 9g saturates), 53g carbohydrate, 1.1g salt • Easy

**125ml (4fl oz) crème fraîche**
**5 tbsp coconut milk**
**4 pitta breads**
**200g (7oz) mixed salad leaves**
**400g (14oz) cooked chicken tikka fillets, sliced**
**2 spring onions, finely sliced**
**2 tbsp Mango Chutney (see page 282)**
**15g (½oz) flaked almonds**
**25g (1oz) raisins**

1 Mix the crème fraîche and coconut milk together in a bowl and put to one side.

2 Split each pitta bread to form a pocket, then fill each pocket with a generous handful of salad leaves. Divide the chicken among the pitta breads. Sprinkle some spring onion over the chicken, add the mango chutney and drizzle with the crème fraîche mixture. Top with a sprinkling of flaked almonds and raisins. Serve immediately.

# Chicken and Coconut Curry

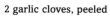

Preparation Time 15 minutes • Cooking Time 35 minutes • Serves 6 • Per Serving 204 calories, 6g fat (of which 1g saturates), 10g carbohydrate, 1.5g salt • Gluten Free • Dairy Free • Easy

2 garlic cloves, peeled
1 onion, quartered
1 lemongrass stalk, trimmed and
   halved
2.5cm (1in) piece fresh root ginger,
   peeled and halved
2 small hot chillies (see Cook's
   Tips, page 10)
a small handful of fresh coriander
1 tsp ground coriander
grated zest and juice of 1 lime

2 tbsp vegetable oil
6 boneless, skinless chicken
   breasts, each cut into three
   pieces
2 large tomatoes, peeled and
   chopped
2 tbsp Thai fish sauce
900ml (1½ pints) coconut milk
salt and ground black pepper
finely sliced red chilli to garnish
basmati rice to serve

**1** Put the garlic, onion, lemongrass, ginger, chillies, fresh coriander, ground coriander and lime zest and juice into a food processor and whiz to a paste. Add a little water if the mixture gets stuck under the blades.

**2** Heat the oil in a wok or large frying pan. Add the spice paste and cook over a fairly high heat for 3–4 minutes, stirring constantly. Add the chicken and cook for 5 minutes, stirring to coat in the spice mixture.

**3** Add the tomatoes, fish sauce and coconut milk. Cover and simmer for about 25 minutes or until the chicken is cooked. Season with salt and pepper, garnish with red chilli and serve with basmati rice.

# Easy Thai Red Curry

Preparation Time 5 minutes • Cooking Time 20 minutes • Serves 4 • Per Serving 248 calories, 8g fat (of which 1g saturates), 16g carbohydrate, 1g salt • Dairy Free • Easy

1 tbsp vegetable oil

3 tbsp Thai red curry paste

4 skinless chicken breasts, about 600g (1lb 5oz) total weight, sliced

400ml can coconut milk

300ml (½ pint) hot chicken (see page 266) or vegetable stock

juice of 1 lime, plus lime halves to serve

200g pack mixed baby sweetcorn and mangetouts

2 tbsp freshly chopped coriander, plus sprigs to garnish

rice or rice noodles to serve

**1** Heat the oil in a wok or large frying pan over a low heat. Add the curry paste and cook for 2 minutes or until fragrant.

**2** Add the sliced chicken and fry gently for about 10 minutes or until the chicken is browned.

**3** Add the coconut milk, hot stock, lime juice and baby sweetcorn to the pan and bring to the boil. Add the mangetouts, then reduce the heat and simmer for 4–5 minutes until the chicken is cooked. Stir in the chopped coriander, garnish with coriander sprigs and serve immediately with rice or noodles, and lime halves to squeeze over.

# Thai Green Curry

Preparation Time 10 minutes • Cooking Time 15 minutes • Serves 6 • Per Serving 132 calories, 2g fat (of which 0g saturates), 4g carbohydrate, 1.4g salt • Dairy Free • Easy

2 tsp vegetable oil

1 green chilli, seeded and finely chopped (see Cook's Tips, page 10)

4cm (1½in) piece fresh root ginger, peeled and finely grated

1 lemongrass stalk, trimmed and cut into three pieces

225g (8oz) brown-cap or oyster mushrooms

1 tbsp Thai green curry paste

300ml (½ pint) coconut milk

150ml (¼ pint) chicken stock (see page 266)

1 tbsp Thai fish sauce

1 tsp light soy sauce

350g (12oz) boneless, skinless chicken breasts, cut into bite-size pieces

350g (12oz) cooked peeled large prawns

fresh coriander sprigs to garnish

Thai rice (see page 281) to serve

1 Heat the oil in a wok or large frying pan. Add the chilli, ginger, lemongrass and mushrooms and stir-fry for about 3 minutes or until the mushrooms begin to turn golden. Add the curry paste and fry for a further 1 minute.

2 Pour in the coconut milk, stock, fish sauce and soy sauce and bring to the boil. Stir in the chicken, then reduce the heat and simmer for about 8 minutes or until the chicken is cooked.

3 Add the prawns and cook for a further 1 minute. Garnish with coriander sprigs and serve immediately with Thai rice.

# Thai Poached Chicken

★

Preparation Time 10 minutes • Cooking Time 1½ hours • Serves 4 • Per Serving 579 calories, 36g fat (of which 10g saturates), 1g carbohydrate, 1g salt • Gluten Free • Dairy Free • Easy

2 limes, halved
1.4kg (3lb) chicken
a knob of butter
2 lemongrass stalks, crushed
450ml (¾ pint) dry white wine
450ml (¾ pint) chicken stock (see page 266)
1 small bunch of coriander, chopped
salt and ground black pepper
rice and vegetables to serve

**1** Preheat the oven to 200°C (180°C fan oven) mark 6. Put 2 lime halves into the cavity of the chicken. Rub the chicken with the butter and season with salt and pepper. Put the chicken into a flameproof casserole.

**2** Add the lemongrass and remaining lime to the casserole, then pour in the wine and stock. Cover with a tight-fitting lid and cook in the oven for 1 hour.

**3** Uncover and cook for a further 30 minutes or until the chicken is cooked and the juices run clear when the thickest part of the thigh is pierced with a skewer. Sprinkle the coriander over the chicken and serve with rice and vegetables.

# Chilli-fried Chicken with Coconut Noodles

Preparation Time 15–20 minutes • Cooking Time 15 minutes • Serves 6 • Per Serving 580 calories, 29g fat (of which 8g saturates), 37g carbohydrate, 3.2g salt • Dairy Free • Easy

2 tbsp plain flour

1 tsp mild chilli powder

1 tsp ground ginger

½ tsp salt

1 tsp caster sugar

6 boneless, skinless chicken breasts, about 150g (5oz) each, cut diagonally into three

250g (9oz) thread egg noodles

3 tbsp groundnut oil

1 large bunch of spring onions, sliced

1½ tsp Thai red curry paste or tandoori paste (see page 283)

150g (5oz) salted roasted peanuts, finely chopped

6 tbsp coconut milk

1 Mix the flour, chilli powder, ground ginger, salt and sugar in a bowl. Dip the chicken into the spiced flour and coat well.

2 Cook the noodles in boiling water according to the pack instructions, then drain.

3 Heat the oil in a frying pan. Add the chicken and fry for 5 minutes or until cooked. Put to one side, cover and keep warm. Add the spring onions to the pan and fry for 1 minute. Put to one side and keep warm.

4 Add the curry paste to the pan with 75g (3oz) peanuts and fry for 1 minute. Add the noodles and fry for 1 minute. Stir in the coconut milk and toss the noodles over a high heat for 30 seconds.

5 Put the chicken and spring onions on the coconut noodles. Scatter with the remaining peanuts and serve.

### ★ COOK'S TIP

*Coconut milk gives a thick creaminess to stir-fries, soups and curries.*

# Spiced One-pot Chicken

Preparation Time 10 minutes, plus marinating • Cooking Time 1 hour 10 minutes • Serves 6 • Per Serving 604 calories, 36g fat (of which 10g saturates), 20g carbohydrate, 0.5g salt • Dairy Free • Easy

3 tbsp Thai red curry paste
150ml (¼ pint) orange juice
2 garlic cloves, crushed
6 chicken pieces, 2.3kg (5lb) total
    weight, with bone in
700g (1½lb) squash or pumpkin,
    peeled and cut into 5cm
    (2in) cubes
5 red onions, quartered
2 tbsp capers, drained and chopped
salt and ground black pepper

1 Combine the curry paste, orange juice and garlic in a bowl. Put the chicken pieces in the marinade and leave to marinate for 15 minutes.

2 Preheat the oven to 220°C (200°C fan oven) mark 7. Put the vegetables into a large roasting tin, then remove the chicken from the marinade and arrange on top of the vegetables. Pour the marinade over and season with salt and pepper. Mix everything together, so that it's covered with the marinade, then scatter with the capers.

3 Cook in the oven for 1 hour 10 minutes, turning from time to time, or until the chicken is cooked through and the skin is golden.

★ GET AHEAD
**To prepare ahead** *Complete the recipe to the end of step 2. Cover and chill for up to one day.*
**To use** *Complete the recipe, but cook for a further 5–10 minutes.*

# Other Birds

# Turkey and Broccoli Stir-fry

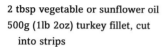

Preparation Time 15 minutes • Cooking Time 8–12 minutes • Serves 4 • Per Serving 254 calories, 8g fat
(of which 1g saturates), 8g carbohydrate, 1.3g salt • **Dairy Free** • **Easy**

2 tbsp vegetable or sunflower oil
500g (1lb 2oz) turkey fillet, cut
    into strips
2 garlic cloves, crushed
2.5cm (1in) piece fresh root ginger,
    peeled and grated
1 broccoli head, cut into florets
8 spring onions, finely chopped
150g (5oz) button mushrooms,
    halved
100g (3½oz) bean sprouts
3 tbsp oyster sauce
1 tbsp light soy sauce
125ml (4fl oz) hot chicken stock
    (see page 266)
juice of ½ lemon

**1** Heat 1 tbsp oil in a wok or large non-stick frying pan. Add the turkey strips and stir-fry for 4–5 minutes until golden and cooked through. Remove from the pan and put to one side.

**2** Heat the remaining oil in the same pan over a medium heat. Add the garlic and ginger and cook for 30 seconds, stirring so that they don't burn. Add the broccoli, spring onions and mushrooms, increase the heat and cook for 2–3 minutes until the vegetables start to brown but are still crisp.

**3** Return the turkey to the pan and add the bean sprouts, oyster and soy sauces, hot stock and lemon juice. Cook for 1–2 minutes, stirring well, until everything is heated through.

★ TRY SOMETHING DIFFERENT
*Use pork fillet instead of turkey, cutting the fillet into thin slices.*

# Turkey and Sesame Stir-fry with Noodles

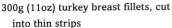

Preparation Time 10 minutes, plus marinating • Cooking Time 10 minutes • Serves 4 • Per Serving 672 calories, 18g fat (of which 4g saturates), 97g carbohydrate, 0.7g salt • Dairy Free • Easy

300g (11oz) turkey breast fillets, cut into thin strips
3 tbsp teriyaki marinade
3 tbsp clear honey
500g (1lb 2oz) medium egg noodles
about 1 tbsp sesame oil, plus extra for the noodles
300g (11oz) ready-prepared mixed stir-fry vegetables, such as carrots, broccoli, red cabbage, mangetouts, bean sprouts and purple spring onions
2 tbsp sesame seeds, lightly toasted in a dry wok or heavy-based pan

1 Put the turkey strips into a large bowl with the teriyaki marinade and honey and stir to coat. Cover and put to one side for 5 minutes.

2 Cook the noodles in boiling water for about 4 minutes or according to the pack instructions. Drain well, then toss in a little oil.

3 Heat 1 tbsp oil in a wok or large frying pan and add the turkey, reserving the marinade. Stir-fry over a very high heat for 2–3 minutes until cooked through and beginning to brown. Add a drop more oil, if needed, then add the vegetables and reserved marinade. Continue to cook over a high heat, stirring, until the vegetables have started to soften and the sauce is warmed through.

4 Scatter with the sesame seeds and serve immediately with the noodles.

# Roast Turkey with Sage, Lemon and Thyme

★

Preparation Time 40 minutes, plus chilling • Cooking Time 3¾ hours • Serves 16 • Per Serving 280 calories, 10g fat (of which 2g saturates), 11g carbohydrate, 2.2g salt • Easy

**FOR THE STUFFING**
4 tbsp olive oil
2 large onions, finely chopped
4 garlic cloves, crushed
150g (5oz) fresh white breadcrumbs
75g (3oz) medium cornmeal or polenta
100g (3½oz) hazelnuts, toasted and chopped
finely grated zest of 2 lemons and juice of 1 lemon
4 tbsp freshly chopped flat-leafed parsley
4 tbsp freshly chopped sage
2 medium eggs, lightly beaten
salt and ground black pepper

**FOR THE SEASONING**
1 tbsp whole pink peppercorns
2 tsp sea salt
2 tbsp paprika
2 tbsp celery salt

**FOR THE TURKEY**
6.3kg (14lb) turkey, with giblets
2 small red onions, cut into wedges
2 lemons, cut into wedges
6 whole garlic cloves
8 fresh thyme sprigs
8 fresh sage leaves
8 fresh flat-leafed parsley sprigs
250ml (8fl oz) olive oil
roast vegetables to serve

**1** To make the stuffing, heat the oil in a pan. Add the onions and garlic and fry gently for 10 minutes to soften but not brown. Tip into a bowl to cool. Meanwhile, put the breadcrumbs, cornmeal or polenta, hazelnuts, lemon zest, parsley, sage and eggs into a large bowl and squeeze over the lemon juice. Add the cooled onion and garlic and season with salt and pepper. Stir to bind together and leave to cool.

**2** For the seasoning, put the peppercorns, sea salt, paprika and celery salt into a pestle and mortar and pound to crush, or whiz in a mini processor.

**3** For the turkey, stand it upright on a board, with the parson's nose (the rear end) facing upwards. Sprinkle the inside cavity with 1 tbsp of the peppercorn seasoning, then pack the cavity with half the onions and lemon wedges, garlic cloves, thyme, sage and all the parsley sprigs.

**4** Sit the turkey with the parson's nose facing away from you. Lift up the loose skin at the neck end with one hand and, using the other, fill the cavity with handfuls of cold stuffing. Turn the turkey over on to its breast, then lift the neck flap up and over the stuffing to cover and bring the wing tips round on top.

**5** Thread a trussing needle with 2m fine string and sew the neck flap to the turkey to enclose the stuffing. Push the skewer firmly through the wings, twist the string around the ends and pull to tighten so that both wings are snug against the breast. Turn the turkey over, tuck in the parson's nose, cross the legs together, then bring the string up and over the legs and wrap around tightly, finishing with a double knot to secure. Cut off any excess.

**6** Pour the olive oil into a large roasting tin. Immerse a piece of muslin, about 60cm (23½in), in it to coat completely, then stretch it out, with the edges overhanging the tin. Sit the turkey on the muslin and sprinkle with the remaining peppercorn seasoning. Scatter the remaining thyme and sage across the turkey, then arrange the remaining lemon and onion wedges and the garlic cloves around the bird. Bring the muslin up and over the turkey to wrap completely, then turn it over so that it's breast side down in the roasting tin. Over-wrap with clingfilm and leave to chill overnight in the bottom of the fridge. Remember to take out 30 minutes before cooking so it has time to come to room temperature. Serve with roasted vegetables.

# Spiced Roast Turkey

Preparation Time 30 minutes • Cooking Time 3 hours, plus resting • Serves 8 • Per Serving 611 calories, 40g fat (of which 16g saturates), 12g carbohydrate, 2.0g salt • **Easy**

4.5kg (10lb) oven-ready turkey
Pork, Spinach and Apple Stuffing, thawed if frozen (see page 277)
2 tsp Cajun spice seasoning
150g (5oz) butter, softened
salt and ground black pepper
fresh herbs to garnish

**FOR THE SAUSAGES**
8 sausages
16 thin streaky bacon rashers

**1** Preheat the oven 190°C (170°C fan oven) mark 5. Loosen the skin at the neck end of the turkey, ease your fingers up between the skin and the breast and, using a small, sharp knife, remove the wishbone.

**2** Season the inside of the turkey, then spoon the cold stuffing into the neck end only. Neaten the shape, turn the bird over and secure the neck skin with skewers or cocktail sticks. Weigh to calculate the cooking time (see page 273).

**3** Put the turkey into a roasting tin, mix the spice with the butter, smear it over the turkey and season. Cover with a tent of foil. Roast in the oven for about 3 hours, basting occasionally. If the legs were tied together, loosen after the first hour so that they cook more evenly.

**4** Meanwhile, twist each sausage in half and cut to make two mini sausages. Stretch the bacon rashers by running the blunt side of a kitchen knife along each rasher (this stops them shrinking too much when they're cooked). Roll a rasher around each mini sausage. Put into a small roasting tin or around the turkey and cook for about 1 hour. Remove the foil from the turkey 45 minutes before the end of the cooking time.

**5** To check whether the turkey is cooked, pierce the thickest part of the flesh with a skewer; the juices should run clear. If there is any sign of blood, cook for 10 minutes, then check again in the same way.

**6** When the turkey is cooked, tip the bird so the juices run into the tin, then put it on a warmed serving plate with the sausages. Cover loosely with foil and leave to rest for 20–30 minutes before carving. Garnish with herbs.

# Lemon and Herb Roast Turkey

Preparation Time 25 minutes • Cooking Time 4½–5 hours, plus resting • Serves 8 • Per Serving 457 calories, 25g fat (of which 10g saturates), 2g carbohydrate, 1.2g salt • **Easy**

5.4–6.3kg (12–14lb) turkey, giblets
   removed for stock (see page 266)
½ quantity Chestnut and Butternut
   Squash Stuffing, thawed if frozen
   (see page 275)
125g (4oz) butter, softened
1 lemon, halved
3 fresh bay leaves
3 fresh sage leaves
2 fresh rosemary sprigs
8 rindless streaky bacon rashers
350g (12oz) chipolata sausages
salt and ground black pepper
1 bunch of mixed herbs to garnish
Red Wine Gravy to serve (see
   page 278)

**1** Take the turkey out of the fridge 45 minutes before stuffing. Preheat the oven to 220°C (200°C fan oven) mark 7. Put the turkey on a board and lift the neck flap. Ease the skin away from the turkey breast. Spoon in the stuffing, taking care not to overfill the cavity. Secure with a cocktail stick.

**2** Put a sheet of foil into a roasting tin and put the turkey on top. Smear the turkey over with butter, then squeeze over the lemon. Put the squeezed lemon and bay leaves inside the turkey, with a sage leaf and a rosemary sprig, then snip over the remaining herbs. Season.

**3** Tie the turkey legs together. Bring the foil over the turkey and crimp the edges together, making sure there's lots of space. Roast in the oven for 30 minutes, then reduce the oven temperature to 170°C (150°C fan oven) mark 3 and roast for 3½ hours.

**4** Roll the bacon into rolls. Twist the chipolatas in two to make cocktail sausages and snip with scissors. Take the turkey out of the oven and increase the temperature to 200°C (180°C fan oven) mark 6. Uncover and baste the turkey with the juices. Put the bacon and chipolatas around the turkey, then roast for 40 minutes, basting halfway through.

**5** To check whether the turkey is cooked, pierce the thickest part of the flesh with a skewer; the juices should run clear. If there is any sign of blood, cook for 10 minutes, then check again in the same way.

**6** Tip the juices out of the turkey into the roasting tin, then lift the turkey, bacon and sausages on to a warmed serving plate. Cover with foil and leave in a warm place for 30 minutes while you make the gravy. To garnish, stuff the turkey cavity with a bunch of mixed herbs.

# Pheasant Casserole with Cider and Apples

Preparation Time 1 hour • Cooking Time 1 hour • Serves 8 • Per Serving 463 calories, 27g fat (of which 13g saturates), 13g carbohydrate, 0.7g salt • **Easy**

2 pheasants, each weighing about 700g (1½lb), each cut into four portions

2 tbsp plain flour, plus extra to dust

50g (2oz) butter

4 streaky bacon rashers

225g (8oz) onions, roughly chopped

275g (10oz) celery, roughly chopped

4 eating apples, such as Granny Smith, cored, cut into large pieces and tossed in 1 tbsp lemon juice

1 tbsp dried juniper berries, lightly crushed

2.5cm (1in) piece fresh root ginger, peeled and finely chopped

300ml (½ pint) chicken stock (see page 266)

2 × 440ml cans dry cider

142ml carton double cream

salt and ground black pepper

fried apple wedges, fresh thyme sprigs and juniper berries to garnish

**1** Preheat the oven to 170°C (150°C fan) mark 3. Season each pheasant portion and dust lightly with flour. Melt the butter in a large flameproof casserole and brown the pheasant pieces in batches until deep golden brown. Remove and keep warm.

**2** Put the bacon into the casserole and cook for 2–3 minutes until golden. Add the onions, celery, apples, juniper and ginger and cook for 8–10 minutes. Stir the flour into the vegetables and cook for 2 minutes. Add the stock and cider and bring to the boil. Put the pheasant back into the casserole, cover and cook in the oven for 45 minutes–1 hour or until tender.

**3** Lift the pheasant out of the sauce and keep warm. Strain the sauce through a sieve and pour it back into the casserole with the cream. Bring to the boil and bubble for 10–15 minutes until syrupy. Put the pheasant back into the sauce and season with salt and pepper.

**4** To serve, garnish the pheasant with fried apple wedges, thyme sprigs and juniper berries.

 GET AHEAD

***To prepare ahead*** *Complete the recipe to the end of step 5, cool quickly, cover and chill for up to two days.*

***To use*** *Preheat the oven to 180°C (160°C fan) mark 4. Bring the pheasant to the boil then reheat in the oven for about 20–25 minutes or until hot.*

# Roast Grouse

Preparation Time 10 minutes • Cooking Time 40 minutes, plus resting • Serves 4 • Per Serving 320 calories, 18g fat (of which 4g saturates), trace carbohydrate, 0.3g salt • Gluten Free • Dairy Free • Easy

**2 oven-ready grouse**
**6 streaky bacon rashers**
**2 tbsp vegetable oil**
**2 tbsp freshly chopped rosemary or**
**thyme (optional)**
**salt and ground black pepper**
**deep-fried thinly sliced potatoes**
**and parsnips (see Cook's Tip) or**
**hand-cooked salted crisps and**
**watercress to serve**

**1** Preheat the oven to 200°C (180°C fan oven) mark 6. Put the grouse into a large roasting tin, with enough space between them so that they can brown evenly. Cover the breast of each with bacon, then drizzle with 1 tbsp oil. Season with salt and pepper and sprinkle with herbs, if using.

**2** Roast in the oven for 40 minutes or until the juices run clear when the thigh is pierced with a skewer.

**3** Leave to rest in a warm place for 10 minutes before serving.

**4** Serve with crisp deep-fried slices of potato and parsnip or ready-made hand-cooked crisps, plus watercress to contrast with the richness of the meat.

★ COOK'S TIP
**Parsnip and Potato Crisps**
*Cut thin strips of each vegetable, using a vegetable peeler. Heat a pan half full of sunflower oil to 190°C (test by frying a small cube of bread; it should brown in 20 seconds). Deep-fry the strips, a few at a time, until golden. Drain on kitchen paper and serve the crisps immediately.*

# Turkey Crown with Orange

⭐

**Preparation Time** 20 minutes • **Cooking Time** 2½ hours, plus resting • **Serves 8** • **Per Serving** 181 calories, 6g fat (of which 3g saturates), 3g carbohydrate, 0.2g salt • **Easy**

2 onions, sliced
2 bay leaves
2.7kg (6lb) oven-ready turkey
   crown
40g (1½oz) butter, softened
1 lemon, halved
2 tbsp chicken seasoning
2 oranges, halved
150ml (¼ pint) dry white wine or
   chicken stock (see page 266)

**1** Preheat the oven to 190°C (170°C fan oven) mark 5. Spread the onions in a large roasting tin, add the bay leaves and sit the turkey on top. Spread the butter over the turkey breast, then squeeze the lemon over it. Put the lemon halves in the tin. Sprinkle the chicken seasoning over the turkey and then put the orange halves in the tin, around the turkey.

**2** Pour the wine or stock into the roasting tin, with 250ml (9fl oz) hot water. Cover the turkey loosely with a large sheet of foil. Make sure it's completely covered, but with

enough space between the foil and the turkey for air to circulate.

**3** Roast in the oven for 2 hours or until the turkey is cooked through and the juices run clear when the thickest part of the thigh is pierced with a skewer. Remove the foil and put back in the oven for 30 minutes or until golden.

**4** Lift the turkey on to a warmed carving dish, cover loosely with foil and leave to rest for 15 minutes before carving.

# Goose with Roasted Apples

★

Preparation Time 30 minutes • Cooking Time about 3 hours, plus resting • Serves 8 • Per Serving 646 calories, 41g fat (of which 12g saturates), 11g carbohydrate, 1g salt • Dairy Free • Easy

6 small red onions, halved

7 small red eating apples, unpeeled, halved

5kg (11lb) oven-ready goose, washed, dried and seasoned inside and out

1 small bunch of sage

1 small bunch of rosemary

1 bay leaf

salt and ground black pepper

**FOR THE GRAVY**

1 tbsp plain flour

300ml (½ pint) red wine

200ml (7fl oz) giblet stock (see page 266)

1 Preheat the oven to 230°C (210°C fan oven) mark 8. Put half an onion and half an apple inside the goose with half the sage and rosemary and the bay leaf. Tie the legs together with string. Push a long skewer through the wings to tuck them in. Put the goose, breast side up, on a rack in a roasting tin. Prick the breast all over and season with salt and pepper. Put the remaining onions around the bird, then cover with foil.

2 Roast in the oven for 30 minutes, then remove the tin from the oven and baste the goose with the fat that has run off. Remove and set aside any excess fat. Reduce the oven temperature to 190°C (170°C fan oven) mark 5 and roast for a further 1½ hours, removing any excess fat every 20–30 minutes.

3 Remove the foil from the goose. Remove excess fat, then add the remaining apples. Sprinkle the goose with the remaining herbs and roast for a further 1 hour or until cooked. Test by piercing the thigh with a skewer – the juices should run clear. Remove the goose from the oven and put it on a warmed serving plate. Cover with foil and leave to rest for 30 minutes. Remove the apples and onions and keep warm.

4 To make the gravy, pour out all but 1 tbsp of the fat from the tin, stir in the flour, then add the wine and stock. Bring to the boil and cook, stirring, for 5 minutes. Carve the goose, cut the roast apples into wedges and serve with the goose, onions and gravy.

# Turkey, Pepper and Haricot Bean Casserole

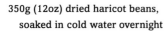

Preparation Time 20 minutes, plus soaking • Cooking Time 1 hour 20 minutes • Serves 6 • Per Serving 326 calories, 6g fat (of which 1g saturates), 41g carbohydrate, 0.1g salt • Gluten Free • Dairy Free • Easy

350g (12oz) dried haricot beans, soaked in cold water overnight
2 large onions
2 small carrots, cut into chunks
1 bouquet garni (see Cook's tip, page 31)
1 tbsp olive oil
2 red chillies, seeded and chopped (see Cook's Tips, page 10)
2 garlic cloves, crushed
350g (12oz) lean turkey meat, cut into bite-size pieces
1 large red pepper and 1 large orange pepper, both seeded and finely diced
2 courgettes, finely diced

400g can chopped tomatoes
1 tbsp sun-dried tomato paste
a large handful of basil leaves
salt and ground black pepper

1 Drain the soaked haricot beans, put them into a large flameproof casserole and cover with fresh water. Quarter 1 onion and add to the casserole with the carrots and bouquet garni. Bring to the boil, then cover, reduce the heat and simmer for 45 minutes or until the beans are tender. Drain the beans, reserving 150ml (¼ pint) of the cooking liquid; discard the flavouring vegetables. Spoon the beans into a bowl and put to one side. Wipe out the casserole.

2 Finely slice the remaining onion. Heat the oil in the casserole, add the onion and cook gently for 5 minutes. Add the chillies and garlic and cook for 1 minute or until softened.

3 Add the turkey to the pan and stir-fry for 5 minutes, then add the diced peppers and courgettes and season well. Cover the casserole and cook for 5 minutes or until the vegetables are slightly softened.

4 Add the tomatoes and tomato paste, cover and bring to the boil. Add the haricot beans and reserved cooking liquid, then stir and season well. Cover the pan, reduce the heat and simmer for 15 minutes. Sprinkle with the basil leaves and serve.

# Turkey and Bean Stew

Preparation Time 15 minutes • Cooking Time 30 minutes • Serves 4 • Per Serving 218 calories, 6g fat (of which 2g saturates), 21g carbohydrate, 1.3g salt • Gluten Free • Easy

1 tbsp olive oil
1 medium onion, finely chopped
2 celery sticks, chopped
2 medium carrots, sliced
900ml (1½ pints) hot chicken stock (see page 266)
200g (7oz) turkey strips
2 rosemary sprigs – one whole and the leaves of one finely chopped (optional)
1 bay leaf
400g can butter beans, drained and rinsed
¼ Savoy cabbage, finely shredded
salt and ground black pepper
25g (1oz) Parmesan shavings, to garnish

1 Heat the oil in a large pan. Add the onion, celery and carrots and gently fry for 10 minutes until softened. Pour in the hot stock, then add the turkey, whole rosemary sprig and bay leaf. Season, then bring to the boil. Reduce the heat and simmer for 15 minutes.

2 Mash half the butter beans with a fork. Stir the mashed and whole butter beans and the cabbage into the pan and simmer for 3 minutes. Check the seasoning and remove the bay leaf and rosemary.

3 Divide among four warmed bowls and garnish with the finely chopped rosemary leaves, if you like, and the Parmesan.

⭐ COOK'S TIP
*The healthiest and cheapest way of bulking up a dish is to add beans. Stars of the pulse world, butter beans are rich in fibre, which keeps you feeling fuller for longer.*

# Duck with Red Onion Marmalade

⭐

Preparation Time 25 minutes, plus marinating • Cooking Time about 1 hour • Serves 4 • Per Serving 979 calories, 79g fat (of which 31g saturates), 53g carbohydrate, 0.7g salt • Gluten Free • Easy

900ml (1½ pints) olive oil
4 duck legs with skin, marinated
   overnight (see Cook's Tips)
red cabbage and roast potato
   wedges to serve

**FOR THE RED ONION**
   **MARMALADE**
125g (4oz) butter
550g (1¼lb) red onions, sliced
125g (4oz) kumquats, halved
125ml (4fl oz) sherry or wine
   vinegar
150g (5oz) golden caster sugar
grated zest and juice of 1 orange
300ml (½ pint) red wine
salt and ground black pepper

1 Preheat the oven to 170°C (150°C fan oven) mark 3. Heat the oil gently in a pan. Pack the prepared duck legs close together in a single layer in a baking dish and pour the oil over, covering the duck completely. Roast in the oven for 45 minutes until the duck is cooked through.

2 Meanwhile, make the red onion marmalade. Melt the butter in a pan. Add the onions, kumquats and vinegar, then cover and simmer, stirring every now and then, for 15–20 minutes until the onions are soft. Add the sugar, turn up the heat and cook for 10 minutes, stirring, to caramelise the onions. Add the orange zest, juice and wine, then cook gently, uncovered, for about 20 minutes or until all the liquid has evaporated. Season.

3 Lift the duck out of the oil and pat dry. Heat a large frying pan and cook the duck over a medium heat for 10–15 minutes until golden and crisp. Serve with the red onion marmalade, red cabbage and roast potato wedges.

⭐ COOK'S TIPS
● *The night before you want to serve this recipe, put the duck legs in a single layer in a plastic container and rub in 3 crushed garlic cloves, 2 tsp freshly chopped thyme and 1 tsp salt. Add 3 bay leaves, then cover and chill overnight. The next day, remove the duck from the fridge, rub off excess salt and rinse thoroughly under cold running water. Pat dry with kitchen paper.*
● *The red onion marmalade can be made in advance; cover and chill for up to three days and reheat to serve.*

# Crispy Duck Salad

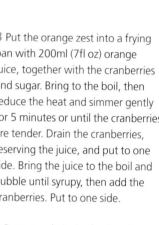

Preparation Time 30 minutes, plus chilling • Cooking Time 1½ hours, plus cooling • Serves 8 • Per Serving 655 calories, 65g fat (of which 11g saturates), 22g carbohydrate, 0.2g salt • Gluten Free • Dairy Free • A Little Effort

6 duck legs, about 200g (7oz) each
1 tsp black peppercorns
2 fresh thyme sprigs and 2 bay leaves
125g (4oz) pecan nuts
finely grated zest and juice of 2 oranges
225g (8oz) cranberries
125g (4oz) caster sugar
4 tbsp white wine vinegar
9 tbsp sunflower oil
3 tbsp walnut oil
125g (4oz) kumquats
salt and ground black pepper
salad leaves, such as frisée to serve

1 Preheat the oven to 180°C (160°C fan oven) mark 4. Put the duck legs into a large flameproof casserole, cover with cold water and bring to the boil. Reduce the heat and simmer for 10 minutes, then skim the surface of the liquid and add the peppercorns, thyme, bay leaves and 2 tsp salt. Transfer to the oven and cook for 45 minutes–1 hour until tender. Cool quickly in the liquid and chill overnight.

2 Preheat the grill. Put the pecan nuts on a baking sheet and toast lightly under the grill.

3 Put the orange zest into a frying pan with 200ml (7fl oz) orange juice, together with the cranberries and sugar. Bring to the boil, then reduce the heat and simmer gently for 5 minutes or until the cranberries are tender. Drain the cranberries, reserving the juice, and put to one side. Bring the juice to the boil and bubble until syrupy, then add the cranberries. Put to one side.

4 Put a good pinch of salt and pepper into a small bowl, then whisk in the vinegar, followed by the oils. Cut the kumquats into quarters, then add to the cranberry mixture with the dressing and pecans. Put to one side.

5 Skim the fat from the surface of the jellied duck liquid and put to one side. Cut the duck into thick shreds, leaving the skin on.

6 Just before serving, heat 1 tbsp reserved duck fat in a large non-stick frying pan and fry half the duck for about 5 minutes or until very crisp and brown; set aside in a warm place. Repeat with the remaining duck. To serve, carefully toss the duck with the cranberry mixture and serve with salad leaves.

# Crispy Duck with Mangetouts

⭐

Preparation Time 15 minutes • Cooking Time about 30 minutes, plus cooling • Serves 6 • Per Serving 308 calories, 17g fat (of which 3g saturates), 18g carbohydrate, 1.7g salt • Dairy Free • Easy

4 duck breast fillets, about
    175g (6oz) each
1½ tbsp clear honey
3 tbsp vegetable oil
1 bunch of spring onions, cut into
    2.5cm (1in) lengths
1 large green pepper, seeded and
    cut into thin strips
225g (8oz) mangetouts
2 garlic cloves, crushed
2–3 good pinches of Chinese
    five-spice powder
3 tbsp caster sugar
3 tbsp dark soy sauce
3 tbsp wine vinegar
16 water chestnuts, sliced
40g (1½ oz) toasted cashew nuts
salt

1 Preheat the oven to 180°C (160°C fan oven) mark 4. Prick the duck skin all over with a skewer or fork and rub well with salt. Put the breasts, skin side up, on a rack or trivet in a roasting tin and cook in the oven for 15 minutes.

2 Remove the duck breasts from the oven and brush the skins with honey. Put them back into the oven and cook for a further 5–10 minutes until the duck is cooked through. Leave to cool, then cut into strips.

3 Heat the oil in a wok or large frying pan. Add the spring onions, green pepper, mangetouts, garlic and five-spice powder and stir-fry for 2 minutes. Add the sugar, soy sauce, vinegar and duck strips and toss in the sauce to heat through and glaze. Add the water chestnuts and cook until heated through.

4 Serve immediately, sprinkled with toasted cashew nuts.

# Duck Terrine with Apple, Apricot and Brandy

Preparation Time 1½ hours, plus soaking, marinating and chilling • Cooking Time 2¼ hours, plus cooling • Cuts into 15 slices • Per Slice 190 calories, 10g fat (of which 6g saturates), 11g carbohydrate, 0.25g salt • Gluten Free • A Little Effort

50g (2oz) pitted prunes, roughly chopped (see Cook's Tips)
50g (2oz) ready-to-eat dried apricots, roughly chopped (see Cook's Tips)
6 tbsp brandy
350g (12oz) turkey breast fillet, cut into 2.5cm (1in) cubes
800g (1¾lb) duck breasts, skinned – there should be 500g (1lb 2oz) meat
a few fresh thyme sprigs
50g (2oz) butter
225g (8oz) shallots or onions, roughly chopped
350g (12oz) eating apples, peeled, cored and chopped
225g (8oz) minced pork
2 tbsp freshly chopped thyme
1 medium egg, beaten
50g (2oz) shelled pistachio nuts
salt and ground black pepper
chutney of your choice such as red onion or Spiced Pepper Chutney (see page 282) to serve

1 The day before, put the prunes and apricots into a bowl with 4 tbsp brandy, cover and leave to soak overnight. Put the turkey and duck into a roasting tin with the thyme sprigs and remaining brandy, then cover, chill and leave to marinate overnight.

2 The next day, heat the butter in a pan. Add the shallots and cook for 10 minutes or until soft. Stir in the apple, then cover and cook for 5–10 minutes until soft. Leave to cool.

3 Preheat the oven to 180°C (160°C fan oven) mark 4. Remove the turkey from the marinade and put into a food processor with the minced pork and the apple mixture. Whiz to a rough purée, then combine with the chopped thyme, egg, marinated fruits and pistachio nuts. Season well with salt and pepper (see Cook's Tips).

4 Remove the duck from the marinade and put between sheets of greaseproof paper. Flatten gently with a rolling pin until the duck is 1cm (½in) thick.

5 Line the base of a 1.2 litre (2 pint) terrine or loaf tin with greaseproof paper or foil. Put a duck breast in the base of the terrine to cover it evenly with no gaps. Spread over half of the stuffing, then repeat the process, finishing with a layer of duck.

6 Cover with foil and put into a roasting tin. Add enough hot water to come three-quarters of the way up the sides of the terrine and cook in the oven for 2–2¼ hours until the juices run clear when tested with a skewer. Transfer to a wire rack, cover with a weighted board and, when cool, leave to chill for 6 hours or overnight.

7 Run a knife around the terrine and turn out on to a board. Remove the greaseproof paper and carve into thin slices. Serve with chutney of your choice.

★ COOK'S TIPS
● *Try this with other dried fruit, such as dried cherries. You'll need 125g (4oz) in place of the prunes and apricots.*
● *Season the stuffing with ½ tsp salt to ensure it has a really good flavour.*

# Crispy Duck with Hot and Sweet Dip

Preparation Time 10 minutes • Cooking Time 1 hour • Serves 4 • Per Serving 504 calories, 29g fat (of which 6g saturates), 42g carbohydrate, 0.5g salt • Gluten Free • Dairy Free • Easy

8 small duck legs
2 pieces star anise
4 fat garlic cloves, sliced
1 dried red chilli
grated zest and juice of 1 orange
1 tbsp tamarind paste or lemon juice
fried garlic slivers, fried chilli pieces and star anise to garnish

**FOR THE HOT AND SWEET DIP**
200ml (7fl oz) white wine vinegar
150g (5oz) golden caster sugar
75g (3oz) each cucumber, spring onion and mango, cut into fine shreds
1 dried red chilli or ¼ tsp seeded and shredded red chilli (see Cook's Tips, page 10)

1 To make the hot and sweet dip, boil the vinegar and sugar together in a pan for 2 minutes, then stir in the cucumber, spring onion, mango and chilli. Transfer to a serving bowl and leave to cool.

2 Prick the duck legs all over with a skewer or fork. Put them into a large pan, cover with cold water and bring to the boil, then reduce the heat and simmer for 45 minutes.

3 Meanwhile, put the 2 star anise, garlic, chilli, orange zest and juice and tamarind paste or lemon juice in a blender and whiz to a paste. Preheat the grill.

4 Drain the duck and put, skin side down, on a foil-lined grill pan. Brush half the spice paste over the duck. Grill for 5 minutes, then turn skin side up and brush the remaining paste over it. Grill for a further 5–7 minutes until the duck skin is well charred and crisp.

5 Garnish with the fried garlic slivers, fried chilli pieces and star anise and serve with the hot and sweet dip.

# Duck with Pineapple

Preparation Time 15 minutes • Cooking Time about 30 minutes, plus resting • Serves 4 • Per Serving 382 calories, 12g fat (of which 2g saturates), 40g carbohydrate, 2.6g salt • Dairy Free • Easy

4 duck breast fillets, about 175g
  (6oz) each
2 tsp clear honey
3 carrots, cut into thin strips
1 bunch of spring onions, sliced
  diagonally
2.5cm (1in) piece fresh root ginger,
  peeled and cut into very thin
  strips
1 garlic clove, crushed
125g (4oz) mangetouts
½ small fresh pineapple, peeled,
  cored and cut into chunks
3 tbsp dark soy sauce

3 tbsp malt vinegar
3 tbsp caster sugar
1 tbsp cornflour
175ml (6fl oz) fresh orange juice
salt

1 Preheat the oven to 180°C (160°C fan oven) mark 4. Prick the duck skin all over with a skewer or fork and rub well with salt. Put the breasts, skin side up, on a rack or trivet in a roasting tin and cook in the oven for 15 minutes.

2 Remove the duck breasts from the oven and brush the skins with honey. Put them back into the oven and cook for a further 5–10 minutes until golden and cooked through. Transfer the duck breasts to a plate and leave to rest for 5 minutes. Set the fat aside in the roasting tin.

3 To make the sauce, heat 3 tbsp of the reserved duck fat in a wok or large frying pan. Add the carrots, spring onions, ginger, garlic and mangetouts and stir-fry for 2 minutes. Using a slotted spoon, remove the vegetables from the pan and put to one side.

4 Add the pineapple to the pan and fry gently for about 20 seconds until heated through. Remove from the pan and keep warm.

5 Stir the soy sauce, vinegar and sugar into the pan. Blend the cornflour with the orange juice, add to the pan and cook for 2 minutes, stirring. Put the vegetables back into the pan and cook until heated through.

6 Cut the duck breasts diagonally into fairly thin slices. Arrange the duck and pineapple on warmed plates and serve the sauce and vegetables alongside the duck.

# Duck with Port and Figs

Preparation Time 15 minutes • Cooking Time 45 minutes • Serves 6 • Per Serving 758 calories, 58g fat (of which 16g saturates), 37g carbohydrate, 0.4g salt • Dairy Free • Easy

4 × 200g (7oz) duck breasts, fat of each breast scored diagonally, making sure you don't cut into the meat, and sinew and excess fat trimmed
1 tsp rapeseed oil
150ml (¼ pint) port
300ml (½ pint) hot chicken stock (see page 266)
zest of 1 orange, plus 1–2 tbsp orange juice
9 fresh figs, halved
salt and ground black pepper
mixed vegetables, garnished with flaked almonds and herbs to serve

1 Preheat the oven to 200°C (180°C fan oven) mark 6. Put the duck, skin side down, with the oil into a large frying pan set over the lowest heat to let the fat run out. This will take 15–20 minutes (see Get Ahead). Pour the fat into a bowl and use to cook roast potatoes later. When the skin has turned golden and most of the fat has drained out, put the duck breasts on a rack set in a roasting tin, skin side up. Cook in the oven for 15 minutes for pink and 20 minutes for well done. Cover loosely with foil and leave to rest while you make the sauce.

2 Put the port, hot stock and orange zest into the frying pan. Bubble rapidly until syrupy and reduced by two-thirds. Stir in orange juice to taste and any juices from the duck. Season and keep warm.

3 Heat a griddle pan over a medium-high heat and griddle the figs, cut side down, for 3 minutes until softened. Slice the duck breasts diagonally or leave whole and arrange on warmed plates with the figs. Drizzle the sauce over and serve with vegetables garnished with flaked almonds and herbs.

 GET AHEAD

**To prepare ahead** *Complete the recipe to the end of step 2, then store the duck in the fridge, covered in clingfilm, for up to 24 hours.*
**To use** *Bring to room temperature before completing the recipe.*
*You can also make the sauce in advance and reheat with the juices from the rested duck. Make sure it is hot before serving.*

# Roast Duck with Orange Sauce

Preparation Time 50 minutes • Cooking Time 1 hour 40 minutes, plus resting • Serves 4 • Per Serving 561 calories, 38g fat (of which 9g saturates), 20g carbohydrate, 0.5g salt • **Dairy Free** • **Easy**

2 large oranges
2 large fresh thyme sprigs
2.3kg (5lb) duck, preferably with
　giblets
4 tbsp vegetable oil
2 shallots, chopped
1 tsp plain flour
600ml (1 pint) chicken stock (see
　page 266)
25g (1oz) caster sugar
2 tbsp red wine vinegar
100ml (3½fl oz) fresh orange juice
100ml (3½fl oz) fruity German
　white wine
2 tbsp orange liqueur, such as
　Grand Marnier (optional)
1 tbsp lemon juice
salt and ground black pepper
glazed orange wedges (see Cook's
　Tip) to garnish
mangetouts and broccoli to serve

**1** Preheat the oven to 200°C (180°C fan oven) mark 6. Using a zester, remove strips of zest from the oranges. Put half the zest into a pan of cold water, bring to the boil, then drain and put to one side. Remove the pith from both oranges and cut the flesh into segments.

**2** Put the thyme and unblanched orange zest inside the duck and season. Rub the skin with 2 tbsp oil, sprinkle with salt and place, breast side up, on a rack over a roasting tin. Roast in the oven, basting every 20 minutes, for 1¼–1½ hours until just cooked and the juices run clear when the thickest part of the thigh is pierced with a skewer. After 30 minutes, turn breast side down, then breast side up for the last 10 minutes.

**3** Meanwhile, cut the gizzard, heart and neck into pieces. Heat the remaining 2 tbsp oil in a heavy-based pan. Add the giblets and fry until dark brown. Add the chopped shallots and flour and cook for 1 minute. Pour in the stock, bring to the boil and bubble until reduced by half, then strain.

**4** Put the sugar and vinegar into a heavy-based pan over a low heat until the sugar dissolves. Turn up the heat and cook until it forms a dark caramel. Pour in the orange juice and stir. Cool, cover and put to one side.

**5** Lift the duck off the rack and keep warm. Skim all the fat off the juices to leave about 3 tbsp sediment. Stir the wine into the sediment, bring to the boil and bubble for 5 minutes or until syrupy. Add the stock mixture and orange mixture. Bring back to the boil and bubble until syrupy, skimming if necessary. To serve the sauce, add the blanched orange zest and segments. Add Grand Marnier, if using, and lemon juice to taste.

**6** Carve the duck and garnish with the glazed orange wedges. Serve with the orange sauce, mangetouts and broccoli.

★ COOK'S TIP
*Glazed Oranges*
*Preheat the grill. Quarter the oranges or cut into wedges. Dust with a little caster sugar and grill until caramelised.*

# Pot-roasted Pheasant with Red Cabbage

Preparation Time 15 minutes • Cooking Time about 1 hour • Serves 4 • Per Serving 659 calories, 21g fat (of which 12g saturates), 11g carbohydrate, 1.4g salt • Gluten Free • Easy

25g (1oz) butter
1 tbsp oil
2 oven-ready young pheasants, halved
2 onions, sliced
450g (1lb) red cabbage, cored and finely shredded
1 tsp cornflour
250ml (9fl oz) red wine
2 tbsp redcurrant jelly
1 tbsp balsamic vinegar
4 rindless smoked streaky bacon rashers, halved
salt and ground black pepper

1 Preheat the oven to 200°C (180°C fan oven) mark 6. Melt the butter with the oil in a large flameproof casserole over a medium to high heat. Add the pheasant and brown on all sides, then remove and put to one side. Add the onions and cabbage to the casserole and fry for 5 minutes, stirring frequently, or until softened.

2 Blend the cornflour with a little water to make a paste. Add to the casserole with the wine, redcurrant jelly and vinegar. Season with salt and pepper. Bring to the boil, stirring.

3 Arrange the pheasant halves, skin side up, on the cabbage. Put the halved bacon rashers on top. Cover the casserole and cook in the oven for 30 minutes or until the birds are tender (older pheasants would take an extra 10–20 minutes).

4 Serve the pot-roasted pheasant and red cabbage with the cooking juices spooned over.

⭐ TRY SOMETHING DIFFERENT
**Pot-roasted Pigeon with Red Cabbage**
*Instead of the pheasant, use oven-ready pigeons; put an onion wedge inside each bird before browning to impart extra flavour.*

# Sweet and Sour Duck

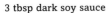

Preparation Time 15 minutes, plus marinating • Cooking Time about 15 minutes • Serves 4 • Per Serving 278 calories, 13g fat (of which 2g saturates), 29g carbohydrate, 1.9g salt • Dairy Free • Easy

3 tbsp dark soy sauce

1 tbsp dry sherry

1 tsp sesame oil

225g (8oz) duck breast fillets, thinly sliced

1 tbsp sugar

2 tsp cornflour

3 tbsp distilled malt vinegar

1 tbsp tomato ketchup

4 tbsp vegetable oil

125g (4oz) aubergine, sliced

1 red onion, sliced

1 garlic clove, sliced

125g (4oz) carrot, sliced lengthways into strips

125g (4oz) sugarsnap peas or mangetouts

1 mango, peeled, stoned and thinly sliced

noodles to serve

1 Mix 1 tbsp soy sauce with the sherry and sesame oil. Pour the mixture over the duck, cover and leave to marinate for at least 30 minutes.

2 Mix together the sugar, cornflour, vinegar, ketchup and remaining 2 tbsp soy sauce. Put to one side.

3 Heat 2 tbsp vegetable oil in a wok or large non-stick frying pan. Drain the duck from the marinade and set the marinade aside. Fry the duck slices over a high heat for 3–4 minutes until golden and the fat is crisp. Remove from the pan and put to one side.

4 Add 1 tbsp vegetable oil to the pan and fry the aubergine for about 2 minutes on each side or until golden. Add the remaining 1 tbsp oil and fry the onion, garlic and carrot for 2–3 minutes, then add the sugarsnap peas or mangetouts and fry for a further 1–2 minutes.

5 Add the mango to the pan along with the duck, the soy sauce mixture and the reserved marinade. Bring to the boil, stirring gently all the time, and allow to bubble for 2–3 minutes until slightly thickened. Serve immediately, with noodles.

# Marinated Duck with Prunes

Preparation Time 30 minutes, plus marinating and soaking • Cooking Time 1¼ hours, plus resting • Serves 4 •
Per Serving 654 calories, 51g fat (of which 14g saturates), 38g carbohydrate, 0.6g salt • Easy

4 duck breasts
8 fat garlic cloves, unpeeled
8 ready-to-eat prunes
25g (1oz) butter
1 tsp plain flour
mashed potato to serve

**FOR THE MARINADE**
1 carrot, finely chopped
2 shallots, finely chopped
1 fresh parsley sprig
1 fresh thyme sprig, plus extra
    to garnish
1 bay leaf
1 tsp black peppercorns
250ml (9fl oz) prune juice
125ml (4fl oz) red wine
4 tbsp brandy
4 tbsp olive oil
½ tsp salt

**FOR THE RED CABBAGE**
1 tbsp olive oil
1 red onion, halved and sliced
2 garlic cloves, crushed
1 large red cabbage, about 1kg
    (2¼lb), shredded
2 tbsp light muscovado sugar
2 tbsp red wine vinegar
8 juniper berries
¼ tsp allspice
300ml (½ pint) vegetable stock
2 pears, cored and sliced
salt and ground black pepper

**1** Combine the marinade ingredients (putting half of the prune juice to one side) in a dish large enough to hold the duck breasts in a single layer, then add the duck. Cover, chill and leave to marinate overnight, turning occasionally.

**2** Soak four small wooden skewers in water for 20 minutes. To make the red cabbage, heat the oil in a large pan. Add the onion and fry for 5 minutes. Add the remaining ingredients except the pears. Season, bring to the boil, then cover, reduce the heat and simmer for 30 minutes. Add the pears and cook for 15 minutes or until nearly all the liquid has evaporated and the cabbage is tender.

**3** Boil the garlic for 10 minutes. Drain, peel and put to one side.

**4** Remove the duck from the marinade and dry on kitchen paper. In a pan, bring the marinade to the boil, then reduce by half. Strain and keep warm. Push the prunes and garlic on to the soaked skewers.

**5** Melt the butter in a large frying pan. Fry the duck, skin side down, for 8 minutes or until golden. Turn and cook for 3–4 minutes. Remove from the pan and leave to rest for 10 minutes. Cook the skewers in the pan, turning, until the garlic colours. Remove from the pan and put to one side.

**6** Add the flour to the pan and cook, stirring, for 2–3 seconds. Add the marinade and remaining prune juice and simmer, stirring, until it thickens and becomes glossy. Serve the duck and skewers with the red cabbage and mashed potato and garnished with thyme.

# Roast Goose with Wild Rice and Cranberry Stuffing

★

Preparation Time 45 minutes • Cooking Time about 3 hours, plus resting • Serves 6 • Per Serving 820 calories, 51g fat (of which 18g saturates), 32g carbohydrate, 1.7g salt • Easy

5kg (11lb) goose (with giblets for stock, page 266)

Wild Rice and Cranberry Stuffing, thawed if frozen (see page 275)

25g (1oz) butter, plus extra to grease

3 red-skinned apples

4 fresh sage sprigs, plus extra to garnish

2 tbsp golden caster sugar

salt and ground black pepper

**FOR THE GRAVY**

2 tbsp plain flour

150ml (¼ pint) red wine

600ml (1 pint) giblet stock (see page 266)

2 tbsp redcurrant jelly

1 To make the goose easier to carve, remove the wishbone from the neck by lifting the flap and cutting around the bone with a small knife. Remove the wishbone. Using your fingers, ease the skin away from the flesh to make room for the stuffing, then put the goose on a tray in the sink and pour a generous amount of freshly boiled water over, then pat dry with kitchen paper.

2 Preheat the oven to 230°C (210°C fan oven) mark 8. Pack the neck of the goose with half of the stuffing and secure the neck shut with skewers or by using a trussing needle with fine string. Put any remaining stuffing on a buttered sheet of foil and wrap it up. Season the cavity of the bird with salt and pepper, then put in 1 whole apple and the sage sprigs.

3 Put the goose on a rack in a roasting tin and season well with salt and pepper. Roast in the oven for 30 minutes, basting occasionally, then remove and set aside any excess fat. Reduce the oven temperature to 190°C (170°C fan oven) mark 5 and cook for a further 2½ hours, removing any excess fat every 20 minutes. Thirty minutes before the end of cooking, put the parcel of stuffing into the oven.

4 Test whether the goose is cooked by piercing the thigh with a skewer – the juices should run clear. Remove the goose from the oven and put it on a board. Cover with foil and leave to rest for at least 20 minutes.

5 Meanwhile, cut the remaining apples into thick wedges. Heat the butter in a heavy-based frying pan until it's no longer foaming. Add the apples and the sugar and stir-fry over a high heat for 4–5 minutes until caramelised, then put to one side.

6 To make the gravy, drain all but 3 tbsp fat from the roasting tin. Add the flour and stir to make a smooth paste. Add the wine and boil for 5 minutes, then add the stock and redcurrant jelly and mix well. Bring to the boil, then reduce the heat and simmer for 5 minutes. Strain before serving. Serve the goose, garnished with sage sprigs, with the stuffing and caramelised apples.

# Roast Guinea Fowl

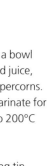

Preparation Time 20 minutes, plus marinating • Cooking Time 1 hour 10 minutes, plus resting • Serves 4 •
Per Serving 585 calories, 27g fat (of which 11g saturates), 5g carbohydrate, 0.7g salt • Gluten Free • Easy

1 guinea fowl
2 lemons: grated zest and juice of
    one, one quartered lengthways
3 bay leaves
5 fresh thyme sprigs
1 tbsp black peppercorns, lightly
    crushed
25g (1oz) butter
150ml (¼ pint) hot chicken stock
    (see page 266)
roast potatoes and green beans
    to serve

**FOR THE GRAVY**
2 tbsp redcurrant jelly
100ml (3½fl oz) dry white wine
salt and ground black pepper

1 Put the guinea fowl into a bowl
and add the lemon zest and juice,
bay leaves, thyme and peppercorns.
Cover, chill and leave to marinate for
1 hour. Preheat the oven to 200°C
(180°C fan oven) mark 6.

2 Put the bird into a roasting tin,
breast side down, put the lemon
quarters and the butter into the
cavity, pour the hot stock over and
roast in the oven for 50 minutes.

3 Turn the guinea fowl breast side
up and continue to roast for about
20 minutes or until cooked and the
juices run clear when the thigh is
pierced with a skewer.

4 Put the guinea fowl on a board,
cover with foil and leave to rest for
10 minutes.

5 To make the gravy, put the
roasting tin on the hob and scrape
up the juices. Add the redcurrant
jelly, wine and 50ml (2fl oz) water
and bring to the boil. Reduce the
heat and simmer for 3–5 minutes.
Season well. Carve the guinea fowl
and serve with the gravy, roast
potatoes and green beans.

# Braised Guinea Fowl and Red Cabbage

Preparation Time 30 minutes • Cooking Time 2 hours 20 minutes • Serves 8 • Per Serving 373 calories, 17g fat (of which 6g saturates), 12g carbohydrate, 0.9g salt • Dairy Free • Easy

2 tbsp rapeseed oil
2 oven-ready guinea fowl
150g (5oz) smoked lardons
400g (14oz) whole shallots, peeled
1 small red cabbage, cored and
    finely sliced
12 juniper berries, crushed
2 tsp dark brown sugar
1 tbsp red wine vinegar
2 fresh thyme sprigs
150ml (¼ pint) hot chicken stock
    (see page 266)
salt and ground black pepper

1 Preheat the oven to 180°C (160°C fan oven) mark 4. Heat 1 tbsp oil in a flameproof casserole large enough for both birds and brown the guinea fowl over a medium to high heat. Remove from the casserole and put to one side.

2 Add the remaining oil to the casserole with the lardons. Fry gently to release the fat, then add the shallots and cook over a medium heat until lightly browned.

3 Stir in the red cabbage and cook for 5 minutes, stirring, or until the cabbage has softened slightly. Add the juniper berries, sugar, vinegar, thyme and hot stock. Season with salt and pepper.

4 Put the guinea fowl on top of the cabbage mixture, then cover the casserole tightly with a lid or double thickness of foil and braise in the oven for 1½ hours. Remove the lid and continue cooking for 30 minutes or until the birds are cooked through – the juices should run clear when you pierce the thighs with a skewer.

5 Transfer the guinea fowl to a board and spoon the cabbage and juices on to a serving platter. Keep warm. Joint the birds into eight, as you would a chicken, then arrange the guinea fowl on the platter on top of the cabbage. Serve at once.

# Fruity Guinea Fowl

Preparation Time 40 minutes, plus marinating • Cooking Time 1½ hours • Serves 6 • Per Serving 811 calories, 49g fat (of which 14g saturates), 24g carbohydrate, 1.7g salt • Dairy Free • Easy

225g (8oz) onion, roughly chopped
125g (4oz) carrot, roughly chopped
125g (4oz) celery, roughly chopped
6–8 guinea fowl joints, 2kg (4½lb)
    total weight
750ml (1¼ pints) red wine
1 tsp black peppercorns, crushed
1 tbsp freshly chopped thyme
2 bay leaves
175g (6oz) ready-to-eat dried
    prunes
3 tbsp vegetable oil
3 garlic cloves, crushed
1 tsp harissa paste (see page 283)
1 tbsp tomato purée
2 tbsp plain flour
300ml (½ pint) chicken stock (see
    page 266)
225g (8oz) streaky bacon, cut
    into strips
2 apples, cored and sliced
salt and ground black pepper
mashed potato to serve

**1** Put the onion, carrot, celery, guinea fowl, 600ml (1 pint) wine, the peppercorns, thyme and bay leaves into a large bowl. Cover, chill and leave to marinate for at least 3–4 hours. Soak the prunes in the remaining wine for 3–4 hours.

**2** Preheat the oven to 170°C (150°C fan oven) mark 3. Drain and pat the joints dry (put the vegetables and wine to one side). Heat 2 tbsp oil in a large flameproof casserole over a medium heat. Cook the joints in batches until browned on both sides. Remove from the pan and put to one side.

**3** Add the marinated vegetables to the same pan (keep the marinade to one side) and stir-fry for 5 minutes. Add the garlic, harissa and tomato purée and cook for 1 minute. Mix in the flour and cook for 1 minute. Pour in the reserved marinade and stock. Bring to the boil, stirring. Put the joints back into the casserole, with the legs at the bottom. Bring to the boil, season, cover and cook in the oven for 40 minutes.

**4** Heat the remaining oil in a pan. Add the bacon and cook, stirring, for 5 minutes or until golden brown. Remove from the pan and put to one side. Cook the apples for 2–3 minutes on each side until golden. Put to one side. Remove the joints from the casserole. Strain the sauce and put back into the pan with the joints. Add the prunes and any juices, the bacon and apples. Heat through in the oven for 10 minutes. Serve with mashed potato.

★ GET AHEAD
**To prepare ahead** *Complete the recipe to the end of step 3, then cool and chill for up to two days.*
**To use** *Preheat the oven to 180°C (160°C fan oven) mark 4. Bring to the boil on the hob, then reheat in the oven for about 30–40 minutes or until hot.*

★ COOK'S TIP
*If you can't find guinea fowl, use corn-fed chicken joints instead.*

# Turkey Breast with Sausage, Cranberry and Apple Stuffing

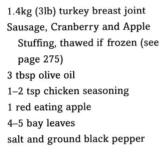

Preparation Time 25 minutes, plus soaking • Cooking Time about 1 hour 20 minutes, plus resting • Serves 8 •
Per Serving 507 calories, 21g fat (of which 8g saturates), 12g carbohydrate, 1.2g salt • Easy

1.4kg (3lb) turkey breast joint
Sausage, Cranberry and Apple
   Stuffing, thawed if frozen (see
   page 275)
3 tbsp olive oil
1–2 tsp chicken seasoning
1 red eating apple
4–5 bay leaves
salt and ground black pepper

**FOR THE GRAVY**
1 tbsp plain flour
2 tbsp cranberry jelly
300ml (½ pint) dry cider
600ml (1 pint) hot chicken stock
   (see page 266)

1 Preheat the oven to 200°C (180°C fan oven) mark 6. Soak three or four wooden skewers in a bowl of water for 20 minutes.

2 Put the turkey joint on a board, skin side down, and cut down the middle, along the length of the joint, to just over three-quarters of the way through. Season with salt and pepper, spoon the stuffing inside, then push the joint back together. Secure with fine string and the soaked skewers. Weigh the joint, then calculate the cooking time: 20 minutes per 450g (1lb), plus 20 minutes extra. For the specified 1.4kg (3lb) turkey, the cooking time will be about 1 hour 20 minutes.

3 Put the turkey joint into a large roasting tin, skin side up, drizzle with oil and sprinkle with the chicken seasoning. Cover with foil and put into the oven.

4 Slice the apple into thin rounds. About 30 minutes before the end of cooking, remove the foil and push the apple slices and bay leaves under the string. Roast, uncovered, for the final 30 minutes or until cooked through and the juices run clear when the thickest part of the meat is pierced with a skewer.

5 Transfer the turkey joint to a warmed plate, cover with foil and leave to rest for about 20 minutes.

6 To make the gravy, drain off all but about 1 tbsp fat from the roasting tin. Add the flour and stir in. Put the roasting tin on the hob over a medium heat and cook for 1 minute, scraping the base of the tin to mix in all the juices. Stir in the cranberry jelly and cider, then bring to the boil and bubble until the liquid has reduced by half. Add the hot stock and cook for 5 minutes or until the gravy has thickened slightly. Remove the skewers from the turkey, cut the meat into slices and serve with the gravy.

# Basics ★

# Preparing stock

Uncooked chicken bones can be used for stock: put the bones to one side when you joint a chicken, or ask your butcher to set some bones aside for you. If the chicken has not been previously frozen, the bones can be kept in a sealed plastic bag in the freezer.

Alternatively, use the leftover carcass of a roast chicken.

## Chicken Stock

**For 1.1 litres (2 pints), you will need:** 1.6kg (3½lb) chicken bones, 225g (8oz) each onions and celery, sliced, 150g (5oz) chopped leeks, 1 bouquet garni (see Cook's Tip, page 31), 1 tsp black peppercorns, ½ tsp salt.

**1** Put all the ingredients into a large pan and add 3 litres (5¼ pints) cold water. Bring slowly to the boil and skim the surface.

**2** Partially cover the pan, reduce the heat and simmer gently for 2 hours. Adjust the seasoning if necessary.

**3** Strain the stock through a muslin-lined sieve into a bowl and cool quickly. Degrease (see right) before using.

★ COOK'S TIPS
● *To get a clearer liquid when making poultry stock, strain the cooked stock through four layers of muslin in a sieve.*
● *Stock will keep for three days in the fridge. If you want to keep it for a further three days, transfer it to a pan and reboil gently for 5 minutes. Leave to cool, put into a clean bowl and chill for a further three days.*
● *When making chicken stock, make sure there is a good ratio of meat to bones. The more meat you use, the more flavour the stock will have.*

## Giblet Stock

**To make 1.3 litres (2¼ pints), you will need:**
turkey giblets, 1 onion, quartered, 1 carrot, halved, 1 celery stick, halved, 6 black peppercorns, 1 bay leaf.

**1** Put all the ingredients into a large pan and add 1.4 litres (2½ pints) cold water. Cover and bring to the boil.

**2** Reduce the heat, then simmer for 30 minutes–1 hour, skimming occasionally.

**3** Strain the stock through a muslin-lined sieve into a bowl and cool quickly. Put into a sealable container and chill for up to three days.

## Degreasing stock

Poultry stock needs to be degreased. You can mop the fat from the surface using kitchen paper, but the following methods are easier and more effective. There are three main methods that you can use: ladling, pouring and chilling.

**1 Ladling** While the stock is warm, place a ladle on the surface. Press down and allow the fat floating on the surface to trickle over the edge until the ladle is full. Discard the fat, then repeat until all the fat has been removed.

**2 Pouring** For this you need a degreasing jug or a double-pouring gravy boat, which has the spout at the base of the vessel. When you fill the jug or gravy boat with a fatty liquid, the fat rises. When you pour, the stock comes out while the fat stays behind in the jug.

**3 Chilling** Put the stock into the fridge until the fat solidifies, then remove the pieces of fat using a slotted spoon.

# Preparing the bird for cooking

Chicken and other poultry and game birds may be bought whole for roasting, or in pieces ready for cooking. It is often cheaper to buy a whole bird, then joint it yourself for cooking as required.

All chickens and turkeys are jointed in much of the same way. The only difference is the size. To prepare chicken and other poultry for cooking you will need a sharp meat knife, poultry shears to cut the bones and a trussing needle.

## Jointing

1 Using a sharp meat knife with a curved blade, cut out the wishbone, then cut off the wings in a single piece. Remove the wing tips.

2 With the tail pointing towards you and the breast side up, pull one leg away and cut through the skin between the leg and breast. Pull the leg down until you crack the joint between the thigh bone and ribcage.

3 Cut through that joint, then cut through the remaining leg meat. Repeat on the other side.

4 To remove the breast without any bone, make a cut along the length of the breastbone. Gently teasing the flesh away from the ribs with the knife, work the blade down between the flesh and ribs of one breast and cut it off neatly. (Always cut in, towards the bone.) Repeat on the other side.

5 To remove the breast with bone in, make a cut along the full length of the breastbone. Using poultry shears, cut through the breastbone, then cut through the ribcage following the outline of the breast meat. Repeat on the other side. Trim off any flaps of skin or fat.

## Trussing

When roasting poultry, it is not necessary to truss it but it gives the bird a neater shape for serving at the table.

1 Cut out the wishbone by pulling back the flap of skin at the neck end and locating the tip of the bone with a small sharp knife. Run the knife along the inside of the bone on both sides, then on the outside. Take care not to cut deep into the breast meat. Use poultry shears or sharp-pointed scissors to snip the tip of the bone from the breastbone and pull the bone away from the breast. Snip the two ends or pull them out by hand.

2 Pull off any loose fat from the neck or cavity. Put the wing tips under the breast and fold the neck flap on to the back of the bird. Thread a trussing needle and use it to secure the neck flap.

3 Push a metal skewer through both legs, at the joint between thigh and drumstick. Twist some string around both ends of the skewer and pull firmly to tighten.

4 Turn the bird over. Bring the string over the ends of the drumsticks, pull tight and tie to secure the legs.

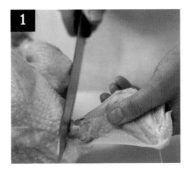

## Skinning breast fillets

**1** Firmly grab the flap of skin at the small end of the breast and pull towards the other end of the breast. Remove the skin and discard, then prepare or cook the fillet as required.

## Slicing breast fillets

**1** Cut or pull out the long strip of flesh lying on the inside of the fillet. Slice it across the grain to the thickness required for your recipe. (Raw chicken should not be cut less than about 3mm/⅛in thick.)

**2** Starting at the small tip of the breast, cut slices of the required thickness. Alternatively, cut into chunks or dice.

## Cutting escalopes

Escalopes are good for quick frying.

**1** Cut or pull out the long strip of flesh lying on the inside of the fillet. (It can be used for stir-fries, stuffings, etc.)

**2** Pressing the breast firmly on to the chopping board with the flat of one hand, carve a thin slice from underneath the breast using a sharp knife. (The knife blade should be parallel with the chopping board.) Remove that slice, then repeat until the breast meat is too small to slice.

**3** To make escalopes, put the slices of chicken between two sheets of clingfilm or greaseproof paper and pound them with a meat mallet until they are about 3mm (⅛in) thick.

## Spatchcocking

A technique to flatten smaller poultry and guinea fowl for grilling.

**1** Hold the bird on a board, breast down. Cut through one side of the backbone with poultry shears. Repeat on other side and remove.

**2** Turn bird over, press down until you hear breastbone crack. Thread skewers through legs and breasts.

## Boning

Boned poultry, stuffed and roasted, makes an attractive dish.

**1** Using a meat knife with a curved blade, remove the wishbone (see step 1, page 267) and the first two sections of the wings.

**2** Lay the chicken breast side down, with the back facing up, and cut down to the backbone along the whole length of the bird. Pulling skin and flesh away as you go, work a sharp knife between the flesh and bone down one side of the bird. Always cut in, towards the bone.

**3** You will soon reach the joints connecting the thigh and wing to the body. Cut through both joints, taking care not to cut through the skin. Do not pierce the skin; it will be the casing for your cooked dish. Continue cutting down between the breast meat and ribcage, again taking care to cut towards the bone.

**4** When you reach the tip of the breastbone, turn the bird around and repeat on the other side. Cut through the soft cartilage along the length of the breastbone to remove the boned flesh in a single piece.

**5** To remove the wings and legs, cut the tendons at the end of the bones and then use a small chopping knife to scrape off the flesh along the full length of the bone. Pull out the bone. Do this twice with the legs to remove the thigh and drumstick.

### HYGIENE

★ Raw poultry contains harmful bacteria that can spread easily to anything they touch.

★ Always wash your hands, kitchen surfaces, chopping boards, knives and equipment before and after handling poultry.

★ Don't let raw poultry touch other foods.

★ Always cover raw poultry and store in the bottom of the fridge, where it can't touch or drip on to other foods.

# Cooking chicken and other poultry

## Deep-frying

**1** Prepare the poultry for frying and chill in the fridge. Prepare the seasoned flour, batter or coating. Heat vegetable oil in a deep-fryer to 180°C (test by frying a small cube of bread; it should brown in 40 seconds). Start battering or coating each piece of poultry.

**2** Using tongs, carefully lower the poultry into the oil. Don't add more than three or four pieces at a time (otherwise the temperature will drop and the poultry will take longer to cook and become greasy). Deep-fry small chunks or strips for about 10 minutes, jointed pieces for about 15 minutes.

**3** As the pieces become golden and crisp, remove them with a slotted spoon and drain on kitchen paper. Sprinkle with a little salt and serve immediately, or keep warm in the oven until everything is cooked.

### ★ COOK'S TIPS
● *Coat each piece of food well and make sure that they are completely covered in the coating.*
● *To speed up the cooking time, cut the chicken into strips or chunks.*

## Pot-roasting

**To serve four to six, you will need:** 2 tbsp vegetable oil, 1 onion, cut into wedges, 2 rashers rindless streaky bacon, chopped, 1.4–1.6kg (3–3½lb) chicken, 2 small turnips, cut into wedges, 6 carrots, halved, 1 crushed garlic clove, 1 bouquet garni (see page Cook's Tip, page 31), 600ml (1 pint) chicken stock, 100ml (3½fl oz) dry white wine, a small handful of freshly chopped parsley, salt and ground black pepper.

**1** Preheat the oven to 200°C (180°C fan oven) mark 6. Heat the oil in a flameproof casserole. Add the onion and bacon and fry for 5 minutes. Put to one side. Add the chicken and brown all over for 10 minutes, then put to one side. Fry the turnips, carrots and garlic for 2 minutes, then put the bacon, onion and chicken back into the casserole.

**2** Add the bouquet garni, stock, wine and season and bring to the boil. Cook in the oven, basting now and then, for 1 hour 20 minutes or until the juices run clear when the thigh is pierced with a sharp knife. Lift out the chicken, stir in the parsley and carve.

## Casseroling

**To serve four to six, you will need:** 1 jointed chicken (see page 267), 3 tbsp vegetable oil, 1 chopped onion, 2 crushed garlic cloves, 2 each chopped celery sticks and carrots, 1 tbsp plain flour, 2 tbsp freshly chopped tarragon or thyme, chicken stock and/or wine, salt and ground black pepper.

**1** Preheat the oven to 180°C (160°C fan oven) mark 4. Cut the chicken legs and breasts in half.

**2** Heat the oil in a flameproof casserole and brown the chicken all over. Remove from the casserole and pour off the excess oil. Add the onion and garlic and brown for a few minutes. Add the vegetables, then stir in the flour and cook for 1 minute. Add the herbs and season. Add the chicken and pour in the stock and/or wine to come three-quarters of the way up the poultry. Cook in the oven for 1–1½ hours or until the chicken is cooked through.

### PERFECT POT-ROASTS

★ Pot-roasting is the perfect way to cook almost any poultry or game bird apart from duck or goose, which are too fatty and do not give good results, and turkey, which are too large to fit in the average casserole dish.

★ Make sure that you use a large enough casserole and that the bird doesn't fit too closely to the sides of the dish.

★ Watch out for overcooking – the closed pot cooks birds almost as fast as an ordinary roast chicken in the oven would cook.

★ Check the liquid level in the casserole from time to time. If it's too dry, add a little more. Water is fine, stock or wine are even better.

★ Timings for pot-roasted poultry: about 45 minutes for small birds such as poussin, or 1–1½ hours for chicken or guinea fowl.

## Poaching

The quick and gentle method of poaching will produce a light broth.

**1** Brown the bird in oil if you wish (this is not necessary but will give a deeper flavour), then transfer to a pan that will hold it easily: a large frying pan or sauté pan is good for pieces, a large pan or casserole for a whole bird.

**2** Add 1 roughly chopped onion, 2 crushed garlic cloves, 2 chopped carrots, 2 chopped celery sticks, 6 whole black peppercorns and 1 tsp dried mixed herbs, scattering them about the whole bird or between the pieces. Pour in just enough stock to cover, then simmer, uncovered, for about 1 hour (for a whole bird) or 30–40 minutes (for pieces).

**3** Gently lift the bird out of the liquid. If you are planning to use the liquid as the basis for a sauce, reduce it by at least half.

 COOK'S TIPS
● *Don't rush the cooking by using a very high heat. If you need to speed things up, cover the pan during the first half of cooking.*
● *Don't let the poultry cook for too long, as it can quickly dry out and toughen over a high heat.*

## Pan-frying

This is a quick method for cooking chicken pieces and you can make a sauce with the pan juices at the end, if you like.

**1** Pour in enough oil (or a mixture of oil and clarified butter) to fill a frying pan to a depth of about 5mm (¼in) and put the pan over a medium heat.

**2** Season the chicken with salt and ground black pepper, then carefully add to the pan, flesh side down, and fry for 10–15 minutes until it's browned. (Don't put too many pieces of chicken in the pan at once or the chicken will cook partly in its own steam.)

**3** Turn the pieces over and cook on the skin side for a further 10–15 minutes until the skin is brown and the flesh is cooked but still juicy all the way through.

**4** Remove the chicken from the pan using a pair of tongs and keep warm. Pour off the excess oil and deglaze the pan with a little wine or stock. Stir thoroughly, scraping up the sediment, then add some herbs and finely chopped garlic or onion and cook for a few minutes. Serve the chicken with the sauce.

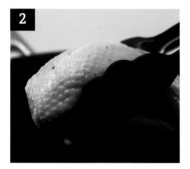

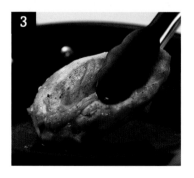

## Steaming

**1** Cut the chicken into thick shreds or chunks, or use thighs, drumsticks or halved breasts. Marinate (see page 279), if you like, for at least 1 hour.

**2** Arrange the chicken in a single layer on a heatproof dish that is small enough to fit inside the steamer. Place in the steamer, cover and steam for 20–40 minutes until just cooked through.

## Grilling

This method is perfect for cooking pieces such as breast fillets or for strips or chunks threaded on to skewers. Small birds can be spatchcocked (see page 268) and grilled.

**1** Marinate (see page 279) the chicken pieces for 30 minutes, then drain and pat dry. Alternatively, brush the chicken with a flavoured oil (see page 279). Put the pieces on a wire rack over a grill pan or roasting tin and set the pan under a preheated grill so that it is about 8cm (3¼in) from the heat source.

**2** Every few minutes brush a little of the marinade or a teaspoon of oil over the chicken.

**3** When cooked on one side, turn with tongs and cook the other side until cooked through. Avoid piercing the flesh when turning. Allow 12–20 minutes for a breast fillet or kebabs and 20–30 minutes for a spatchcocked bird.

## Stir-frying

**1** Cut the chicken into small, even-sized strips or dice no more than 5mm (¼in) thick. Heat a wok or large pan until very hot and add oil to coat the inside.

**2** Add the chicken and cook, stirring constantly, until it is just done. Remove to a bowl. Cook the other ingredients you are using for the stir-fry, then return the chicken to the pan and cook for 1–2 minutes to heat through.

# Roasting and carving

A roast chicken has a luxurious aroma and flavour and it makes an excellent Sunday lunch or special meal with very little preparation. To get the most out of the roast, these few simple guidelines make carving very easy, giving neat slices to serve.

## Preparing the bird

**1** Take the bird out of the fridge 45 minutes–1 hour before roasting to allow it to reach room temperature.

**2** Before stuffing (see page 275) a bird for roasting, clean it thoroughly. Put the bird in the sink and pull out and discard any loose fat with your fingers. Run cold water through the cavity and dry the bird well using kitchen paper.

## Basting

Chicken, turkey and other poultry needs to be basted regularly during roasting to keep the flesh moist. Use an oven glove to steady the roasting tin and spoon the juices and melted fat over the top of the bird. Alternatively, use a bulb baster.

When roasting duck or goose, spoon off the excess fat every 20–30 minutes. Keep the cooled fat in a covered bowl in the fridge: it lasts for months and is excellent for cooking roast potatoes.

## How to tell if poultry is cooked

Test by piercing the thickest part of the meat – usually the thigh – with a skewer. The juices that run out should clear with no trace of pink; if they're not, return the bird to the oven and check at regular intervals. Duck and game birds are traditionally served with the meat slightly pink: if overcooked, the meat may be dry. When tested, the juices should have just a blush of pink.

### CHICKEN

To calculate the roasting time for a chicken, weigh the oven-ready bird (including stuffing, if using) and allow 20 minutes per 450g (1lb) plus 20 minutes extra, in an oven preheated to 200°C (180°C fan oven) mark 6.

| Oven-ready weight | Serves | Cooking time (approx.) |
|---|---|---|
| 1.4–1.6 kg (3–3½lb) | 4–6 | 1½ hours |
| 1.8–2.3kg (4–5lb) | 6–8 | 1 hour 50 minutes |
| 2.5–2.7kg (5½–6lb) | 8–10 | 2¼ hours |

OTHER POULTRY AND BIRDS

Preheat the oven to 200°C (180°C fan oven) mark 6.

| Serves | | Cooking time (approx.) |
|---|---|---|
| Poussin | 1–2 | 20 minutes per 450g (1lb) |
| Guinea fowl 1.4kg (3lb) | 2–4 | 35 minutes per 1kg (2¼lb), plus 15 minutes |
| Duck 1.8–2.5kg (4–5½lb) | 2–4 | 20 minutes per 450g (1lb) |
| Goose, small 3.6–5.4kg (8–12lb) | 4–7 | 20 minutes per 450g (1lb) |
| Goose, medium 5.4–6.3kg (12–14lb) | 8–11 | 25 minutes per 450g (1lb) |
| Grouse | 1 | 25–35 minutes |
| Partridge | 1 | 20–25 minutes |
| Pheasant | 2–3 | 45–60 minutes |

## COOKING A TURKEY

Cooking a turkey can be a daunting prospect, especially since quite often it is a once-a-year meal.

Take the turkey out of the fridge 45 minutes before stuffing it. Coat the turkey with butter and season. Wrap loosely in a 'tent' of foil, then cook in an oven preheated to 190°C (170°C fan oven) mark 5. Allow 45 minutes per 1kg (2¼lb), plus 20 minutes (see chart below for timings). Remove the foil about 1 hour before the end of cooking time to brown the bird. Baste regularly.

Check that the turkey is cooked (see opposite), then remove from the oven and carefully transfer from the roasting tin to a platter. Cover with foil and a clean teatowel and allow to rest for 20–30 minutes before carving. This allows the juices to settle back into the meat, leaving it moist and easier to carve.

| Oven-ready weight of turkey (at room temperature) | Approximate no. of servings | Approximate thawing time | Cooking time (foil-wrapped) |
|---|---|---|---|
| 2.3–3.6kg (5–8lb) | 6–10 | 15–18 hours | 2–3 hours |
| 3.6–5kg (8–11lb) | 10–15 | 18–20 hours | 3–3¼ hours |
| 5–6.8kg (11–15lb) | 15–20 | 20–24 hours | 3¼–4 hours |
| 6.8–9kg (15–20lb) | 20–30 | 24–30 hours | 4–5½ hours |

## Simple roast chicken

**To serve four to six, you will need:**
1.4–1.6kg (3–3½lb) chicken, 5 garlic cloves, 4 lemon slices, juice of 2 lemons (squeezed halves put to one side), 2 tsp Dijon mustard, 4 fresh rosemary sprigs, 4 fresh thyme sprigs, 1 sliced onion, 300ml (½ pint) chicken stock, 300ml (½ pint) dry white wine.

1 Make incisions all over the chicken except the breast. Loosen the breast skin. Crush 3 garlic cloves and slip under the skin with lemon slices, mustard and herbs.

2 Put the lemon halves into the cavity. Put the chicken into a roasting tin. Spoon 2 tbsp lemon juice into the cavity and pour the remaining juice over. Chill for a few hours. Remove from the fridge 30 minutes before cooking.

3 Preheat the oven to 200°C (180°C fan oven) mark 6. Put the chicken, breast side down, on a rack in the tin. Add the onion, remaining garlic and 4 tbsp each stock and wine.

4 Roast in the oven for 20 minutes, turn and roast for 35 minutes or until juices run clear when the leg is pierced. Baste now and then, adding wine if needed.

5 Put the chicken on a platter and cover loosely with foil. Spoon off as much fat as possible, leaving behind the juices in the tin. Put the tin over a medium-high heat, add the remaining stock and wine and scrape up the sediment from the tin. Simmer for 5 minutes to make gravy. Strain.

## Turkey know-how

**Thawing** Leave a frozen turkey in its bag and thaw at a cool room temperature, not in the fridge. Remove any giblets as soon as they become loose. Once there are no ice crystals inside the body cavity and the legs are flexible, cover and store in the fridge. Cook within 24 hours. Take the bird out of the fridge 45 minutes–1 hour before roasting to allow it to reach room temperature.

**Stuffing** Loosely stuff the neck end only. Allow 225g (8oz) stuffing for each 2.3kg (5lb) weight of bird and stuff just before cooking. Secure the neck skin with skewers or cocktail sticks, or sew using a trussing needle threaded with fine string. Weigh the bird after stuffing to calculate the cooking time.

## Carving chicken
After resting, put the bird on a carving board.

**1** Steady the bird with a carving fork. To cut breast meat, start at the neck end and cut slices about 5mm (¼in) thick. Use the carving knife and fork to lift them on to a warmed serving plate.

**2** To cut off the legs, cut the skin between the thigh and breast.

**3** Pull the leg down to expose the joint between the thigh bone and ribcage and cut through that joint.

**4** Cut through the joint between the thigh and drumstick.

**5** To carve meat from the leg (for turkeys and very large chickens), remove it from the carcass and joint the two parts of the leg, as above. Holding the drumstick by the thin end, stand it up on the carving board and carve slices roughly parallel with the bone. The thigh can be carved either flat on the board or upright.

## Storing leftovers
Don't forget the leftovers when the meal is finished – never leave poultry standing in a warm room. Cool quickly in a cold place, then cover and chill.

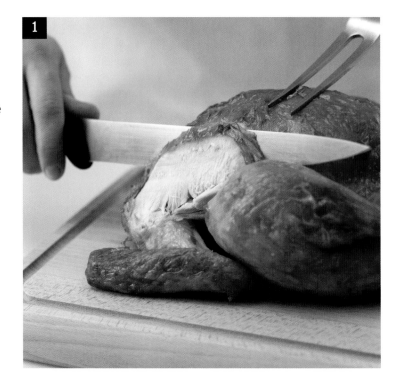

# Stuffings

Some people like moist stuffing, cooked inside the bird, others prefer the crisper result when the stuffing is cooked in a separate dish – why not do half and half and please everyone? All these stuffings – with the exception of the wild rice stuffing – can be made a day ahead or frozen for up to one month. Thaw overnight in the fridge. Cook in a preheated oven, or alongside the roast.

## Best-ever Sage and Onion Stuffing

**To serve eight, you will need:**

1 tbsp olive oil, 1 very finely chopped large onion, 2 tbsp finely chopped fresh sage, 7 heaped tbsp fresh white breadcrumbs, 900g (2lb) pork sausagemeat, 1 medium egg yolk, salt and ground black pepper.

1 Heat the oil in a pan. Add the onion and fry until soft and golden. Stir in the sage and leave to cool.

2 Put 1 tbsp breadcrumbs to one side, then mix the remainder into the sausagemeat with the onion and egg yolk. Season with salt and pepper, then leave to cool. Cover and chill overnight, or freeze.

3 Preheat the oven to 180°C (160°C fan oven) mark 4. Put the stuffing into an ovenproof dish, sprinkle with the breadcrumbs and cook for 35–40 minutes until cooked through and golden.

## Sausage, Cranberry and Apple Stuffing

**To serve eight, you will need:**

50g (2oz) butter, 1 finely chopped onion, 1 crushed garlic clove, 4 pork sausages – about 275g (10oz) – skinned and broken up, 75g (3oz) dried cranberries, 2 tbsp freshly chopped parsley, 1 red eating apple, salt and ground black pepper.

1 Heat the butter in a pan. Add the onion and cook over a medium heat for 5 minutes or until soft. Add the garlic and cook for 1 minute. Tip into a bowl and leave to cool. Add

the sausages, cranberries and parsley, then cover and chill overnight, or freeze.

2 Preheat the oven to 200°C (180°C fan oven) mark 6. Core and chop the apple and add it to the stuffing. Season and stir well.

3 Put the stuffing into an ovenproof dish and cook in the oven for about 30 minutes or until cooked through.

## Wild Rice and Cranberry Stuffing

**This stuffing is great with goose. If you have the goose giblets, use the liver for this recipe.**

**To serve six to eight, you will need:**

125g (4oz) wild rice, 225g (8oz) streaky bacon, cut into short strips, 2 medium red onions, about 225g (8oz) total weight, finely chopped, 75g (3oz) dried cranberries, 1 medium egg, beaten, salt and ground black pepper.

1 Put the rice into a pan and cover with 900ml (1½ pints) cold water. Add ¼ tsp salt and bring to the boil. Reduce the heat and simmer, partly covered, for 45 minutes or until the rice is cooked. Drain and cool.

2 Heat a large frying pan. Add the bacon and dry-fry, turning from time to time, until lightly browned. Remove the bacon with a slotted spoon and transfer to a bowl. (If you have the goose liver, cook it in the same pan for 2–3 minutes, leave to cool, then chop it finely and add it to the bacon.) Add the onions to the

frying pan and cook over a low heat until soft and translucent. Add the cranberries and cook for 1–2 minutes, then add the mixture to the bacon and leave to cool completely.

3 Add the cooked rice and the egg to the bacon mixture. Season, then stir thoroughly to combine. Cover and chill overnight.

4 Preheat the oven to 200°C (180°C fan oven) mark 6. Wrap the stuffing in a buttered piece of foil and cook for 30–40 minutes.

## Chestnut and Butternut Squash Stuffing

**To serve eight, you will need:**

1 tbsp olive oil, 15g (½oz) butter, 1 finely chopped onion, 1 small butternut squash, finely chopped, 2 finely chopped rosemary sprigs, 2 finely chopped celery sticks, 1 firm pear, finely chopped, 200g (7oz) peeled and cooked (or vacuum-packed) chestnuts, roughly chopped, 2 slices – about 100g (3½oz) – walnut bread, cut into small cubes, salt and ground black pepper.

1 Heat the oil and butter in a pan. Add the onion and fry for about 10 minutes or until soft but not brown. Add the squash and rosemary and continue to cook for a further 5 minutes or until everything is soft and golden. Add the celery and pear and cook for 1–2 minutes.

2 Add the chestnuts, season with salt and pepper and mix well. Add

the bread, mix everything together, then leave to cool. Cover and chill overnight, or freeze.

**3** Preheat the oven to 200°C (180°C fan oven) mark 6. Put the stuffing into a buttered ovenproof dish and cook for about 25–30 minutes or until golden.

## Fennel and Pinenut Stuffing

**To serve eight, you will need:**
75g (3oz) butter, 1 bunch of spring onions, sliced, 450g (1lb) roughly chopped fennel, 4 tbsp freshly chopped tarragon, 50g (2oz) pinenuts, toasted, 150g (5oz) goat's cheese, 150g (5oz) fresh breadcrumbs, 2 medium eggs, beaten, grated zest and juice of 1 lemon, salt and ground black pepper.
**1** Heat the butter in a pan. Add the spring onions and cook for 3 minutes. Add the fennel and cook for 5 minutes, then leave to cool.

**2** Add the tarragon, pinenuts, cheese, breadcrumbs, eggs, lemon zest and juice. Season with salt and pepper and mix well. Cover and chill overnight, or freeze.

**3** Preheat the oven to 200°C (180°C fan oven) mark 6. Put the stuffing into a buttered ovenproof dish and cook for 30–40 minutes.

## Orange, Sage and Thyme Stuffing

**To serve eight, you will need:**
2 tbsp olive oil, 1 finely chopped large onion, 2 crushed garlic cloves, 75g (3oz) fresh white breadcrumbs, 50g (2oz) toasted and chopped pinenuts, grated zest of 1 orange, plus 2–3 tbsp juice, 2 tbsp each freshly chopped thyme and sage, 1 medium egg yolk, beaten, salt and ground black pepper.
**1** Heat the oil in a pan. Add the onion and garlic and fry gently for 5 minutes until soft but not brown.

**2** Put the remaining ingredients into a large bowl. Add the onion mixture and stir to bind, adding more orange juice if needed.

## Bacon, Pecan and Wild Rice Stuffing

**To serve eight, you will need:**
900ml (1½ pints) hot chicken stock (see page 266), 1 bay leaf, 1 fresh thyme sprig, 225g (8oz) mixed long-grain and wild rice, 50g (2oz) unsalted butter, 225g (8oz) smoked streaky bacon, roughly chopped, 2 finely chopped onions, 3 finely chopped celery sticks, ½ Savoy cabbage, chopped, 3 tbsp finely chopped marjoram, 85g sachet sage and onion stuffing mix, 125g (4oz) chopped pecans.
**1** Pour the hot stock into a pan, add the bay leaf and thyme and bring to the boil. Add the rice, cover, reduce the heat and cook according to the pack instructions. Drain if necessary, then tip into a large bowl and cool quickly, discarding the herbs.

**2** Melt the butter in a large pan. Add the bacon, onions and celery and cook over a medium heat for 10 minutes until the onions are soft but not brown. Add the cabbage and marjoram and cook for 5 minutes, stirring regularly.

**3** Add the cabbage mixture to the rice, together with the stuffing mix and pecans. Tip into a bowl and cool quickly.

## Falafel Balls

**These stuffing balls are delicious with chicken, but are also great with pitta bread and green salad as a vegetarian meal.**
**To serve eight to ten, you will need:**
275g (10oz) dried chickpeas, 1 roughly chopped small onion, a small handful of fresh coriander, 3 roughly chopped garlic cloves, juice of ½ lemon, 2 tsp ground cumin, ½ tsp bicarbonate of soda, olive oil for shallow-frying, salt and ground black pepper.
**1** Put the chickpeas into a pan and cover with plenty of cold water. Bring to the boil and boil for 2 minutes, then leave to soak for 2 hours. Drain.

**2** Put the drained chickpeas into a food processor with the onion, coriander, garlic, lemon juice, cumin, bicarbonate of soda and ½ tsp salt and pepper. Whiz until everything is finely ground and beginning to stick together. Take small handfuls of the mixture and squeeze in the palm of your hand to extract any excess moisture. Shape into walnut-sized balls.

**3** Heat the oil in a frying pan over a medium-high heat and fry the falafel for 3–4 minutes until they are deep golden brown all over. Drain well on kitchen paper. Serve immediately, or chill for later use.

**4** To use, put the falafel into a parcel of foil and reheat alongside the roast for 15–20 minutes.

## Rosemary and Lemon Stuffing

**To serve four to six, you will need:**
25g (1oz) butter, 1 finely chopped onion, 125g (4oz) fresh white breadcrumbs, 1 tbsp freshly chopped rosemary leaves, grated zest of 1 lemon, 1 medium egg, beaten, salt and ground black pepper.

**1** Melt the butter in a pan. Add the onion and fry over a low heat for 10–15 minutes until soft and golden. Tip into a bowl and cool.

**2** Add the breadcrumbs, rosemary leaves and lemon zest. Season well, then add the egg and stir to bind.

## Pork, Chestnut and Orange Stuffing

**To serve eight to ten, you will need:**
50g (2oz) butter, 6 roughly chopped shallots, 4 roughly chopped celery sticks, 1 fresh rosemary sprig, snipped, 1 tbsp freshly chopped flat-leafed parsley, 175g (6oz) firm white bread, cut into rough dice, 2 cooking apples, about 225g (8oz) total weight, peeled, cored and chopped, 125g (4oz) cooked, peeled (or vacuum-packed) chestnuts, roughly chopped, grated zest of 1 large orange, 450g (1lb) coarse pork sausagemeat, salt and ground black pepper.

**1** Melt the butter in a large frying pan. Add the shallots, celery and rosemary and gently fry for 10–12 minutes until the vegetables are soft and golden. Tip into a large bowl. Add the parsley, bread, apples, chestnuts and orange zest to the bowl. Season and mix well.

**2** Divide the sausagemeat into walnut-sized pieces. Fry, in batches, until golden and cooked through. Add to the bowl and stir to mix.

## Pork, Spinach and Apple Stuffing

**To serve eight, you will need:**
2 tbsp olive oil, 150g (5oz) finely chopped onion, 225g (8oz) fresh spinach, torn into pieces if the leaves are large, 2 sharp apples, such as Granny Smith, peeled, cored and cut into chunks, 400g (14oz) pork sausagemeat, coarsely grated zest of 1 lemon, 1 tbsp freshly chopped thyme, 100g (3½oz) fresh white breadcrumbs, 2 large eggs, beaten, salt and ground black pepper.

**1** Heat the oil in a frying pan. Add the onion and cook for 10 minutes or until soft. Increase the heat, add the spinach and cook until wilted.

**2** Add the apples and cook, stirring, for 2–3 minutes, then leave to cool. When the mixture is cold, add the sausagemeat, lemon zest, thyme, breadcrumbs and eggs, then season and stir until evenly mixed.

## Cranberry and Lemon Stuffing

**To serve four to six, you will need:**
25g (1oz) butter, 1 finely chopped large onion, 1 crushed garlic clove, 450g (1lb) best-quality sausages, 4 tbsp freshly chopped parsley, 2 tbsp freshly chopped sage, the zest of 2 lemons, 1 tbsp brandy or Calvados (optional), 75g (3oz) dried cranberries, salt and ground black pepper.

**1** Melt the butter in a frying pan. Add the onion and sauté for about 10 minutes or until soft but not brown. Add the garlic and cook for a further 1 minute, then transfer to a bowl and leave to cool.

**2** Preheat the oven to 190°C (170°C fan oven) mark 5. Squeeze the sausagemeat out of the skins into the bowl with the onions and garlic. Add all the remaining ingredients and season, then mix well, using your hands. Shape into 18 balls and place in muffin tins or pack into an oiled baking dish and bake in the oven for 30 minutes or until cooked through and golden on top.

# Accompaniments

Bread Sauce and Cranberry Sauce can be made ahead and then frozen for up to one month.

## Red Wine Gravy

**To serve eight, you will need:**

juices from the roasted bird, 1 tbsp plain flour, 150ml (¼ pint) red wine, about 1.4 litres (2½ pints) giblet stock (see page 266), 1 tbsp fine-shred marmalade.

**1** Pour off all but 2 tbsp fat from the roasting tin. Put the roasting tin on the hob over a low heat.

**2** Stir in the flour using a wooden spoon, scraping up the juices from the base of the tin, and cook for 2 minutes, stirring constantly.

**3** Add the wine, stirring constantly, then gradually add the stock. Bring to the boil, then add the marmalade and simmer for 5–10 minutes until thick and syrupy.

## Glazed Chipolatas

**To serve eight, you will need:**

450g (1lb) chipolata sausages, 3 tbsp cranberry sauce, 1 tbsp clear honey, a pinch of ground ginger, 1 tbsp olive oil.

**1** Preheat the oven to 200°C (180°C fan oven) mark 6. Put the sausages into a plastic container, add the cranberry sauce, honey, ground ginger and oil and toss together until evenly coated.

**2** Spread the chipolatas on a baking sheet and cook for 30–40 minutes. Serve immediately.

## Bacon-wrapped Prunes

**To serve eight, you will need:**

12 rashers rindless streaky bacon, 24 ready-to-eat pitted prunes, 2 tbsp olive oil.

**1** Preheat the oven to 190°C (170°C fan oven) mark 5. Cut each bacon rasher in half. Roll half a rasher around each prune.

**2** Put on a baking sheet and drizzle with the oil. Roast for 20 minutes or until the bacon is crisp.

★ GET AHEAD

***To prepare ahead*** *Complete the recipe to the end of step 1, then put the prunes into a sealed container and chill in the fridge overnight.*

***To use*** *Complete the recipe.*

## Bread Sauce

**To serve eight, you will need:**

1 onion, quartered, 4 cloves, 2 bay leaves, 600ml (1 pint) milk, 125g (4oz) fresh white breadcrumbs, 4 tbsp double cream, 25g (1oz) butter, a little freshly grated nutmeg, salt and ground black pepper.

**1** Stud each onion quarter with a clove, then put into a pan with the bay leaves and milk. Bring to the boil, remove from the heat and leave to infuse for 10 minutes.

**2** Use a slotted spoon to lift out the onion and bay leaves and discard. Add the breadcrumbs to the pan and bring to the boil, stirring. Reduce the heat and simmer for 5–6 minutes.

**3** Stir in the cream and butter, then add the nutmeg and salt and pepper. Spoon into a warmed serving dish and keep warm (see Cook's Tip) until ready to serve.

★ COOK'S TIP

*To keep bread sauce warm without congealing, put it into a small bowl, cover with clingfilm and put this into a large bowl filled with hot water for 30 minutes.*

★ GET AHEAD

***To prepare ahead*** *Put the sauce into an airtight container, press a damp piece of greaseproof paper on the surface to prevent a skin forming, then cool, cover and chill for up to two days.*

***To use*** *Put the sauce into a small pan with 2 tbsp cream, reheat gently, then simmer for 2 minutes until piping hot.*

## Cranberry Sauce

**To serve eight, you will need:**

225g (8oz) fresh cranberries, grated zest and juice of 1 orange, 4 tbsp fine-shred marmalade, 125g (4oz) light muscovado sugar, 50ml (2fl oz) port.

**1** Put the cranberries into a pan. Add the orange zest and juice, marmalade, sugar and port and mix. Bring to the boil, reduce the heat and simmer for 5–10 minutes, stirring occasionally, until thickened.

# Marinades, spice rubs and flavoured butters

### Quick and Easy Marinade

Combine olive oil, lemon or lime juice and chopped garlic, pour over chicken and marinate in the fridge for at least 1 hour.

### Lemon and Rosemary Marinade

Mix together the coarsely grated zest and juice of 1 lemon with 2 tbsp freshly chopped rosemary and 6 tbsp olive oil. Pour over chicken and marinate in the fridge for at least 1 hour.

### Spicy Tomato Marinade

Mix together 8 tbsp tomato ketchup with 2 tbsp soy sauce, 2 tbsp chilli sauce and 4 tbsp red wine. Add 2 tsp Jamaican jerk seasoning. Pour over chicken and marinate in the fridge for at least 1 hour.

### Pineapple and Coconut Marinade

Blend ¼ peeled chopped pineapple with the scooped-out flesh of ½ a lime until smooth. Add 200ml (7fl oz) coconut milk and 1 tsp Tabasco. Pour over chicken and marinate in the fridge for at least 1 hour.

### Hot and Spicy Marinade

Combine 1 crushed garlic clove, 2 tbsp ground coriander, 2 tbsp ground cumin, 1 tbsp paprika, 1 seeded and chopped red chilli (see Cook's Tips, page 10), the juice of ½ lemon, 2 tbsp soy sauce and 8 fresh thyme sprigs. Pour over chicken and marinate in the fridge for 1 hour.

### ★ COOKS TIPS

● *Use a large sealable plastic bag when marinating food: it coats the food more easily, cuts down on washing up, and takes up less space in the fridge than a bowl.*

● *Marinades will not penetrate poultry skin, so remove the skin or cut slashes in it before mixing the poultry with the marinade.*

● *Use just enough marinade to coat the flesh generously: it is wasteful to use too much, as most will be left in the base of the container. It cannot be reused once it has been in contact with raw flesh.*

● *Dry marinated meat to remove liquid from the surface before cooking. Shake off excess marinade and pat dry with kitchen paper.*

● *Pay attention when using marinades or sweet glazes made with sugar or honey, as they tend to burn if not watched carefully.*

### SPICE RUBS

Sometimes referred to as a dry marinade, spice rubs are a great way to add flavour to poultry. They don't penetrate far into the flesh, but give an excellent flavour on and just under the crust. Make them with crushed garlic, dried herbs or spices and plenty of ground black pepper. Rub into the poultry and leave to marinate in the fridge for at least 30 minutes or up to 8 hours.

### FLAVOURED OILS

★ Look for lemon, garlic, basil and chilli flavoured oils – they can be used as a marinade. Alternatively, just brush the oil over the food before grilling.

★ Even quicker are ready-made tikka and teriyaki marinades, which are perfect for most kinds of poultry.

### FLAVOURED BUTTERS

A pat of flavoured butter makes an instant sauce for simply grilled chicken. Per serving, you will need: 25g (1oz) soft unsalted butter, plus flavouring (see below).

1 Beat the softened butter together with the flavouring. Turn out on to clingfilm, shape into a log and wrap tightly.

2 Chill in the fridge for at least 1 hour. It will keep for up to one week (or freeze for up to one month).

### FLAVOURINGS:

*For 125g (4oz) unsalted butter.*
**Anchovy butter:** *6 mashed anchovy fillets.*
**Herb butter:** *2 tbsp finely chopped herbs, a squeeze of lemon juice.*
**Garlic butter:** *1 crushed garlic clove, 2 tsp freshly chopped parsley.*

# Sauces

## The Ultimate Barbecue Sauce

**To make 300ml (½ pint), you will need:**

3 tbsp olive oil, 3 finely chopped garlic cloves, 3 tbsp balsamic vinegar, 4 tbsp dry sherry, 3 tbsp sun-dried tomato paste or tomato purée, 3 tbsp sweet chilli sauce, 300ml (½ pint) passata, 5 tbsp clear honey.

**1** Put the oil, garlic, vinegar, sherry, tomato paste or purée and the chilli sauce into a bowl and mix well. Pour into a pan, then add the passata and honey. Bring to the boil, reduce the heat and simmer for 10–15 minutes until thick.

## Avocado Salsa

**To serve four to six, you will need:**

3 large ripe tomatoes, 1 large red pepper, 2 small red chillies, (see Cook's Tips, page 10) 1 finely chopped red onion, 4 tbsp freshly chopped coriander, 2 tbsp freshly chopped parsley, 2 ripe avocados, salt and ground black pepper.

**1** Quarter, seed and dice the tomatoes. Core, seed and finely chop the pepper. Halve, seed and finely chop the chillies and combine with the tomatoes, peppers, onion and herbs.

**2** Halve, stone, peel and dice the avocados. Add to the salsa and season well with salt and pepper. Toss well and serve within about 10 minutes. (Cut avocado flesh will discolour if left for longer than this.)

### FOR QUICK SAUCES

### Mango Mayo

Put the flesh of 1 large mango into a bowl and mash together with 2 tsp freshly chopped coriander, 1 tsp grated fresh root ginger and the juice of 1 lime. Season with salt and pepper. Gradually whisk in 200ml (7fl oz) sunflower oil until thick. Great with barbecued chicken.

### Basil Mayo

Stir 2 tbsp basil Pesto (see Cook's Tips, page 10) into 200ml (7fl oz) mayonnaise. This is great with barbecued chicken.

### Avocado Crush

Toss 1 large peeled chopped avocado in 4 tbsp lemon juice. Blend with 100ml (3½fl oz) olive oil and 2 tbsp water. Great with chicken salad.

### Almond and Herb Pesto

Whiz together 50g (2oz) fresh flat-leafed parsley, 1 thick slice stale bread (crust removed), 2 tbsp lemon juice and 1–2 garlic cloves, then whiz in 50g (2oz) toasted almonds and 200ml (7fl oz) olive oil. Great with barbecued chicken.

# Rice and chutneys

## Saffron Rice

**To serve eight, you will need:**

500g (1lb 2oz) basmati rice, 900ml (1½ pints) stock made with 1½ chicken stock cubes, 5 tbsp sunflower or light vegetable oil, ½ tsp saffron threads, salt, 75g (3oz) blanched almonds and pistachio nuts, roughly chopped, to garnish (optional).

**1** Put the rice into a bowl and cover with warm water, then drain well through a sieve.

**2** Put the stock, oil and a good pinch of salt into a pan, then cover and bring to the boil. Add the saffron and the rice.

**3** Cover the pan and bring the stock back to the boil, then stir, reduce the heat to low, replace the lid and cook gently for 10 minutes until little holes appear all over the surface of the cooked rice and the grains are tender. Leave to stand, covered, for 15 minutes.

**4** Fluff up the rice with a fork and transfer it to a warmed serving dish. Sprinkle the nuts on top of the rice, if using, and serve.

## Pilau Rice

**To serve four, you will need:**

50g (2oz) butter, plus a generous knob to serve, 225g (8oz) long-grain white rice, rinsed and drained, 750ml (1¼ pints) hot chicken stock (see page 266), salt and ground black pepper.

**1** Melt the butter in a pan. Add the rice and fry gently for 3–4 minutes until translucent.

**2** Slowly pour in the hot stock, season, stir and cover with a tight-fitting lid. Leave undisturbed over a very low heat for about 10 minutes or according to the pack instructions until the water has been absorbed and the rice is just tender.

**3** Remove the lid and cover the surface of the rice with a clean cloth or teatowel. Replace the lid and leave to stand in a warm place for about 15 minutes to dry the rice before serving.

**4** Fork through and add a knob of butter to serve.

## Coconut Rice

**To serve eight, you will need:**

25g (1oz) butter, 450g (1lb) long-grain white rice, rinsed and drained, 1 tsp salt, 50g (2oz) creamed coconut, crumbled.

**1** Melt the butter in a large pan. Add the rice and stir to coat in butter. Add 1.2 litres (2 pints) cold water and the salt. Cover the pan and bring to the boil. Reduce the heat and simmer for about 10–12 minutes or according to the pack instructions until all the water has been absorbed.

**2** Once the rice is cooked, remove the pan from the heat. Add the creamed coconut. Cover the pan with a clean teatowel and replace the lid to allow the coconut to dissolve and the teatowel to absorb any steam. Fluff up with a fork before serving.

## Thai Rice

**To serve six, you will need:**

500g (1lb 2oz) Thai rice, a handful of mint leaves, salt.

**1** Cook the rice and mint in lightly salted boiling water for about 10–12 minutes until tender. Drain well and serve.

## Fresh Mango Chutney

**To make 225g (8oz), you will need:**
1 large ripe mango, 1 fresh green chilli, seeded (see Cook's Tips, page 10), juice of 1 lime, ¼ tsp cayenne pepper, ½ tsp salt.

**1** Cut the mango in half lengthways, slicing either side of the large flat stone; discard the stone. Using the point of a knife, cut parallel lines into the mango flesh, almost to the skin. Score another set of lines to cut the flesh into squares. Turn the skin inside out so that the cubes of flesh stand up, then cut these off and place in a bowl.

**2** Cut the chilli into fine rings and mix with the mango cubes, lime juice, cayenne and salt. Chill for 1 hour before serving. It will keep for up to two days in the fridge.

## Fresh Coriander Chutney

**To make 275g (10oz), you will need:**
100g (4oz) fresh coriander, 1 roughly chopped medium onion, 2 fresh green chillies, seeded (see Cook's Tips, page 10), 2.5cm (1in) piece fresh root ginger, peeled, 1 tsp salt, 2 tbsp lemon or lime juice, 1 tbsp desiccated coconut.

**1** Put all the ingredients into a blender or food processor and whiz until smooth.

**2** Transfer to a glass or plastic bowl, cover and chill in the fridge. It will keep for up to one week.

## Spiced Pepper Chutney

**To make 1.6kg (3½lb), you will need:**
3 red peppers and 3 green peppers, seeded and finely chopped, 450g (1lb) chopped onions, 450g (1lb) peeled and chopped tomatoes, 450g (1lb) cooking apples, peeled, cored and chopped, 225g (8oz) demerara sugar, 1 tsp ground allspice, 450ml (¾ pint) malt vinegar, 1 tsp peppercorns, 1 tsp mustard seeds.

**1** Place the peppers in a preserving pan or large heavy-based pan with the onions, tomatoes, apples, sugar, allspice and vinegar. Tie the peppercorns and mustard seeds in a piece of muslin and add to the pan. Heat gently, stirring, until the sugar has dissolved. Bring to the boil, then reduce the heat and simmer, uncovered, over a medium heat for about 1½ hours, stirring occasionally, until soft, pulpy and well reduced. Remove the muslin bag.

**2** Spoon the chutney into jars, cover and seal. It will keep for up to three months.

## Chilli Chutney

**To make 900g (2lb), you will need:**
900g (2lb) very ripe tomatoes, roughly chopped, 8 red chillies, seeded (see Cook's Tips, page 10), 6 crushed garlic cloves, 5cm (2in) piece fresh root ginger, grated, 1 lemongrass stalk, trimmed and outer layer removed, 1 star anise, 550g (1¼lb) golden caster sugar, 200ml (7fl oz) red wine vinegar.

**1** Put half the tomatoes into a food processor or blender. Roughly chop the chillies, add to the blender with the garlic and ginger and whiz to a purée. Transfer to a large heavy-based pan.

**2** Crush the lemongrass and cut in half. Tie the cut halves together with string, then add to the pan with the star anise, sugar and vinegar.

**3** Bring the mixture to the boil, add the remaining tomatoes, then reduce the heat. Cook gently for 45–50 minutes, stirring occasionally and skimming off any foam, until the mixture has thickened and reduced slightly. Remove the star anise and lemongrass.

**4** Spoon the chutney into jars, cover and seal. Chill and use within one month.

# Pastes and sauces

Ready-made pastes and sauces, consisting of ingredients such as spices, fresh chillies, onion, ginger and oil, are widely available, but most are also easily made at home.

## Pastes

**Harissa** is a spicy paste flavoured with chillies, coriander and caraway and is used as a condiment or ingredient in North African cooking, particularly in Morocco, Tunisia and Algeria.

**To make your own harissa:**
Grill 2 red peppers until softened and charred, cool, then peel, core and seed.

Put 4 seeded and roughly chopped red chillies (see Cook's Tips, page 10) into a food processor with 6 peeled garlic cloves, 1 tbsp ground coriander and 1 tbsp caraway seeds and whiz to a rough paste. Add the grilled peppers, 2 tsp salt and 4 tbsp olive oil and whiz until smooth. Put the harissa into a screw-topped jar, cover with a thin layer of olive oil and store in the fridge. It will keep for up to two weeks.

**Tandoori paste** is used on foods such as chicken to add flavour and to give it a reddish-orange colour common in tandoor cooking.

**To make your own tandoori paste:**
Put 24 crushed garlic cloves, a 5cm (2in) piece fresh root ginger, peeled and chopped, 3 tbsp each coriander seeds, cumin seeds, ground fenugreek and paprika, 3 seeded and chopped red chillies (see Cook's Tips, page 10), 3 tsp English mustard, 2 tbsp tomato purée and 1 tsp salt into a food processor with 8 tbsp water and whiz to a paste. Divide the paste into three equal portions, then freeze for up to three months.

## Sauces

**Soy sauce** – made from fermented soy beans and, usually, wheat, this is the most common flavouring in Chinese and Southeast Asian cooking. There are light and dark soy sauces; the dark kind is slightly sweeter and tends to darken the food. It will keep indefinitely.

**Tabasco** – a fiery hot sauce based on red chillies, spirit vinegar and salt, and prepared to a secret recipe. A dash of Tabasco may be used to add a kick to soups, casseroles, sauces, rice dishes and tomato-based drinks.

**Tamari** – similar to soy sauce, this fermented sauce is made from soy beans and is dark in colour and rich in flavour. Usually wheat-free.

**Teriyaki sauce** – a Japanese sauce made from soy sauce, mirin (a sweet Japanese cooking wine) and sugar.

# Salad dressings

### Balsamic Dressing

**To make about 100ml (3½fl oz), you will need:**

2 tbsp balsamic vinegar, 4 tbsp extra virgin olive oil, salt and ground black pepper.

**1** Whisk the vinegar and oil in a small bowl. Season to taste with salt and pepper.

**2** If not using immediately, store in a cool place and whisk before using.

 COOK'S TIPS
● *To help it emulsify easily, add 1 tsp cold water to the dressing.*
● *To get a really good emulsion, shake the dressing vigorously in a screw-topped jar.*

### French Dressing

**To make 100ml (3½fl oz) you will need:**

1 tsp Dijon mustard, a pinch of sugar, 1 tbsp red or white wine vinegar, 6 tbsp extra virgin olive oil, salt and ground black pepper.

**1** Put the mustard, sugar and vinegar into a small bowl and season with salt and pepper.

**2** Whisk thoroughly until well combined, then gradually whisk in the oil until thoroughly combined. If not using immediately, store in a cool place and whisk before using.

⭐ TRY SOMETHING DIFFERENT
*Herb Dressing Use half the mustard, replace the vinegar with lemon juice and add 2 tbsp freshly chopped herbs, such as parsley, chervil and chives.*
*Garlic Dressing Add 1 crushed garlic clove to the dressing at step 2.*

### Basic Vinaigrette

**To make about 300ml (½ pint) you will need:**

100ml (3½fl oz) extra virgin olive oil, 100ml (3½fl oz) grapeseed oil, 50ml (2fl oz) white wine vinegar, a pinch each of sugar and English mustard powder, 1 garlic clove, crushed (optional), salt and ground black pepper.

**1** Put both oils, the vinegar, sugar, mustard powder and garlic, if using, into a large screw-topped jar. Tighten the lid and shake well. Season with salt and pepper.

**2** If not using immediately, store in a cool place and shake before using.

### Lemon Vinaigrette

**To make about 150ml (¼ pint) you will need:**

2 tbsp lemon juice, 2 tsp runny honey, 8 tbsp extra virgin olive oil, 3 tbsp freshly chopped mint, 4 tbsp roughly chopped flat-leafed parsley, salt and ground black pepper.

**1** Put the lemon juice, honey and salt and pepper to taste into a small bowl and whisk to combine.

**2** Gradually whisk in the oil and stir in the chopped herbs. If not using immediately, store in a cool place and whisk before using.

### Mustard Dressing

**To make about 100ml (3½fl oz) you will need:**

1 tbsp wholegrain mustard, juice of ½ lemon, 6 tbsp extra virgin olive oil, salt and ground black pepper.

**1** Put the mustard, lemon juice and oil into a small bowl and whisk together. Season to taste with salt and pepper.

**2** If not using immediately, store in a cool place and whisk before using.

### Lemon and Parsley Dressing

**To make about 100ml (3½fl oz), you will need:**

juice of ½ lemon, 6 tbsp extra virgin olive oil, 4 tbsp freshly chopped flat-leafed parsley, salt and ground black pepper.

**1** Put the lemon juice, olive oil and parsley into a medium bowl and whisk together. Season to taste with salt and pepper.

**2** If not using immediately, store in a cool place and whisk before using.

### Blue Cheese Dressing

**To make 100ml (3½fl oz), you will need:**

50g (2oz) Roquefort cheese, 2 tbsp low-fat yogurt, 1 tbsp white wine vinegar, 5 tbsp extra virgin olive oil, salt and ground black pepper.

**1** Crumble the cheese into a food processor with the yogurt, vinegar and oil.

**2** Whiz for 1 minute until combined. Season with salt and pepper. Use within one day.

## Chilli Lime Dressing

**To make 125ml (4fl oz), you will need:**
¼ red chilli, seeded and finely chopped (see Cook's Tips, page 10), 1 garlic clove, crushed, 1cm (½in) piece fresh root ginger, peeled and finely grated, juice of 1½ large limes, 50ml (2fl oz) olive oil, 1½ tbsp light muscovado sugar, 2 tbsp coriander leaves, 2 tbsp mint leaves.

**1** Put the chilli, garlic, ginger, lime juice, oil and sugar into a food processor or blender and whiz for 10 seconds to combine.

**2** Add the coriander and mint and whiz together for 5 seconds to chop roughly. Store in a cool place and use within two days.

## Garlic, Soy and Honey Dressing

**To make about 100ml (3½fl oz), you will need:**
1 garlic clove, crushed, 2 tsp each soy sauce and honey, 1 tbsp cider vinegar, 4 tbsp olive oil, ground black pepper.

**1** Put the garlic into a small bowl. Add the soy sauce, honey, vinegar and oil, season to taste with pepper and whisk together thoroughly.

**2** If not using immediately, store in a cool place and whisk before using.

## Mint Yogurt Dressing

**To make about 175ml (6fl oz), you will need:**
150g (5oz) Greek yogurt, 3–4 tbsp chopped mint leaves, 2 tbsp extra virgin olive oil, salt and ground black pepper.

**1** Put the yogurt into a bowl and add the mint and oil. Season to taste with salt and pepper.

**2** If not using immediately, store in a cool place and use within one day.

## Sun-dried Tomato Dressing

**To make about 100ml (3½fl oz), you will need:**
2 sun-dried tomatoes in oil, drained, 2 tbsp oil from sun-dried tomato jar, 2 tbsp red wine vinegar, 1 garlic clove, 1 tbsp sun-dried tomato paste, a pinch of sugar (optional), 2 tbsp extra virgin olive oil, salt and ground black pepper.

**1** Put the sun-dried tomatoes and oil, the vinegar, garlic and tomato paste into a blender or food processor. Add the sugar, if using.

**2** With the motor running, pour the oil through the feeder tube and whiz briefly to make a fairly thick dressing. Season with salt and pepper. If not using immediately, store in a cool place and whisk before using.

## Caesar Dressing

**To make about 150ml (¼ pint), you will need:**
1 medium egg, 1 garlic clove, juice of ½ lemon, 2 tsp Dijon mustard, 1 tsp balsamic vinegar, 150ml (¼ pint) sunflower oil, salt and ground black pepper.

**1** Put the eggs garlic, lemon juice, mustard and vinegar into a food processor and whiz until smooth then, with the motor running, gradually add the oil and whiz until smooth.

**2** Season with salt and pepper, cover and chill for up to three days.

## Classic Coleslaw Dressing

**To make about 175ml (6fl oz), you will need:**
2½ tbsp red wine vinegar, 125ml (4fl oz) olive oil, 1 tbsp Dijon mustard, salt and ground black pepper.

**1** Pour the vinegar into a screw-topped jar. Add the oil and mustard and season with salt and pepper. Screw on the lid and shake.

**2** Combine with the coleslaw ingredients and chill until needed.

## Chilli Coleslaw Dressing

**To make about 100ml (3½fl oz), you will need:**
½ tsp harissa paste (see page 283), 100g (3½oz) natural yogurt, 1 tbsp white wine vinegar.

**1** Put all the ingredients into a small bowl and whisk to combine.

**2** Combine with the coleslaw ingredients and chill until needed.

# Index

# CONVERSION TABLES

## TEMPERATURE

| °C | FAN OVEN | GAS MARK | °C | FAN OVEN | GAS MARK |
|----|----------|----------|-----|----------|----------|
| 110 | 90 | ¼ | 190 | 170 | 5 |
| 130 | 110 | ½ | 200 | 180 | 6 |
| 140 | 120 | 1 | 220 | 200 | 7 |
| 150 | 130 | 2 | 230 | 210 | 8 |
| 170 | 150 | 3 | 240 | 220 | 9 |
| 180 | 160 | 4 | | | |

## LIQUIDS

| METRIC | IMPERIAL | METRIC | IMPERIAL |
|--------|----------|--------|----------|
| 5ml | 1 tsp | 200ml | 7fl oz |
| 15ml | 1 tbsp | 250ml | 9fl oz |
| 25ml | 1fl oz | 300ml | ½ pint |
| 50ml | 2fl oz | 500ml | 18fl oz |
| 100ml | 3½ fl oz | 600ml | 1 pint |
| 125ml | 4fl oz | 900ml | 1½ pints |
| 150ml | 5fl oz / ¼ pint | 1 litre | 1¾ pints |
| 175ml | 6fl oz | | |

## MEASURES

| Metric | Imperial | Metric | Imperial |
|--------|----------|--------|----------|
| 5mm | ¼ in | 10cm | 4in |
| 1cm | ½ in | 15cm | 6in |
| 2cm | ¾ in | 18cm | 7in |
| 2.5cm | 1in | 20.5cm | 8in |
| 3cm | 1¼ in | 23cm | 9in |
| 4cm | 1½ in | 25.5cm | 10in |
| 5cm | 2in | 28cm | 11in |
| 7.5cm | 3in | 30.5cm | 12in |